D0884649

THE EFFECTS OF
RADIATION on MATERIALS

Edited by

J. J. Harwood
U. S. Office of Naval Research

Henry H. Hausner
Consultant to The Martin Co.

J. G. Morse
Nuclear Division, The Martin Co.

W. G. Rauch
U. S. Office of Naval Research

REINHOLD PUBLISHING CORPORATION
NEW YORK
CHAPMAN & HALL, LTD., LONDON

REINHOLD PUBLISHING CORPORATION

Publishers of Chemical Engineering Catalog, Chemical Materials Catalog, "Automatic Control," "Materials in Design Engineering," "Progressive Architecture"; Advertising Management of the American Chemical Society.

Printed in U. S. A

FOREWORD

The behavior of materials depends to a large extent on the environmental conditions. In nuclear engineering a new "environment" has to be considered—irradiation.

The subject of the effect of radiation on materials is one which currently is receiving much attention. To the layman, the biological effects of radiation are of more vital and immediate concern and consequently have received widespread publicity. However, to nuclear engineers, materials engineers, metallurgists, physicists and chemists, the various phenomena associated with irradiation of materials by neutrons, gamma rays, fission fragments or other energetic particles are of great scientific and practical interest. In each of the fields of science and engineering, the subject of radiation effects is approached from different viewpoints and objectives. Thus, we find that radiation damage has imposed an additional design parameter in the selection and use of materials for fuel elements or structural members in nuclear power reactors. Studies of the mechanism of radiation effects in solids indicate that the use of radiation can be a powerful tool for increasing our understanding of the physics of solids, particularly of imperfections in their structure. The striking effect of radiation upon polymerization processes, leading to the preparation of new polymeric materials of commercial importance, has opened up an entirely new field of organic synthesis.

Until relatively recently, much of the information concerning the effects of radiation upon materials was not readily available to the scientific and engineering community. The 1955 Geneva Conference on the Peaceful Uses of Atomic Energy provided the impetus for the release of a large body of information by the U. S. Atomic Energy Commission and foreign sources. Much of the current research being conducted in AEC National Laboratories, universities and other research institutions, both in this country and abroad, on the effect of radiation is now finding its way into the open scientific literature.

As the civilian usage of nuclear power expands, so will the necessity increase for engineers and scientists to become familiar with this fascinating subject. A start in this direction was made at a Colloquium on "The Effects of Radiation on Materials" sponsored by the Office of Naval Research jointly with The Martin Company at Johns Hopkins University in Baltimore in March, 1957. Its purpose was to present a series of unclassified reviews that were educational in nature and gave broad coverage to this field. The presentations were designed to appeal to both research scientists and engineers working on radiation effects and on the development and design of nuclear power reactors, as well as to manufacturers of structural parts and instruments for reactors, and to college students interested in nuclear engineering who wish to broaden their education. Some 600 people attended this three-day meeting and in response to the unusually heavy demand, it was decided to make the proceedings of the Colloquium available in book form.

These papers deal with metals, alloys, inorganic dielectrics, semiconductors, organic and polymeric materials and materials for nuclear reactor components including fuel elements, moderators, coolants and shielding materials. Theories and concepts of radiation effects, radiation sources and measurements of radiation, and the known effects of radiation on the physical, metallurgical, mechanical, corrosion, and electrical properties are presented. In addition, there is discussion of the current thinking on behavior of organic materials, including effects of radiation upon polymeric reaction processes, e.g., graft copolymerization. It will be obvious to the reader that much remains to be done, from both a theoretical and practical viewpoint, to improve our knowledge of the resistance of materials to radiation.

The editors are indebted to Mr. T. F. Nagey, General Manager of the Nuclear Division of The Martin Company and Dr. I. Estermann, Chief of Materials, Office of Naval Research for their continued encouragement and support throughout the preparation of the Colloquium. They also wish to express their gratitude to Dr. L. Himmel of the Office of Naval Research, and Mr. N. Dernbach and Mrs. J. Pankoff of The Martin Company for their assistance in arranging the Colloquium and in the handling of the manuscripts.

Editorial Committee

J. J. HARWOOD, (U. S. Office of Naval Research)
H. H. HAUSNER, (Consultant to The Martin Company)
J. G. MORSE, (The Martin Company)
W. G. RAUCH, (U. S. Office of Naval Research)

CONTENTS

Chapter 1

DEFECTS IN SOLIDS AND CURRENT CONCEPTS OF RADIATION EFFECTS*

G. J. Dienes

Brookhaven National Laboratory
Upton, New York

Introduction

Nuclear radiations are known to alter the properties of solid materials, often to such an extent that the changes are of great engineering significance.[1-33]. The physical consequences of the interaction of high energy radiation with matter are that several types of disturbances (crystalline defects and radiation-induced processes) are introduced which affect the properties of a solid. These disturbances are: (a) vacancies, (b) interstitial atoms, (c) thermal spikes, (d) impurity atoms, (e) ionization effects, (f) displacement spikes and (g) replacement collisions. Each of these defects is described briefly below.

Vacancies. Vacant lattice sites may be created by collisions of energetic neutrons, fission fragments or other fast particles with the atoms in a solid lattice. The energy transferred in these collisions is usually sufficient for the recoiling atom to create further vacant lattice sites by subsequent collisions. Thus, for each primary collision, a cascade of collisions resulting in vacancies is initiated.

Interstitial atoms. The atoms that are displaced from their equilibrium positions in the lattice will stop in an interstitial or nonequilibrium position, provided they do not recombine immediately with a nearby vacancy.

Thermal spikes. This concept in its modern form originated with Seitz[28] who took into account the lattice oscillations set up in a wake of either a fission fragment or a charged knocked-on atom of the lattice. Calculations by Brooks[27] and others indicated that the possible duration of a high temperature region of approximately 1000°K involving some thousands of atoms might be 10^{-10} to 10^{-11} second.

Impurity atoms. The fission process, which introduces foreign fission products, and the capture of the neutron by a nucleus resulting in a different

* Under contract with the U. S. Atomic Energy Commission.

atomic species are the means of introducing impurity atoms. The effect of fission fragments is usually the more pronounced of the two, although both mechanisms are often insignificant compared to the other effects.

Ionization effects. The passage of charged particles through a solid may cause extensive ionization and electronic excitation, which in turn lead to bond rupture, free radicals, coloration, luminescence, etc., in many types of solids. These effects are most important in the various insulators and dielectrics, ionic crystals, glasses, organic high polymers, etc.

Displacement spikes. Brinkman[34] has suggested recently that displacement spikes are produced at the end of the range of a fast moving atom. His calculations indicate that, when the energy of the fast moving atom falls below a transition value (which depends on the atomic number), the mean free path between displacement collisions becomes of the order of the atomic spacing. Thus, each collision results in a displaced atom and the end of the trail is believed to be a region containing of the order of one to ten thousand atoms in which local melting and turbulent flow have occurred during a very short time interval. Brinkman suggests that vacancies and interstitials will anneal more or less completely in this region and that the damage is left in the form of dislocation loops and small misoriented regions. Brinkman's estimate of the mean free path between collisions is probably too low[11,27] and the existence of displacement spikes is rather speculative. This mechanism is probably only important in heavy metals.

Replacement collisions. Theoretical considerations of radiation damage have led Kinchin and Pease[35] to the introduction of the concept of replacement collisions. If a collision between a moving interstitial atom and a stationary atom results in ejection of the stationary atom leaving the interstitial with insufficient kinetic energy for it to escape from the vacancy it has created, then this atom will fall into the vacancy, dissipating its kinetic energy through lattice vibrations as heat. Kinchin and Pease show that for a reasonable choice of energy parameters the number of replacement collisions exceeds the number of displacement collisions, and they obtain satisfactory agreement with the experimentally determined disordering rate of $MnNi_3$ found by Aronin.[36]

The thermal spike and displacement spike processes are evidently rather complex and it is difficult to carry out reliable calculations. They have been invoked to explain the unexpectedly efficient disordering of ordered alloys by irradiation. Seitz[37] has indicated recently that the simple picture provided by a thermal spike, namely rapid heating and quenching, is inadequate to explain the disordering. He suggests that the irreversible plastic strain which originates in thermal stresses about displacement spikes is the source of the disorder. Alternatively, the experiments may be interpreted in terms of replacement collisions.

In the present chapter attention will be focussed on production of displaced atoms, i.e. interstitials and vacancies. The theoretical calculation of the number of displaced atoms produced by energetic particles will be described briefly. The number of displaced atoms has also been measured by a variety of techniques in several solid types. The main purpose of the present paper is to compare theory and experiment. Some illustrative examples of important changes in physical properties are given in Section V.

A very important phenomenon, namely annealing of the damage (reversion of physical properties to their initial values upon raising the temperature), will not be treated in detail in this paper although some examples are given in Section V. The reader is referred to recent review articles for a full discussion of this topic.[6,8,11,12,15,16,27] The annealing of damage is often of great practical importance since it provides a method of minimizing radiation effects. The annealing processes are usually complex and intricate and detailed interpretation of these effects is not yet at hand.

Calculation of the Number of Displaced Atoms

Theoretical work in the field of radiation effects is concerned with three major aspects of the problem:[12] (a) the production of displaced atoms and other associated imperfections by high energy bombarding particles; (b) the nature and mobility of the imperfections and their role in annealing; and (c) the relations between physical properties of solids and crystalline imperfections. For the purposes of this chapter the major results of item (a) will be needed as well as selected topics under (c). The latter will be covered in the experimental section as the need arises.

E. P. Wigner[38] made the first quantitative estimates of the number of displaced atoms produced by high energy particles. A brief discussion of the theory, developed in detail by Seitz,[28] is given here without going into the details of the mathematical treatment. Seitz, in his early theory,[28] calculated the fraction of energy lost in elastic collisions using the Born approximation. These are the collisions which are effective in displacing atoms. The early theory led to a square root dependence on the energy which gave a rather good approximation up to an energy of $E' \sim 10 E_d$ although the theory is subject to question and has been superseded by improved treatments. E' is the average energy of all the primary knock-ons and E_d is the threshold energy for displacement, i.e., the energy required to displace an atom permanently from a stable site in the lattice. E_d is an important parameter in all of the displacement theories. Theoretical estimates of E_d will be discussed in connection with its experimental determination.

Recent advances in the theory are due to Snyder and Neufeld[39] and

Harrison and Seitz.[40] A complete account of the present status of the theory has been given by Seitz and Koehler.[11] These investigators have pointed out that the Born approximation is not valid and that the problem is better treated on the basis of classical scattering. The theoretical results are given below.

The basic equation for the number of displaced atoms, N_d, is

$$N_d = \bar{\nu}\, n\varphi \tag{1}$$

where $\bar{\nu}$ is the number of atoms displaced per primary collision, n is the number of primary displacements per incident particle and φ is the total number of incident particles. It will be assumed that φ is known in any given experimental arrangement. $\bar{\nu}$ is given by the following equations [11]

$$\bar{\nu} = \left(0.885 + 0.561 \log \frac{X_m + 1}{4}\right) \frac{X_m + 1}{X_m}\,;\ X_m \geq 3 \tag{2}$$

in which X_m is

$$X_m + 1 = \frac{4M_1 M_2}{(M_1 + M_2)^2} \frac{E}{E_d} = E_m/E_d \tag{3}$$

and M_1 and E are the mass and energy of the incident particle, M_2 is the mass of the atoms of the lattice, and E_m is the maximum energy transferred by the moving particle to the atom of the lattice. $\bar{\nu}$ varies slowly with X_m and is rather insensitive to the quantities in (3). In the case of copper bombarded by 12 mev deuterons X_m is 5.64×10^4 if E_d is taken as 25 ev. The corresponding value of $\bar{\nu}$ is 6.23.

For charged particle irradiation n in Eq. (1) is calculated as follows. The number of primary atoms displaced by an incident particle of charge Z_1, mass M_1, and energy E, in traversing a distance dR through a solid is

$$dn = n_0 \sigma_d\, dR \tag{4}$$

where n_0 is the number of atoms per unit volume and σ_d, which is the cross-section for displacement, is given for the non-relativistic case by

$$\sigma_d = \mu/E \tag{5}$$

where

$$\mu = 4\pi a_h \frac{M_1}{M_2} \frac{Z_1^2 Z_2^2 R_h^2}{E_d} \tag{6}$$

and Z_2 and M_2 are the charge and mass of the stationary atom, R_h is the Rydberg energy and a_h is the Bohr radius. The total number of atoms displaced when the incident particle traverses a distance dR and its total range drops from R_1 to $R_1 - \Delta R$, is

$$n = n_0 \mu \int_{R_1 - \Delta R}^{R_1} \frac{dR}{E} \tag{7}$$

For fast neutrons[8] the collisions of the neutrons are of the hard sphere type. Only a very small fraction, E_d/E_m, of the struck atoms are not displaced and, therefore, the cross section for producing a primary knock-on is the total neutron cross section. For the heavy elements E_m does not usually exceed the ionization limit L_c. L_c is the energy limit below which ionization losses may be neglected. In this case the total number of displaced atoms per fast neutron collision is given, in terms of the average energy transferred E', by

$$\tilde{\nu} = \frac{E'}{2E_d} \tag{8}$$

or in terms of the maximum energy transferred by

$$\tilde{\nu} = \frac{E_m}{4E_d} \tag{9}$$

where E_m is given by Eq. (3). For lighter elements E_m generally exceeds L_c. In most cases the primary knock-ons effectively lose all the excess energy in ionization and in this case

$$\tilde{\nu} = (2 - L_c/E_m)\frac{L_c}{4E_d} \tag{10}$$

L_c may be estimated from the lowest excitation potential of the valence electrons in insulators and from the Fermi energy of the free electrons for metals.[8]

In the case of bombardment[11,9] with fast electrons relativistic formulas have to be used. The range of charged particles becomes nearly proportional to the energy in the relativistic region. Below 2.5 mev the range of electrons satisfies the relation[41] (E in mev)

$$R(\text{mg/cm}^2) = 412 \, e^{(1.265 - 0.0954 \ln E)} \tag{11}$$

Above 2.5 mev the linear relation

$$R(\text{mg/cm}^2) = 530 \, E - 106 \tag{12}$$

becomes satisfactory. A convenient approximation may be used for specimens thin enough so that E remains larger than the threshold value E_d. In this case, the cross section may be expressed as

$$\sigma(R) = \sigma(R_1)\frac{R - R'}{R_1 - R'} \tag{13}$$

where $\sigma(R)$ is the cross section when the range is R, R_1 is the initial range, and $\sigma(R_1)$ the corresponding cross section for the incident particles of energy E_1. R' is to be adjusted to give the best fit of the $\sigma_d(E)$ curve over the range of interest. Whenever (13) is valid the number of primary atoms displaced per electron can be calculated from

$$n = n_0 \int_{R_0}^{R_1} \sigma(R) \, dR = n_0 \sigma(R_1)(R_1 - R_0) \left[\frac{(R_1 + R_0) - 2R'}{2(R_1 - R')} \right] \quad (14)$$

where R_0 is the residual range after penetration so that $R_1 - R_0$ is the thickness.

For incident electrons near the threshold energy the value of $\bar{\nu}$ (number of atoms displaced per primary collision) is expected to be unity since the primary displaced atoms then have insufficient energy to displace others. For higher energies the value of $\bar{\nu}$ has to be calculated using Eq. (3). The very attractive feature of electron bombardment experiments is, of course, the simple nature of the damage which results at low energies, i.e. one displaced atom per primary collision, with the collisions quite widely separated in space.

The Threshold Energy for Displacement

It was shown in the previous section that an important parameter which enters the theory of displacement production is the "threshold energy for displacement," E_d, which is the energy required to displace an atom permanently from a stable site in the lattice. This parameter has been studied both theoretically and experimentally in recent years.

Theoretical Calculations. Seitz[28] estimated the magnitude of E_d qualitatively as follows. The energy required to remove a typical atom from an interior site in a solid in an adiabatic or reversible manner is about $2E_c$, where E_c is the energy of sublimation. If, however, the process is carried out dynamically, as in a fast collision, the process is highly irreversible and the energy required is expected to be of the order of $4E_c$. Since E_c in tightly bound solids is of the order of 5–6 ev Seitz suggested 25 ev as a reasonable value for E_d.

More detailed theoretical calculations have been carried out recently by Huntington[42] for copper and Kohn[43] for germanium. Huntington has considered low energy collisions and has assumed that the principal interaction between colliding atoms in a typical close packed metal, such as copper, is the repulsion of the closed ion shells. This interaction he approximated by a Born-Meyer type function

$$V(r) = A \exp \left[\frac{-(r - r_0)}{r_0} \rho \right] \quad (15)$$

where r_0 is the equilibrium separation of to adjacent ions and ρ and A are constants. Since this force law is short range, a billiard ball model was used for the collision calculations. For copper the value of ρ can be bracketed[44] between 13 and 17. For $\rho = 13$ an energy of 18.5 ev is required to move an atom to an interstitial position in the (111) direction through the triangle formed by its three nearest neighbors and 17.5 ev for displacement creation in the (100) direction. In the latter case the original fast atom moves to another lattice site displacing its nearest neighbor into an interstitial pattern. For $\rho = 17$ the corresponding energies were found to be 43 and 34 ev. The experimental value for copper, to be discussed in the next section, lies well inside these rather wide theoretical limits.

Kohn[43] has carried out similar calculations for germanium and found that some of the nearest interstitial positions can be reached by substantially smaller energies, of the order of 10 ev. The main reason for the lower theoretical value is the open structure of the Ge lattice in contrast to the close packed face-centered-cubic structure of Cu. Kohn's calculations also show that the energy required to displace an atom in the diamond lattice may vary substantially with direction. For example, it is found that an atom can escape more easily in the $(-1, -1, -1)$ direction than in a direction close to (111) which is blocked by a nearest neighbor. The discrepancy between the theoretical and experimental values and its implications will be discussed in the next section.

Once the displacement energy is known it is a simple matter to calculate for various types of radiations the minimum energy required to produce displacements. In the case of massive particle irradiation

$$E_m = \mu E \tag{16}$$

where

$$\mu = \frac{4M_1M_2}{(M_1 + M_2)^2}$$

and E_m is the maximum energy transferred by moving particle of mass M_1 and energy E to a stationary atom of mass M_2. For electron bombardment, relativistic effects must be taken into account and the following expression,

$$E_m = \frac{2E(E + 2mc^2)}{M_2c^2} \tag{17}$$

where m is the electron mass and c is the velocity of light, is valid for $E_d \ll E$ and $m \ll M_2$.[9] In the case of γ-rays the radiation effect is primarily caused by the Compton electrons or photoelectrons permitting one to use the electron thresholds.

Experimental Determinations. The first published result on threshold energy determination came from the work of Klontz (as discussed by Lark-

Horovitz[9]) on germanium bombarded with high energy electrons at room temperature. In this experiment *n*-type Ge was bombarded with electrons of increasing energy with the total number of incident particles per bombardment kept constant. The change in conductivity was observed as a function of the energy of the incident particles. The conductivity vs. electron energy curve showed a level portion, indicating no change in conductivity, followed by a sharp decrease in the conductivity. Extrapolation to the level portion gave a threshold energy of about 0.65 mev.

Klontz[45] followed up this study with a detailed investigation of conductivity changes in germanium as a function of electron energy. These later experiments were done at liquid nitrogen temperature in order to minimize annealing. The sample was subjected to electron bombardment in a Van de Graaff machine at various well-defined energies. Typical curves are shown in Fig. 1. The initial horizontal line (up to about 0.6 mev) is followed by a large decrease in conductivity, the extent of which depends on the original conductivity and the number of electrons incident at each energy. The threshold is obtained by extrapolating the region of large change to its intersection with the initial horizontal position. For the two samples of Fig. 1 thresholds of 0.63 and 0.65 mev are observed. Klontz concludes that

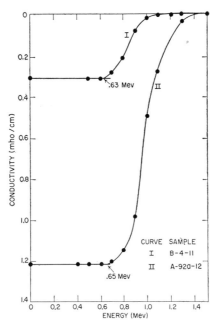

Figure 1.1. Extrapolation curves used in determination of threshold for lattice displacements in Ge (from ref. 45).

the most probable value of the threshold is 0.63 ± 0.02 mev. By Eq. (17) this corresponds to a threshold energy, E_d, of 30 ± 1 ev.

Loferski and Rappaport[46] have used changes in minority carrier lifetime, a property far more sensitive than the resistivity to the presence of defects, to measure threshold energies. In this experiment changes in the short circuit current of an electron voltaic cell are measured as a function of bombardment time at various bombarding energies. In this case, therefore, a transient phenomenon due to the incident electrons is measured as influenced by defects created by a small fraction of the same electrons. By an extrapolation procedure similar to that used by Klontz these investigators conclude that E_d is 13 ev for both Ge and Si.

These two sets of experiments are in disagreement, with Loferski and Rappaport's values being closer to Kohn's theoretical predictions. The discrepancy is difficult to resolve. Sensitivity may have been lost in Klontz's experiments at low bombardment energies since both the cross section for displacement and the volume of suitably irradiated material decrease rapidly with decreasing energy. On the other hand, Loferski and Rappaport, because of the high sensitivity of their method, may well have measured the results of a few very favorable collisions. The gradual appearance of damage near the threshold indicates that the threshold is actually quite spread out in agreement with the ideas of Sampson et al.[47] It is not clear which value or what distribution of values should be used in theoretical displacement calculation. It is clear, however, that the cross section for displacement should be determined experimentally in great detail as a function of bombarding energy. Further, because of the indications from Huntington's and Kohn's theoretical work, the displacement energy also has to be studied as a function of crystalline direction.*

The threshold energy for graphite was determined by similar methods by D. T. Eggen.[48] He found a value near 25 ev for E_d in this material.

Eggen and Laubenstein[49] have determined the threshold energy for copper using low temperature electron irradiation. In this experiment thin Cu specimens were mounted on a heavy copper plate which was immersed in liquid air during the irradiation and measurements. The rate of change of resistance was determined as a function of electron energy in the 0.45 to 1.0 mev range. Extrapolation to zero damage gave 0.49 ± 0.02 mev for the threshold electron energy corresponding to E_d for copper of 25.0 ± 1.0 ev. This value falls well within the theoretical limits obtained by Huntington.

* The influence of crystalline direction on damage has been observed recently by W. L. Brown and W. M. Augustyniak (*Bull. Am. Phys. Soc.* II, **2**, 156, 1957) in germanium. These workers found that the damage rate in the (111) direction is about 40 per cent higher than either in the (110) or (100) directions.

Denney[50] has found that irradiation of a metastable alloy of iron in copper (2.4 w/o Fe) initiates the transformation of the face-centered-cubic iron to the stable ferromagnetic body-centered-cubic structure. Upon bombarding with electrons of varying energy and measuring the saturation magnetization Denney was able to deduce the threshold energy for the production of displaced atoms. This occurred at 0.45 mev. Denney concludes that the displaced iron atoms are responsible for initiating the transformation. Thus, 0.45 mev corresponds to an E_d of 27 ev in iron.

Dugdale[51] has found that ordering in AuCu$_3$ can be induced at temperatures where thermal ordering rates are unobservably low by bombarding with electrons of about 0.3 mev energy. Dugdale interprets this low temperature ordering as due to the formation of vacancies and interstitials which are sufficiently mobile to allow the necessary microdiffusion for ordering to take place. If this interpretation is correct the threshold energy in AuCu$_3$ is about 10 ev.

The experimental and theoretical results on threshold energy determinations are summarized in Table 1. For the present it appears quite satisfactory to use a value of 25 ev for E_d in theoretical calculations of the number of displaced atoms produced by irradiation. This value of E_d will be used in the rest of this paper unless otherwise stated.

TABLE 1. THEORETICAL AND EXPERIMENTAL THRESHOLD ENERGIES (from ref. 12b)

| Bombarded material | Property measured | Threshold energy, ev | | Reference |
		Experiment	Theory	
n-Germanium at −196°C	resistivity	30		Klontz[45]
n-Germanium at room T	minority carrier lifetime	13		Loferski and Rappaport[46]
p-Silicon at room T	minority carrier lifetime	13		Loferski and Rappaport[46]
Germanium			∼10	Kohn[43]
Graphite	resistivity	25		Eggen[48]
Copper	resistivity	25		Eggen and Laubenstein[49]
Copper			17–34	Huntington[42]
Iron-copper alloy, Fe displaced	saturation magnetization	27		Denney[50]
Cu$_3$Au	ordering	∼10		Dugdale[51]

Experimental Determination of the Number of Displaced Atoms— Comparison with Theory

In this section those experiments which lead to rather clear-cut estimates of the number of displaced atoms in solids will be discussed in some detail. One of the central problems of modern solid state physics is the relation between physical properties and lattice imperfections. The theories are generally rather crude. Consequently, although most physical properties, are altered by the presence of displaced atoms, only a few are well enough understood to serve as a quantitative measure of the concentration of displaced atoms. Different methods have been used with different solids and the material of this section is organized around the different types of solids involved.

Metals. The electrical resistivity of pure metals is increased upon irradiation with massive fast particles.[52] Ionizing radiation alone has no effect. The increase in resistance is mainly due to an increase in the residual resistivity although some changes in the thermal part of the resistivity have been observed.[53] The residual (or very low temperature) resistivity of metals is very sensitive to the presence of impurities and imperfections in the crystal. Any disturbance of the ideal periodic potential leads to scattering of the conduction electrons and thereby to an increase in the resistance. At low concentrations there should be very little interference among the various defects and the increase in resistivity is expected to be proportional to the number of defects introduced into the material. The proportionality constant has to be calculated theoretically and will be discussed in detail in conjunction with the interpretation of the experimental data.

It is clear from the discussion so far that the resistivity measurement must be made at low temperature in order to measure the residual resistivity. The irradiation itself must be done at low temperature because the radiation-induced defects in metals are known to anneal out at quite low temperatures. The experiments of Cooper, Koehler, and Marx[54] satisfied the above requirements. These investigators irradiated 5-mil (0.13 mm) wires of pure Cu, Ag and Au with 12 mev deuterons. The samples were mounted on a liquid helium cryostat and the temperature was maintained near 10°K. The range of 12 mev deuterons is 8 mils (.20 mm) in Cu and, therefore, the particles penetrated through the wires.

Fig. 2 shows the changes in the resistivity of Cu, Ag and Au as a function of the time-integrated flux for specimens irradiated near 10°K. The curves start linearly from the origin but have a slight negative curvature. The resistivity change, $\Delta\rho$, obtained after a given amount of irradiation near 10°K, is stable at the bombardment temperature. The negative curvature, therefore, is due to an annealing process associated with bombardment.

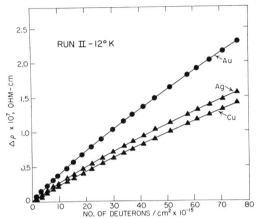

Figure 1.2. Resistivity increase as a function of integrated deuteron flux. (from ref. 54).

This process is generally termed radiation annealing. For the present discussion it is the initial slope of the curve which is pertinent in giving the number of displaced atoms to be compared with the theory of displacement production. The data are given in Table 2.

At low concentration of defects the change in resistivity, $\Delta\rho$, is proportional to the concentration of defects. The interpretation is now straightforward provided we know the proportionality constant relating $\Delta\rho$ to the concentration of interstitials and vacancies, i.e. the cross section for the scattering of the conduction electrons by such defects. Unfortunately, there is no obvious independent experimental method for determining these cross sections and they have to be evaluated theoretically. These calculations are very intricate and the results are still highly controversial in spite of the considerable amount of work done on this problem over the last few years. The theoretical work is briefly summarized below since it is central to the interpretation of the experimental results.

Dexter[55] approximated the scattering potential associated with the imperfections by a shielded coulomb interaction and computed electronic transition-matrix elements by the Born approximation. The shielding constant was adjusted so as to yield the experimental values when applied to substitutional impurities having adjacent atomic number. Dexter took into

TABLE 2. 12 MEV DEUTERON IRRADIATION DATA AT 12°K

Sample	Initial slope $\mu\Omega$ cm per 10^{17} d/cm^2
Cu	0.221
Ag	0.263
Au	0.379

account the effect of lattice distortions around the defects and concluded that they represent only a minor correction. His result for Cu, Au and Ag was that one atomic percent of vacancies would give an extra resistivity of about 0.4 $\mu\Omega$ cm. A similar calculation for interstitials gave about 0.6 $\mu\Omega$ cm.

Jongenburger[56,57] suggested that a more reliable calculation is obtained if Born's approximation is not used. He carried out detailed calculations for vacancies based on the free electron approximation, using for the scattering potential the negative of the Hartree potential of a free copper ion. This potential was adjusted to take care of the screening of the conduction electrons which was approximated by creating in the electron gas a spherical hole of unit charge and of radius r_s, where r_s is defined by $(4\,\pi/3)r_s^3 = \Omega$ (Ω = atomic volume). On calculating the phase shifts he found that they gave good agreement with the Friedel[58] sum rule. He also confirmed Dexter's conclusion that distortion around the defects can be neglected. For one per cent vacancies in Cu, Ag and Au, Jongenburger obtained the following $\Delta\rho$ values: 1.3, 1.5 and 1.5$\mu\Omega$ cm, respectively.

Jongenburger[59] also estimated by the same method the extra resistivity caused by interstitial atoms. For the contribution of the interstitial scattering potential alone a value of 1–2 $\mu\Omega$ cm was found. An additional resistivity of 3.5 $\mu\Omega$ cm is contributed by the nearest neighbor displacements, leading to a final value of about 5$\mu\Omega$ cm per per cent of interstitials.

More recently Blatt[60] has calculated the resistivity associated with one atomic per cent of interstitials by assuming that the effect of the associated displacements can be neglected. He derived the scattering potentials for the imperfections from the appropriate Hartree self-consistent fields and employed the partial wave method in evaluating the scattering cross sections. The potentials were adjusted until the phase shifts satisfied the Friedel sum rule. The calculated resistivities do not appear to depend critically on the choice of potential. Blatt[61] finds, however, that the choice of potential is important for the calculation of thermoelectric power. His calculation of thermoelectric power leads to good agreement with experiment in the case of substitutional arsenic in copper. Blatt's final value for the extra resistivity due to 1 per cent of interstitial atoms in copper is 1.4 $\mu\Omega$ cm., which is practically the same as that due to vacancies. For substitutional impurities approximate agreement was obtained with resistivity changes measured by Linde, although the calculated resistivities were consistently too high. In view of this Blatt suggests that his, as well as Jongenburger's, calculations overestimate the resistivity increase due to vacancies and interstitials by about a factor of two.

Overhauser and Gorman[62] have reexamined the whole problem of scattering by imperfections. In particular, they studied in detail the contribu-

TABLE 3. THEORETICAL RESIDUAL RESISTIVITY OF INTERSTITIAL ATOMS AND VACANCIES IN CU, AG AND AU. THE UNITS ARE $\mu\Omega$ CM PER ATOMIC PER CENT OF THE IMPERFECTION

Material	Interstitials	Vacancies	Reference
Copper	0.6	0.4	Dexter[55]
	5.0	1.3	Jongenburger[56, 57, 59]
	1.3	1.4	Blatt[60, 69]
	10.5	1.5	Overhauser-Gorman[62]
Silver	0.6	0.4	Dexter[55]
	—	1.5	Jongenburger[56]
Gold	0.6	0.4	Dexter[55]
	—	1.5	Jongenburger[56]

tion of the elastic displacement of atoms near the imperfections to the increase in the residual resistivity. They found that, for interstitials, scattering from the strained regions is an order of magnitude greater than that from the defect itself. The effect is smaller for a vacancy but not negligible. Interference terms were found to be small. In the Overhauser-Gorman treatment unknown parameters, such as effective mass and electron-lattice interaction constant, are eliminated by comparing the final formula with the theoretical resistivity associated with lattice vibrations. The residual resistivity of the strained lattice is obtained then from the experimental lattice resistivity. The final results for $\Delta\rho$ are: 10.5 $\mu\Omega$ cm. per per cent of interstitials and 1.5$\mu\Omega$ cm. per per cent of vacancies.

The results of the various theoretical investigations are summarized in Table 3.

It is clear from the large discrepancies among the various theoretical values that the experiments cannot yet be interpreted in a definite way. The proportionality constant required to derive the number of displaced atoms from the experimental measurements is apparently only known within an order of magnitude. Seitz and Koehler[11] adopted the value of 2.7$\mu\Omega$ cm per vacancy-interstitial pair in Cu based essentially on Blatt's calculation. The number of displaced atoms per 10^{17} d/cm^2 is, then, 0.082 per cent using the experimental number in Table 4. The theoretical value corresponding to the experiments of Cooper, Koehler and Marx[54] is 0.43 per cent. Eq. (3), (4) and (8) were used in this calculation. The discrepancy between theory and experiment is, therefore, about a factor of 5 with the theory apparently overestimating the number of displaced atoms. The discrepancy is less if Dexter's numbers are used and becomes very large, of the order of a factor of 20, if Overhauser's numbers are used for the theoretical value of the residual resistivity (see Table 3). Similar results have been obtained by Blewitt and co-workers[63,11] recently, using neutron irradiation at 17°K.

Recent work by Denney and co-workers[64,65,66] using electron irradiation

TABLE 4. NUMBER OF DISPLACED ATOMS PRODUCED IN GRAPHITE BY
REACTOR IRRADIATION (from ref. 12b)

Exposure (nvt)	Per cent of Displaced Atoms						
	Theory[a]	Neutron Transmission	Electronic Properties + Chem. traps[b]	Magnetic Susceptibility + Theory[b]	Hall Coeff. + Theory[b]	Stored Energy + Theory[c]	Percent of Displaced Atoms per 10^20 nvt total
1 × 10^20 fast or ~4.5 × 10^20 total	5.0						1.11
1.1 × 10^20 fast of ~5 × 10^20 total		2.6					0.52
5 × 10^17 total			5×10^{-3}				1.0
1.7 × 10^17 fast or ~7.5 × 10^17 total				7×10^{-3}			.93
5 × 10^19 total					5×10^{-2}		.10
10^20 total[d] (room temp) 10^20 total[d] (liquid nitrogen temperature)						.27 ~.50	.27 ~.50

[a] Calculated using 1 mev for neutron energy.
[b] Assuming 2 trapped electrons per displaced atom.
[c] Using 440 Kcal/mole of displaced atoms.
[d] From initial rise of stored energy with exposure.

on copper at 10°K led to somewhat different results. These workers found that upon irradiation with 1.35 mev electrons the increase in resistivity observed experimentally agrees with that calculated theoretically within a factor of two, provided Blatt's numbers are used for the resistivity increment per per cent defect (see Table 3). From preliminary annealing experiments, however, it appears that Blatt's value is too low while that calculated by Overhauser and Gorman is too high. It was assumed here that all the interstitials anneal out below 80°K. Thus, while it is likely that the simple defects formed by electron irradiation conform to theory better than those produced by massive particles, the question is by no means resolved at the present time.

Graphite. Antal, Weiss and Dienes[67] used the scattering of very slow neutrons by interstitials and vacancies to determine the defect concentration. This technique is limited to materials of low neutron capture cross-section. Detailed experimental studies have been carried out on graphite.

Neutrons of sufficiently long wave length are scattered isotropically by isolated point defects and the scattering can be measured when crystalline effects (Bragg scattering) are absent. Babinet's principle may be applied under such conditions and, therefore, vacancies and interstitials scatter in exactly the same manner. The cross section for this nuclear type of scattering is accurately known from other measurements. The pertinent cross section is the bound atom cross section σ_b. Thus, if the scattering from the defects is measurable an absolute method is at hand for determining their concentration. Thus, while the physics of the situation is quite analogous to the scattering of conduction electrons by defects in metals, the great advantage of the neutron technique is the accurate knowledge of the corresponding nuclear cross sections.

It is not practical to attempt to measure directly the isotropically scattered neutron intensity. Instead, the attenuation of a long wave-length neutron beam during its passage through the material is measured in a transmission experiment. There are other sources of attenuation which have to be taken into account and whose cross sections should be very small compared to the cross section for defect scatterings.

In the absence of defects and past the last Bragg cut-off ($\lambda > 2d_{max}$), the transmitted intensity, I_s, is given by

$$I_s = I_0 \exp\left[-NX(\sigma_a + \sigma_i + \sigma_{dis})\right] \tag{18}$$

where I_0 = incident intensity

N = number of nuclei per cm^3

X = path length traversed through the sample

σ_a = cross section for absorption

σ_i = cross section for inelastic scattering

σ_{dis} = cross section for disorder scattering other than defects (isotopic spin, etc).

If f defects per atom are present the transmitted intensity, I_d, is

$$I_d = I_0 \exp\left[-NX(\sigma_a + \sigma_i + \sigma_{dis} + \sigma_b f)\right] \tag{19}$$

A direct comparison of a crystal containing a fraction, f, of defects to a control crystal gives

$$\frac{I_d}{I_s} = e^{-NX\sigma_b f} \tag{20}$$

Measurement of the ratio I_d/I_s immediately gives a value for f.

Graphite was chosen for study because of inherent interest in this material and because it fulfilled very well the theoretical and experimental requirements. Samples were available which were estimated to contain of the order of a few per cent defects on the basis of Seitz' theory. This concentration should be easily measurable. For graphite

$$\sigma_b = 4.7 \text{ barns}$$

$$\sigma_a + \sigma_i \simeq 0.9 \text{ barns at 8 A}$$

and there is no spin or isotopic incoherence. The graphite specimen served also as a neutron filter, which resulted in a most economical use of the very low intensity available in a long wave-length neutron beam.

The slow neutron beam was obtained from the Brookhaven reactor by filtering the thermal neutron spectrum. This spectrum of flux has a Maxwellian energy distribution peaked near 1A with a "tail" on the long wavelength side. If a polycrystalline material of sufficient length is placed in such a beam, Bragg scattering removes all neutrons from the incident beam except those having $\lambda > 2d_{max}$, where d_{max} is the largest interplanar spacing for which diffraction is possible. In these experiments the graphite specimens were made long enough (approx. 9″) to constitute efficient filters by themselves. A typical spectrum of the neutrons transmitted by a 9-in. graphite specimen is shown on Figure 3 as the "unirradiated" curve. The "cut-off" wave length is clearly marked by an abrupt increase in transmitted intensity at $\lambda = 2d_{(002)} = 6.70$ A.

In order to avoid spurious effects due to the increase in the c-axis of graphite upon pile irradiation, a plot of transmitted intensity vs. wave length was obtained using a crystal spectrometer. Any irrelevant change in intensity could then be disregarded and the transmitted intensity obtained by measuring the area under the curves for $\lambda > 7.30$ A (See Fig. 3). Onset of second order reflections at about 13.4 A would place a limit on the usable wave-length region, but is of no consequence in these experiments since the beam intensity is too weak to be detected past 12 A. Care was taken to accept all small angle scattered neutrons, thus eliminating effects of small particle size in the sample.

Several spectra were obtained from the spectrometer for the irradiated and standard (unirradiated) specimen run alternatively and averaged. Figure 3 shows the results. The areas under each curve give

$$\frac{I_d}{I_s} = 0.607$$

The estimated accuracy of this figure is about ± 10 per cent. By Eq. (20) $f = 0.0526$. The fraction of displaced atoms is $f/2 = 0.0263$.

The f value obtained by the above method may now be compared to the number of displaced atoms expected theoretically using Eq. (10). For 1 mev neutrons in graphite, using $E_d = 25$ ev and $L_c = 10^4$ ev, Eq. (10) gives

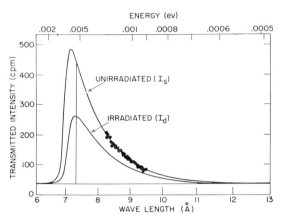

Figure 1.3. Slow neutron intensity transmitted by an irradiated and unirradiated graphite specimen. For clarity, only a typical group of experimental points have been reproduced along one curve to indicate their number and spread. Only intensities to the right of the vertical line at 7.30 Å were considered in computing I_s and I_d (from ref. 67).

for the number of atoms displaced per 1 mev neutron

$$N_d = 200$$

The fraction of displaced atoms which corresponds to 1.1×10^{20} *nvt* (neutrons per cm^2) of 1 mev neutrons is, therefore, 0.055 or 5.5 per cent using for σ_s, the collision cross section for the carbon atom, the value 2.5×10^{-24} cm^2. This value is an overestimate because the effective neutrons were assumed to be of 1 mev energy. Further, the value of L_c is rather uncertain. (Formula 2.6b of reference 8 was used to estimate L_c.) The number to be used for *nvt* is rather uncertain since the fast flux and its energy distribution are not known with any accuracy. Our best estimate of the effective *nvt* for the graphite sample used in these experiments is 1.1×10^{20} neutrons/cm^2 (total integrated neutron flux of about 4×10^{20} n/cm^2). The uncertainty in this number is of the order of 50 per cent.

The experimentally determined value of f is known, therefore, with greater accuracy than any theoretically derived value, partly because of uncertainties in the value of *nvt*. Consequently, the theory itself cannot be judged too critically. The fraction of displaced atoms determined experimentally by this method is in good agreement with the theory within the limitations mentioned above.

The value of f determined in these experiments may be in error. One reason is that if the defects are aggregated into pairs or larger clusters their scattering will not be equivalent to those of isolated interstitials and vacancies. Another reason is that the inelastic cross section may be altered by the irradiation. It has been assumed that this effect is unimportant. It has also been assumed that there is negligible inhomogeneous distortion (i.e. distortion rather than just displacement of the graphite planes) in the neighborhood of the defect. An outward inhomogeneous distortion around the interstitial can be shown to reduce the effective cross section of the interstitial. (A similar distortion would increase the cross section of the vacancy.) Theoretical estimates of this correction are at present unreliable but it is probably not greater than 20 per cent. In principle the occurrence of pairs is detectable by examining the wave-length dependence of the attenuation. These preliminary experiments are not sufficiently accurate past 9 A to establish the existence of a wave-length dependence. The fact that no wave-length dependence which would be outside experimental error is observable indicates that only a small fraction of the displaced atoms may be present in the form of pairs. More refined experiments will be necessary to establish this point definitely.

Some annealing undoubtedly has occurred during irradiation near room temperature since it is known that about one-third of the damage introduced at about $-190°C$ anneals out in warming to room temperature.[68] Because of all these uncertainties one cannot claim a better agreement between theory and experiment than within a factor of two. Because of annealing one expects that the experimental value is smaller than the theoretical one.

Changes in electrical properties can also be used to determine the fraction of defects, or rather the fraction of electron traps.[16] Typical experimental curves as a function of reactor exposure are shown in Figure 4. The damage centers are both electron traps and electron scatterers.

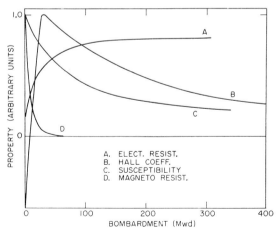

Figure 1.4. Electrical properties after bombardment of graphite (from ref. 16).

Changes in electrical properties must be separated into contributions from each of these two effects. Electron traps actually increase the number of carriers by lowering the Fermi energy to a region of higher density of states as indicated by the Hall coefficient data. The electrical resistance nevertheless increases upon irradiation because of the large increase in scattering probability. The magnetoresistance, which probably changes as the inverse square of the scattering probability, decreases very rapidly with increasing bombardment. The magnetic susceptibility of graphite is highly diamagnetic due to the presence of electrons near the edge of the Brillouin zone. Since these electrons are trapped upon irradiation the diamagnetism decreases rapidly as a function of irradiation. The magnetic susceptibility is nearly independent of the scattering probability.

A theoretical derivation of the number of displaced atoms from the above property changes is difficult. Fortunately, the concentration of electron traps in irradiated graphite can be determined independently[69,70] by comparing the irradiated material to unirradiated graphite into which known amounts of electron traps have been introduced as chemical impurities. These chemical traps do not materially change the electron scattering. By this method the electron trap concentration in graphite is found to be 10^{-4} trap per carbon atom for a bombardment of 5×10^{17} nvt integrated slow neutron flux. This value differs by less than a factor of two from the total number of displaced atoms expected theoretically.

There has been some success recently in calculating the number of trapped electrons from changes in magnetic susceptibility.[71,72] A value of 1.4×10^{-4} electron trapped per carbon atom is obtained after a bombardment of 1.7×10^{17} nvt of fast neutrons. This value is in good agreement with the figure quoted above which was determined by the use of bromine-graphite residue compounds. Similar calculations based on radiation-induced changes in the Hall coefficient appear to be far less successful.[73] A value of 10^{-5} electron trap per carbon atom is derived for a neutron irradiation of 5×10^7 nvt of integrated slow neutron flux. This value is a factor of 10 below that obtained above by a number of different methods. The number of traps produced by neutron bombardment still has to be converted into the number of displaced atoms. Unfortunately, the number of electron traps per displaced atom is not known with any accuracy. It is likely that the number of traps per interstitial plus vacancy, i.e. per displaced atom, is near 2.[16] With this value, generally satisfactory agreement is observed among the determinations for the number of displaced atoms based on neutron transmission and on changes in electronic properties (with the exception of the theoretical change in Hall coefficient).

One can also estimate the number of displaced atoms from measurements of stored energy. The heat content of a sample is raised by the production of interstitials and vacancies. If their energies of formation are known their concentration is immediately calculable from total stored energy values, determined calorimetrically as an increase in the heat of combustion. A value for the stored energy of 100 cal/gm for an irradiation at room temperature of 10^{20} total integrated neutron flux appears to be representative.[22] Dienes[74] has calculated theoretically the energy of formation of an interstitial and a vacancy in graphite and obtained the values 420 Kcal/mole and 120 Kcal/mole, respectively. Hennig[75] has pointed out that some of the attractive terms were neglected unjustifiably in the Van der Waals potential employed in the interstitial calculation. For the interstitial 320 Kcal/mole is a better value giving 440 Kcal/mole of displaced atoms. Using this figure leads to 0.27 per cent displaced atoms per 10^{20} *nvt* of total flux. The neutron transmission experiments, which gave a value of 2.6 per cent, were carried out on samples which received 1.1×10^{20} *nvt* of fast neutrons, or about 5×10^{20} *nvt* of total integrated neutron flux. The corresponding value from stored energy is, therefore, 1.35 per cent. The agreement is not too bad, particularly if it is recalled that the irradiations were not carried out in the same reactor or on the same samples.

There is also evidence of a higher damage rate at liquid nitrogen than at room temperature.[68,76] The extra damage anneals out below room temperature. The amount of energy stored below room temperature is about the same as that stored above[76] and, therefore, the number of displaced atoms calculated from this measurement should be approximately doubled. However, corresponding neutron transmission experiments are not yet available and it is impossible at this point to say whether some of the defects have annealed out or found energetically more favorable places in the lattice.

The various experiments on graphite are summarized in Table 4 and compared with theory. The conclusion from this table is that the various experimental methods agree quite well among themselves, well within the large uncertainties in the flux. The only exception is the value derived from a theoretical analysis of Hall coefficient measurements; this value is unreasonably low. The experiments also agree quite well with theory, although the theory cannot be judged too critically because of large uncertainties both in the theory and in the exposures. The agreement, which is of the order of a factor of two, is considerably better than in the case of metals. The results suggest that the simple collision theory is reasonably adequate for a material like graphite and that E_d is not spread out over a wide range of values.

Semiconductors. The electrical properties of semiconductors are generally very sensitive to bombardment with energetic particles that produce displaced atoms in the crystal.[9,77] The reason is that the concentration of charge carriers is extremely small in a semiconductor and the introduction of a very few traps can lead to very large changes in the carrier concentration.

It is now generally agreed that in specimens of n-type germanium of high conductivity[78,79] the displaced atoms introduce acceptor levels, at least initially, which are sufficiently low for electrons to be removed from the conduction band. In the early stages of irradiation the Fermi level remains almost unaltered and the decrease in number of carriers is directly proportional to the increase in the number of acceptor levels. At higher irradiations the Fermi level drops and the situation is far more complex.[79] Eventually the sample becomes p-type. The initial rate of loss of conductivity of n-type Ge should give a good measure of the rate of production of displaced atoms.

Klontz's work,[45,80] carried out at liquid nitrogen temperature on 0.35 mm thick samples, showed that in n-type germanium bombardment with 1.5 mev electrons resulted in the loss of 0.065 carriers per bombarding electron. Similar experiments with 4.5 mev electrons gave 6.15 times more damage. Recent work with neutron bombardment[81] shows that two types of electron traps are produced by both electron and neutron bombardment. This is compatible with the model suggested by James and Lark-Horovitz[78] provided two traps are associated with each Frenkel pair. This means that two acceptors are produced per displacement. On this basis the above experiments give 0.032 displacements per electron at 1.5 mev and 0.196 displacements per electron at 4.5 mev. The corresponding theoretical values[11] are 0.06 and 0.156, respectively. The calculations were made using Eq. (11) to (14) and $E_d = 30$ ev.

Brown, Fletcher and Wright[82] bombarded Ge with 3 mev electrons at room temperature. They found a cross section of 30×10^{-24} cm^2 for the production of traps. This corresponds to 0.106 displacements per electron in their samples ($\frac{1}{16}$ in. thick) using two traps per displacement. The corresponding theoretical figure is about a factor of 4 bigger[11], .424 displacements per electron (using 30 ev for E_d). However, in this case some annealing has occurred.[74]

Similar results are obtained from alpha particle bombardments at room temperature. Brattain and Pearson[83] bombarded layers of n-type Ge with 5.3 mev alpha particles which were stopped in the specimens. They found that each alpha-particle introduces about 78 acceptors or 39 displaced atoms. Lark-Horovitz and colleagues obtained a value of 95 acceptors (47 displaced atoms) under similar conditions.[79] The corresponding theoretical value[11] is 123 displaced atoms per alpha particle. Again, some annealing has undoubtedly occurred. A similar result is obtained upon deuteron bombardment (9.5 mev) at 200°K.[79] The calculated[11] number of displaced atoms

TABLE 5. NUMBER OF DISPLACED ATOMS PRODUCED IN GERMANIUM
BY VARIOUS IRRADIATIONS* (from ref. 12b)

Experimental Technique	Experimental Value for Number of Displaced Atoms, N_e	Theoretical Value for Number of Displaced Atoms, N_{th}	N_{th}/N_e	Reference
1.5 mev electrons at 90°K	0.032 per incident electron	0.06 per incident electron	2.3	45, 80, 11
4.5 mev electrons at 90°K	0.196 per incident electron	0.156 per incident electron	0.8	45, 80, 11
3 mev electrons at 25°C	0.106 per incident electron	0.424 per incident electron	4.0	11, 82
5.3 mev α at 25°C	39 per incident alpha particle	123 per incident alpha particle	3.1	11, 83
5 mev α at 25°C	47 per incident alpha particle	123 per incident alpha particle	2.6	11, 79
9.5 mev deuteron at 200°K	8 per incident deuteron	31 per incident deuteron	3.9	11, 79
Neutron bombardment at 90°K	2.5 per incident fast neutron	15 per incident fast neutron	6.0	27, 81

* Two acceptors per displaced atom are assumed throughout; estimates, therefore, differ by a factor of 2 from those in ref. 11.

per incident deuteron is found to be 31 and the experimentally observed value is 8 (17 acceptors).

For neutron bombardment at liquid nitrogen temperature[81] an average of 5 acceptor levels per unit of fast effective *nvt* was found. This corresponds to about 2.5 displaced atoms per fast neutron. The theoretical values are higher by about a factor of 6. The discrepancy may actually be larger than this since some of the resistivity change may be due to changes in mobility.[27]

The above results for semiconductors are summarized in Table 5. The conclusion from this table is that the agreement between theory and experiment is about the same as in the case of metals and is not as good as in the case of graphite, particularly for neutron bombardment. The number of displaced atoms are apparently overestimated theoretically.

Corundum and Fused Silica. It is attractive to study the number and nature of displaced atoms produced by fast particle bombardment by means of changes in optical properties, e.g. color centers, trapping centers, etc. The optical methods are generally very sensitive and can be rendered absolute by independent measurement of the oscillator strength involved in any given absorption band. In order to use such methods, however, it is necessary to separate unequivocally the effects due to displaced atoms

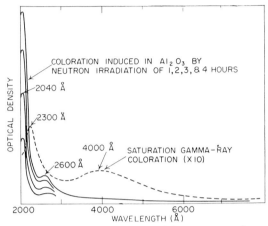

Figure 1.5. Optical absorption bands induced by reactor and gamma-ray irradiation in Al_2O_3. All these measurements were made with the Beckman DU spectrophotometer. The optical density scale for γ-coloration has been multiplied by 10. (from ref. 84.).

from those produced by ionizing radiation. Such a separation of displacement and ionizing effects is difficult, particularly in the case of the otherwise very attractive simple ionic crystals.

A clear-cut separation of the two effects has been reported by Levy and Dienes[84,85] for alpha aluminum oxide (Al_2O_3). This material turns out to be very resistant to coloration by ionizing radiation and the slight coloration due to such radiation saturates at a very low exposure. Upon reactor irradiation α-Al_2O_3 was found to show two optical absorption bands in the 2-8000 A region, one at approximately 2040 A and one at 2600 A. (There appears to be an additional band at 1650 A which has not yet been studied.) Typical experimental data are shown in Figure 5. All neutron irradiations were carried out in the same pneumatic tube facility at the Brookhaven reactor with flux constant to 10 per cent and at a temperature of $100 \pm 5°C$. The optical absorption spectrum is independent of any further exposure to ionizing radiation.

The growth of the absorption bands as a function of irradiation was studied. It was found that the growth may be resolved into a linear part and an initial part which saturates exponentially. The linear part is interpreted as due to the steady rate of production of defects by fast neutrons. Theory and experiment may now be compared in terms of this steady rate of defect production.

The theoretically expected number can be calculated from Eq. (10). For Al_2O_3 the following numbers were used: $L_c = 3.72 \times 10^4$ ev ($L_t = 8$ ev),

$M_1 = 20.4$ (average atomic mass), $E_d = 25$ ev. With these numbers Eq. (10) gives

$$N_d = 744$$

The number of nuclei per cc is 1.2×10^{23} and the average cross-section for primary neutron collision in the neighborhood of 1 mev is 3 barns. The calculation was made for a sample which was exposed in a flux of 2.8×10^{12} nv total, corresponding to a fast flux of about 0.7×10^{12} nv. Under these conditions the expected rate of production is

$$n = 6.6 \times 10^{17} \text{ displaced atoms/cc/hr}$$

The number of color centers times the oscillator strength, $n_0 f$, was calculated from the optical absorption band at 2040 A using the measured half width and Smakula's equation.[86,87] The corresponding number is

$$n_0 f = 6.0 \times 10^{15} \text{ color centers cc hr}$$

It is evident that n_0 can be made equal to n if the oscillator strength, f, is chosen to be 0.011. This is an unreasonable value. A value of 0.2 for f was deduced by Crawford and Wittels[15] from a comparison of optical absorption bands and magnetic susceptibility in vitreous SiO_2 colored by reactor irradiation. If f is taken to be 0.1, a reasonable value, the number of color centers is less than the theoretically expected number of displaced atoms by a factor of 10. Further work is needed before this discrepancy can be interpreted.

Early experiments by Levy[88] and more detailed experiments by Mitchell and Paige[89] have shown that similar results obtain in the case of crystalline and vitreous silica. In crystalline quartz two absorption bands have been found, at 5.7 and 7.6 ev respectively, which are associated with atomic displacements. The bands occur at about the same energies in fused quartz indicating that the short range atomic arrangement determines the energy of the transition. Mitchell and Paige suggest that the defects responsible for the 5.7 and 7.6 ev bands are oxygen vacancies and interstitials, respectively. A comparison with collision theory calculation shows that the lower limits to the oscillator strength are 0.05 (5.7 ev band) and 0.2 (7.6 ev band). Thus, the results are qualitatively similar to those for Al_2O_3, i.e. agreement with collision theory calls for very low values of the oscillator strengths.

Various experimental and theoretical methods have been described in this section for determining the concentration of displaced atoms produced by exposure to fast neutrons in a nuclear reactor. It is concluded that theory and experiment are in essential agreement in the case of graphite (i.e. within about a factor of two). For other types of solids the number of displaced atoms appear to be overetimated theoretically and agreement with experiment can be claimed only within an order of magnitude. It is not possible to decide at this time whether the discrepancies are due to inadequacies in the theory of displacement production or in theories linking changes in physical properties to the concentration of lattice defects.

Illustrative Changes in Physical Properties

Some of the changes in physical properties brought about by fast particle irradiation have already been discussed in connection with the determination of the concentration of displaced atoms. The changes mentioned could be interpreted, more or less simply, in terms of simple isolated crystalline defects. Many other changes occur in physical properties, some of them of considerable engineering importance, which cannot always be interpreted on the basis of the presence of simple defects. Some illustrative examples will be given in this chapter.

Dimensional Changes

Dimensional changes occur in many materials upon fast particle irradiation and are of particular practical importance in such reactor materials as graphite and uranium. The effects in these two substances are discussed briefly in this section.

The crystal lattice of graphite expands in a highly anisotropic way upon reactor irradiation.[16,22,23] There is a large expansion in the C_o, or interplanar, direction and a small shrinkage along the a direction. The large expansion in C_o is almost certainly caused by the introduction of interstitial atoms between the loosely bound graphite planes. These are the energetically most favorable positions for the interstitials.[74] The crystallite changes induced by irradiation have been studied extensively by x-ray diffraction. At low exposures there is a decrease in the crystalline peak intensity, a shift in the angle of diffraction corresponding to the expansion of the c-axis, but the peak shape remains essentially constant. At exposures above 5×10^{20} neutrons/cm^2 the peak is progressively broadened until at high exposures the peak becomes very diffuse.

Some typical data are shown in Fig. 6 for the c-axis expansion as a function of exposure.*[22] The corresponding over-all dimensional changes are only qualitatively related to the crystallite expansion and are generally smaller in magnitude. The behavior varies widely with the degree of orientation in the graphite. Fig. 7 shows the dimensional changes in several grades of graphite after irradiation. The abrupt change in the rate of expansion near 6×10^{20} neutrons/cm^2 may be associated with the broadening of the x-ray lines and hence the rather severe distortion of the crystal at higher exposures.

* MWD/T = megawatt days per ton, 1 $MWD/T \sim 7 \times 10^{17}$ *nvt*.

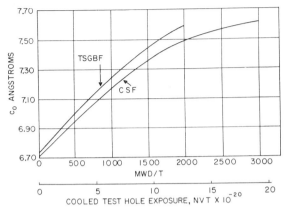

Figure 1.6. C_o displacement in irradiated graphite. (MWD/T = megawatt days per ton, 1 MWD/T $\sim$ 7 $\times$ 10^{17} mvt) (from ref. 22).

The interstitials between the graphite planes are relatively mobile. Thus, the expanded *c*-axis begins to recover at rather low temperatures when the material is heated up. As a corollary, if the irradiation is carried out at an elevated temperature much less *c*-axis expansion is observed. Some typical results are shown in Fig. 8.

Dimensional changes are generally large in anisotropic materials. Another material of great practical importance, whose dimensional changes can be very large, is uranium.[20,21] The dimensional change in this material is an

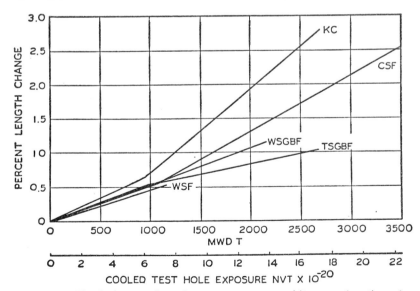

Figure 1.7. Physical expansion of transverse cut graphite as a function of exposure (from ref. 22).

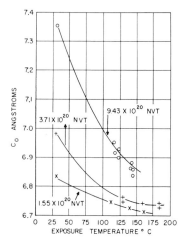

Figure 1.8. Variations in C_o displacement of CSF graphite with exposure temperature (from ref. 22).

order of magnitude larger than the more or less normal distortions expected in other materials and is not a change in density (which is small). Uranium, of course, is fissionable and a sample of the material is subjected both to fast neutron and fission-fragment damage. Thus, severe damage is to be expected in any case. The effects to be discussed, however, appear to be connected with the highly anisotropic crystal structure of uranium rather than any particular mode or irradiation.

The phenomenon of radiation growth. Fig. 9 shows a series of photographs of a single crystal of alpha-uranium before and after irradiation. The crystal was originally nearly a right circular cylinder 0.125 inch in diameter.

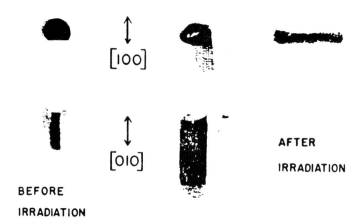

Figure 1.9. Aspects of a cylindrical single crystal of alpha uranium before and after irradiation in a reactor. 0.1% atom burnup (from ref. 21).

TABLE 6. IRRADIATION GROWTH COEFFICIENTS OF A SINGLE CRYSTAL
OF ALPHA-URANIUM

(Argonne National Laboratory, specimen irradiated to 0.1% burnup at approximately 100°C)

Direction Pole	Irradiation Growth Coefficient, G_i (Eq. 21)
(100)	-420 ± 20
(010)	$+420 \pm 20$
(001)	0 ± 20

A great deal of lengthening and shortening has occurred in the (010) and (100) directions, respectively, and the circular cross section has become elliptical. It is convenient to express the growth caused by irradiation in terms of the dimensionless quantity, G_i, defined by

$$G_i = \frac{\ln (L/L_0)}{\text{Ratio of fissions to total atoms}} \qquad (21)$$

For small elongations the relation

$$G_i = \frac{\text{Percent Growth}}{\text{Percent Burnup}} \qquad (22)$$

is adequate. Typical growth values are shown in Table 6. These numbers show that the length of a uranium rod would roughly double for about 0.2 per cent burnup.

Imperfect lineage crystals have the same general behavior as single crystals, but the magnitude of the elongation is greater and the geometrical regularity of the distorted specimens is less.

Cylindrical polycrystalline specimens in which the grains are not randomly oriented also deform under irradiation. The magnitude and character of the deformation and surface distortion depend upon structural factors. Longitudinal growth rates more than double those measured in single crystals have been observed in highly oriented polycrystalline specimens irradiated at the same temperature.

Polycrystalline uranium also exhibits marked deformation as a result of thermal cycling. This effect does not occur in single crystals. There are some similarities to irradiation growth but the above difference in single crystals shows clearly that there must be a basic difference in the mechanism and this analogy will not be pursued any further.

Suggested interpretations. A number of mechanisms have been proposed to account for the irradiation growth of alpha-uranium. It is clear that anisotropy plays an important role in leading to differential strains which have to be at least partly irreversible. Two major mechanisms in single crystals are generally considered important at the present time: (1) anisotropic diffusion and (2) plastic deformation accompanying fission spikes.

(1) Diffusion mechanism. Seigle and Opinsky[21,90] have proposed a mechanism which is based upon anisotropic diffusion of interstitials and vacancies. The alteration of shape arises from this diffusion by gross material transfer[91,92,93]. Seigle and Opinsky propose that interstitials migrate with some preference for the [010] direction while vacancies would migrate in the [100] and [001] directions. It is assumed that the diffusion of interstitials and vacancies essentially balance in the [001] direction leading to a net shrinkage in the [100] direction. The theory predicts that the rate of growth in the [010] direction will vary as the $3/4$ power of the neutron flux and the square root of the diffusion coefficient for interstitials. As in all diffusion mechanisms, a temperature dependence is, of course, predicted. An estimate[28] of the number of defects produced per fission shows that there is a plentiful supply of defects for the operation of this mechanism. The model is partially supported by the work of Kunz and Holden[24] who showed that the deformation rate of cold rolled uranium foil is greatly reduced when irradiation is done at liquid air where diffusion would be largely suppressed.

(2) *Plastic deformation accompanying fission spikes.* A growth mechanism can be based on the thermal expansion in the fission spike. An essential part of such a mechanism is that plastic deformation should be caused by the local expansion and that there should be a difference in behavior on heating and cooling. Pugh[20] ascribed growth to fission spikes accompanied by anisotropic plastic deformation. The anisotropic plastic properties of uranium have been deduced by Cahn[94] from the observed slip and twin systems. The proposed mechanism is as follows. The uniform compressive stress around the site of fission causes local preferential plastic yielding by twinning in uranium single crystals in the longitudinal [010] direction. When the fission spike cools, the outer region is subjected to a uniform tensile stress and therefore yields plastically, this time by twinning in the [100] and [001] directions. The net result is a local increase in length in the [010] direction in the outer region. This local extension throws a stress on the surrounding matrix which is relieved by equal amounts of slip on both the (110) planes. Since tension in the [010] direction produces no resolved shear stress on the (010) plane, slip in this plane does not occur even though it is the major slip mode. The macro-deformation of the crystal is, therefore, by (110) <110> shears which agrees with experiment in that extension occurs in the [010] direction, contraction in the [100] direction, and no change in the [001] direction. No limit is imposed on the extent of growth.

Since slip is a reversible process in a geometrical sense it could not be the basis of a ratchet mechanism. The above model predicts, therefore, that growth rates would diminish above 350°C and be practically zero at 600°C because at the higher temperature slip would occur rather than twinning and slip. Below 200°C growth would diminish with decreasing temperature because of the increase in the yield strength of the crystal. Experimental observations are in agreement with these predictions.

The main difficulty with the above model is that fission spikes are of very short duration and are rather small. The two recoiling fission fragments will dissipate the energy of fission along a line 10^{-4} to 10^{-3} cm. long. At distances greater than about 500 atoms from this line the yield stress will no longer be exceeded while usually 1000 atoms need to be affected to cause operation of a Frank-Read source. A part of the energy, however, is temporarily stored as interstitials and vacancies which also cause a local expansion. Above 500°C these defects recombine very fast but below this temperature they will keep the fission spike expanded somewhat, although the concentration of defects is probably too small to be very effective. If flow occurs, therefore, it must occur very rapidly. More detailed calculations by Seitz and Koehler[11] indicate, however, that plastic flow is likely to occur in the zone of highest stress as a result of the generation of dislocation rings of the order of five atomic distances in diameter. Thus, the twinning mechanism appears to be a plausible mechanism. It will take much detailed experimentation to decide between this and the diffusion mechanism.

Stored Energy. Irradiation of a crystal increases the energy content of the lattice. This increase in energy is referred to as the stored energy. In many ways perhaps this is the most basic physical change accompanying the production of defects. If the energy of formation of the defects is known theoretically and if the total stored energy is measured, then the number of defects is immediately calculable. This method of determining the fraction of displaced atoms has been used for graphite and has already been described in a previous section.

For simplicity of interpretation it is essential that the increase in enthalpy be measured by starting and terminating an experiment in well defined thermodynamic states. This was done in the graphite experiments referred to above where the stored energy was measured as an increase in the heat of combustion. This extra heat content is clearly the total energy content of the defects. If the irradiation is done at low temperature so that no annealing of the defects has taken place then the above energy change is simply the total energy of formation of a given fraction of defects. If, say, aggregation has already taken place via annealing, the corresponding stored energy is no longer interpretable in such a simple way. Stored energy experiments have also been done on diamond[95] and the results for this substance are very similar to that for graphite.

The nature of the released stored energy during annealing is of greater interest than the simple accumulation of increase in enthalpy. Fig. 10 shows the total stored energy in irradiated graphite and the stored energy which remains after prolonged annealing at 1000°C.[22] By difference one obtains

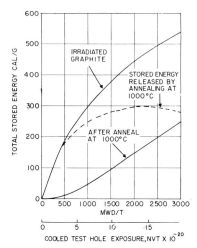

Figure 1.10. Buildup of total stored energy in graphite (from ref. 22).

the amount of stored energy which was released during the annealing—shown as a dotted line in Fig. 10. Note first that these stored energy effects are large; 500 cal/gm of stored energy represents the energy required to raise the temperature of a gram of graphite to more than 1200°C. The second observation is that most of the stored energy accumulated during brief irradiations can be released by annealing at a temperature of 1000°C. However, at exposures greater than about 13×10^{20} neutrons/cm^2 essentially none of the incremental amounts of stored energy can be released by annealing at 1000°C (i.e. the two solid curves in Fig. 10 become essentially parallel). Annealing temperatures approaching that of graphitization are required for complete recovery of the material.

The writer is not aware of any other experiments in which the total stored energy has been measured in an unambiguous way. The release of stored energy over limited temperature ranges has been studied in various materials[96,97,98]. From such experiments often important information is obtainable concerning the annealing of radiation damage, particularly if other physical properties are measured and correlated with the release of energy. More work in this field would be welcome since suitable measurements are clearly interpretable and, in principle, interstitials and vacancies can be distinguished since their energy contents are expected to differ by a factor of 2 to 5.

Mechanical Properties of Metals. The first observation on a change in elastic properties upon irradiation came from early work on graphite[22,99]. Reactor irradiation of graphite was found to produce a stronger, harder and more brittle material. Young's modulus was increased by about a factor of 3 upon an exposure of 10^{20} *nvt*.

Theoretical interpretation of these changes is difficult because of the complicated structure of graphite. The first theoretical calculations were carried out for metals by Dienes[100,101,102] who investigated the effect of vacancies and interstitials on the elastic constants of simple close-packed metallic crystals. In such substances the elastic constants are determined primarily by the repulsive interactions of the closed ion shells. This potential is of an exponential nature and varies extremely rapidly with interatomic distance. As the interatomic distance is shortened by creating an interstitial, the energy of the system increases sharply on the repulsive side of the potential curve. The creation of vacancies results essentially in the destruction of some normal interactions. Thus, one expects the influence of the interstitials to outweigh heavily the effect of vacancies.

Detailed calculations, in which relaxation of nearest neighbors was taken into account, led to the following conclusions. The presence of a small fraction of interstitials and vacancies results in large increases in the elastic moduli of copper, of the order of 5–7 per cent per one per cent interstitial. Lattice vacancies alone were found to decrease the moduli by essentially a bulk effect. Consequently, increases in the elastic moduli are to be attributed primarily to the presence of interstitial atoms. There is a complicating factor arising from modulus changes which may occur by a mechanism of dislocation pinning.[103] A proper experimental test of this theory has not yet been carried out. It is essential to make pre- and post-irradiation measurement at very low temperatures (below $40°K$) on low-temperature irradiated crystals because of annealing. It would also be advantageous to do the experiments on a low concentration alloy so as to eliminate the dislocation contribution to the modulus by pinning the dislocations. It should also be mentioned that the theory indicates that the above effect would be absent in a soft body-centered-cubic crystal such as sodium. In this case the relaxation around the interstitial is large enough to essentially eliminate the crowding upon which the modulus increase depends.

A rather large increase in modulus has been observed experimentally by Thompson and Holmes in copper single crystals after reactor irradiation[104,105,106]. These workers found that the modulus increase, which may be as high as 15–20 per cent, is not proportional to the amount of irradiation and saturates (i.e. no further change in modulus) at a very low irradiation level, namely of the order of 4×10^{12} *nvt* of fast flux. During this process the logarithmic decrement, which also saturates, decreases by almost an order of magnitude. It is quite clear that this effect cannot be due to the production of defects in the bulk as calculated by Dienes for two reasons.

First, the required flux is orders of magnitude too small and, second, no appreciable internal friction effects are to be expected from the presence of isolated interstitials and vacancies. The pinning of dislocations by the radiation-produced defects is a very reasonable explanation and this is the interpretation advanced by Thompson and Holmes. They show that this interpretation leads to generally accepted values for the dislocation densities and average segment lengths.

A change in modulus without an accompanying change in attenuation has been observed by Truell, Teutonico and Levy[107] in silicon. These workers carried out ultrasonic velocity and double refraction measurements on a cube of silicon which had been bombarded with a beam of approximately collimated fast neutrons. They found that the ultrasonic velocities were lowered by the irradiation and that double refraction became observable with waves propagated perpendicular to the neutron beam but not parallel to it. Since there was no observable change in attenuation it is reasonable to attribute the velocity changes to changes in the elastic moduli without any change in the dislocation network. If an analogy to Dienes' calculation for close-packed metals is valid for the diamond structure the results suggest, since the moduli decreased, that vacancies are responsible for the observed effects. This is not unreasonable for a room-temperature irradiation since the interstitials may have annealed out. The double refraction then is due to a clustering of defects along the path of the primary knock-on since the recoiling atom is expected to produce a region of damage roughly ellipsoidal in shape with the long direction oriented, on the average, along the direction of the incident particle.

Particle irradiation brings about large changes in some of the other mechanical properties of metals. The increase in elastic modulus has already been discussed above and has been attributed to the pinning of dislocations by radiation-induced defects. By the same argument it is expected that the critical shear stress would increase since it depends on the break-away of pinned dislocations. This is the case, and indeed this effect was observed first. Blewitt and Coltman[108] have studied the stress-strain curves of irradiated and unirradiated single crystals of copper. Some typical experimental results are shown in Fig. 11. The critical shear stress increased from 0.241 to 2.00 kg/mm^2 for a fast neutron flux of about 2×10^{18} nvt.^{3} After appreciable plastic deformation the differences in the stress-strain curves essentially disappear as shown in Fig. 11. The discontinuities at a shear strain of about 0.6 are due to an additional irradiation of about 2×10^{18} nvt. It is clear that after cold work the effect of irradiation is much smaller than for annealed samples. It is also clear from Fig. 11 that there is no 1-to-1 correspondence between cold work and radiation hardening. On the basis of the shape of the stress-strain curve of the irradiated specimen Blewitt and

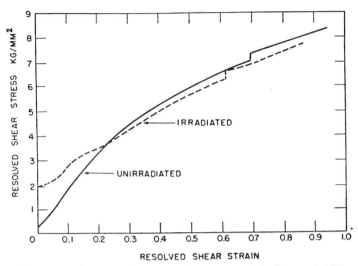

Figure 1.11. Stress-strain curve of copper crystals (from ref. 108).

co-workers suggest that irradiation is somewhat similar to solid-solution hardening.[109,110] The slip characteristics of the irradiated crystal are similar to those of α-brass and the critical shear stress vs. bombardment curves, shown in Fig. 12, are similar to the effect of alloying.

Kunz and Holden[111] obtained similar results for iron and zinc single crystals. McReynolds et al.[112] studied copper and aluminum after reactor bombardment at 80°K and found that the effects in Al annealed out before reaching room temperature while temperatures of about 300°C were required before the increase in the shear stress of copper annealed out in agreement with the observations of Blewitt and Coltman. The values of the critical shear stress obtained in these experiments are much larger than those obtainable by alloying. On the basis of the original number of

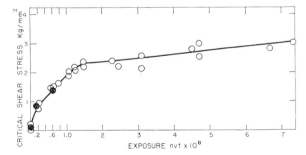

Figure 1.12. Effect of Neutron Irradiation on the critical shear stress of copper (from ref. 110).

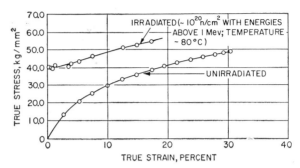

Figure 1.13. The effect of reactor exposure on the stress-strain curve of nickel (from ref. 114).

defects introduced by irradiation, Blewitt[113] estimated that one interstitial atom was forty times as effective as a Zn atom in raising the critical shear stress. It is very unlikely that the defects are still present as simple point defects and many of them must have annealed out. However, whatever the nature of the defects responsible for this effect it is clear that they are extremely effective in raising the critical shear stress.

In some metals the whole stress-strain curve is appreciably altered by irradiation. A typical example is the curve for nickel shown in Fig. 13, taken from the work of Bruch, McHugh and Hockenbury.[114]

Irradiation also affects the brittle to ductile transition temperature in those metals which exhibit a brittle behavior below a certain temperature and a ductile behavior above this temperature. Meyer[115] studied in some detail this effect in mild steel using 18.6 mev deuterons for irradiation. Fig. 14 illustrates the results obtained in impact tests before and after

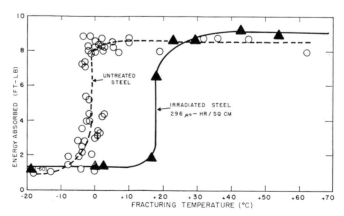

Figure 1.14. Transition curve for untreated and irradiated impact specimens (from ref. 115).

irradiation with an average total exposure of 6.7×10^{17} particles per cm^2 ($29.6\mu a - $ hrs/cm^2). This irradiation increased the transition temperature from $-1°C$ to about $18°C$. Such embrittlement appears to be characteristic of body-centered-cubic structures. Bruch, McHugh, and Hockenbury[116] found that molybdenum exhibited brittle behavior in tensile tests after an exposure of about 10^{20} neutrons/cm^2. The transition temperature was increased from $-30°C$ to about $70°C$.

Diffusion. It is generally accepted at the present time that diffusion in solids takes place via defects in the crystal, which are primarily vacancies in metals and either vacancies or interstitials in ionic salts.[117] Since fast particle irradiation results in the production of such defects a close connection between diffusion and irradiation is to be expected. Some aspects of this connection had been discussed by Feldman and Dienes[118] and a full theoretical calculation has been carried out by Lomer.[119] The main point is that by means of irradiation a non-equilibrium number of defects can be produced in a crystal and therefore, diffusion rates can be increased in a temperature region where they are normally very low. The diffusion coefficient, D, can be expressed as a function of temperature by the relation

$$D = AC_v e^{-E_m/RT} \tag{23}$$

where C_v = atomic fraction of vacancies

E_m = activation energy for motion of a vacancy

A = constant

In the following it will be assumed that diffusion occurs by means of vacancies. The same argument is applicable to interstitials or to a combination of the two defects. In equilibrium C_v is given by

$$C_v = A'e^{-E_f/RT} \tag{24}$$

where E_f = energy of formation of a vacancy. Under irradiation with fast particles additional vacancies are formed. Suppose that the steady state concentration of these vacancies is C_v', which, of course, depends on the flux, ψ, of bombarding particles. Then

$$D = Ae^{-E_m/RT}[C_v + C_v'(\psi)] \tag{25}$$

Qualitatively, then, one can say the following:

(a) At high temperature C_v is larger than C_v' because most of the extra defects anneal out and the irradiation has a very small effect on D.

(b) At very low temperature $C_v' > C_v$ and the diffusion coefficient can be increased enormously by irradiation. At low temperature the temperature dependence will be characterized by E_m alone since all the defects are frozen in and C_v' becomes independent of the temperature.

(c) In the intermediate temperature range D will be increased and the temperature dependence will not be purely exponential in $1/T$, since C_v depends in a complicated way on the temperature because of annealing, but is always less temperature-dependent than C_v .

Detailed calculations by Lomer[119] for copper confirm this qualitative picture. His main results are shown in Fig. 15 where the diffusion length expected in three months in copper is plotted against $1/T$ under various conditions. The assumed energy parameters are indicated in the figure and both vacancies and interstitials are taken into account as well as annihilation at trapping sites (fraction 10^{-10}) at low temperature where equilibrium concentrations are not valid. Lomer also indicates the practical limits of detection in a macroscopic diffusion experiment as well as by indirect techniques such as internal friction. It is quite clear that as far as macroscopic diffusion measurements are concerned the expected irradiation effects are practically undetectable, primarily because the defects anneal out too fast.

There is some experimental evidence which supports Lomer's analysis. Johnson and Martin[120] investigated the effect of 10 mev protons on the self diffusion of silver in the 525–852°C temperature range by conventional tracer techniques. Their data show no observable effect of proton irradiation in agreement with the above theoretical considerations.

There are some indirect effects of defect motion which do not require that the defect stay in the crystal but depend only on the total number of

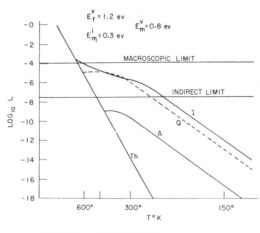

Th = THERMAL EQUILIBRIUM CORE
A = ANNEALED ie COOLED VERY SLOWLY
Q = QUENCHED
I = EXPERIMENT UNDER PILE IRRADIATION

Figure 1.15. The diffusion length L in an experiment lasting three months plotted against temperature for various conditions of "copper" (from ref. 119).

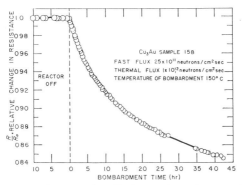

Figure 1.16. The effect of neutron irradiation on the resistance of partially ordered Cu_3Au. The original resistivity was 7.92 micro-ohm cm. The resistivity of Cu_3Au at equilibrium at 150°C is 5.50 micro-ohm cm. After 500 hours at a flux of 2.5×10^{11} fast neutrons/cm² sec and 1×10^{12} thermal neutrons/cm²/sec the resistivity dropped to 5.94 micro-ohm cm. (from ref. 123).

defect jumps which have occurred. Increased rate of ordering in an alloy is such an effect and has been studied in several systems. These studies are described below as important examples of radiation-induced solid state reactions.

Adam and Dugdale[121] and Blewitt and Coltman[122, 123] were the first ones to observe ordering in an alloy, in this case Cu_3Au, brought about by neutron bombardment. If a disordered specimen of Cu_3Au is irradiated in the reactor at a somewhat elevated temperature, say 150°C, the resistivity decreases and approaches the equilibrium-ordered value after a long irradiation. Slight ordering can be achieved even at 80°C[124]. A typical curve is shown in Fig. 16. Thermal ordering at these temperatures is far too slow to be observable. Similar effects have been achieved with 3 mev electrons[125] and with gamma-rays.[126] X-ray measurements proved that the long range order has been increased as a result of the irradiation.[127] The interpretation of these experiments is that the diffusion rate has been increased by the production of vacancies and interstitials during the irradiation. Those defects which are not immediately annihilated by recombination migrate through the crystal leaving a wake of partial order, until they are annihilated or trapped either at dislocation or at severely damaged regions of the lattice. Blewitt and Coltman[123] estimate that, in their irradiation experiment at 200°C with a fast neutron flux of about 10^{12} n cm^{-2} sec^{-1}, the mean path of defects before annihilation is of the order of 100 A.

Another set of experiments was performed by Rosenblatt, Smoluchowski and Dienes on α-brass[128]. These workers found that reactor irradiation at 50°C resulted in a decrease in the resistivity of α-brass and interpreted this

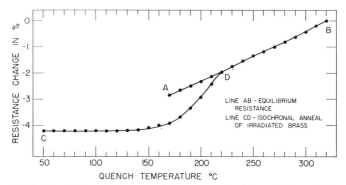

Figure 1.17. Line AB-equilibrium resistance quenched from indicated datum point temperature and measured at liquid nitrogen; line CD-isochronal anneal (measurements made in liquid nitrogen) of specimen equilibrated at 210°C and irradiated 20 days at 50°C (from ref. 129).

change as an increase in the short range order. Damask[129] investigated these resistivity effects in some detail by studying the annealing of kinetics of resistance changes producted in 30 per cent Zn α-brass by quench, neutron irradiation at 50°C, and cold work. His studies indicate the following: (1) Resistance decreases in α-brass can be induced by proper heat treatment. The rate of change of resistance with annealing time follows the same kinetics as that of stress induced changes in local order. Thus, the resistance changes arise from changes in short range order. (2) Reactor irradiation of α-brass at 50°C in an equilibrium resistance state produces a decrease in resistance. Some typical data are shown in Fig. 17. An anneal of this decrease results in the same kinetic behavior as that of stress induced order and, therefore, neutron irradiation has increased the short range order. More recent experiments indicate that the change in relaxation time due to irradiation can be very large[130]. At 50°C the thermal relaxation time is about 10^{11} seconds while that in a neutron flux (2×10^{12} $n/cm^2/sec$) or 2 mev electron flux (2×10^{14} $e/cm^2/sec$) is about 10^4 seconds giving a ratio of about 10^7. (3) The first step of annealing of resistance induced by cold work shows essentially the same kinetic behavior as (1) and (2) and, therefore, this step probably arises from reordering of the cold-work-induced disorder. This first step is not annealed by neutron irradiation and, therefore, local heating from neutron irradiation is not an important mechanism in changing the state of local order. The defects themselves are ineffective in this case because they are apparently trapped by dislocations introduced by the cold work.

    These two sets of experiments fully support the conclusion that local or microdiffusion has been greatly enhanced by the presence of the extra defects produced by fast particle irradiation.

References

1. J. C. Slater, "The Effects of Radiation on Materials," *J. Appl. Phys*, **22**, 237 (1951).

2. G. J. Dienes, "Radiation Effects in Solids," *Ann. Rev. Nucl. Sci.* **II**, 187 (1953).

3. G. J. Dienes, "Effects of Nuclear Radiations on the Mechanical Properties of Solids," *J. Appl. Phys.*, **24**, 666 (1953).

4. F. Seitz, "Radiation Effects in Solids," *Physics Today* **5**, 6 (1952).

5. S. Siegel, "Radiation Damage as a Metallurgical Research Technique," Chapter in "Modern Research Techniques in Physical Metallurgy," ASM, 1953, pp. 312–324.

6. J. W. Glen, "A Survey of Radiation Effects in Metals," *Phil. Mag. Suppl.* **4**, 381 (1955).

7. C. R. Sutton and D. O. Leeser, "How Radiation Affects Structural Materials," *Iron Age* **174**, 97 (1954).

8. G. H. Kinchin and R. S. Pease, "The Displacement of Atoms in Solids by Radiation," *Rep. Prog. Phys.* **18**, 1 (1955).

9. K. Lark-Horovitz, "Nucleon Bombarded Semiconductors," "Reading Conference on Semiconducting Materials," Butterworth's Scientific Publications, London, England, 1951, pp. 47–78.

10. K. Lintner and E. Schmid, "Bedeutung von Korpuskularbestrahlung für die Eigenschaften von Fest Körpern," *Ergebnisse d. exakt. Naturwiss.* **28**, 302 (1955).

11. F. Seitz and J. S. Koehler, "Theory of Lattice Displacements," Proceedings of the International Conference on the Peaceful Uses of Atomic Energy, United Nations, 1956, Vol. 7, p. 615 (Paper No. 749); Solid State Physics, Vol. 2, Academic Press, New York 1956, pp. 307–449 (edit. F. Seitz and D. Turnbull).

12. G. J. Dienes, (a) "Theoretical Aspects of Radiation Damage," Proceedings of the International Conference on the Peaceful Uses of Atomic Energy, United Nations, 1956, Vol. 7, p. 634 (Paper No. 750); (b) "Displaced Atoms in Solids—Comparison between Theory and Experiment," in "Symposium on Radiation Effects of Materials," ASTM, 1957.

13. J. H. O. Varley, "Damage in Non-Fissile Materials," Proceedings of the International Conference on the Peaceful Uses of Atomic Energy, United Nations, p. 642 (Paper No. 444), 1956.

14. G. Mayer, P. Perio, J. Gigon and M. Tournarie, "Irradiations of Non-Metallic Materials," *ibid.*, Vol. 7, p. 647 (Paper No. 362).

15. J. H. Crawford, Jr. and M. C. Wittels, "Radiation Effects in Crystals," *ibid.*, Vol. 7, p. 654 (Paper No. 753).

16. G. R. Hennig and J. E. Hove, "Radiation Damage to Graphite," *ibid.*, Vol. 7, p. 666 (Paper No. 751), see also special article by M. Burton, T. J. Neubert, *et al.* on "Neutron-Induced Decomposition in Graphite," *J. Appl. Phys.* **27**, 557–572 (1956) in which the early work in this field is covered.

17. R. Smoluchowski, "Irradiation of Ionic Crystals," Proceedings of the International Conference on the Peaceful Uses of Atomic Energy, United Nations, 1956, Vol. 7, p. 682 (Paper No. 748).

18. D. S. Billington, "Radiation Damage in Reactor Materials," *ibid.*, Vol. 7, p. 421 (Paper No. 744).

19. S. T. Konobeevsky, N. F. Pravdyuk, and V. I. Kutaitsev, "Irradiation of Fissionable Materials," *ibid.*, Vol. 7, p. 433 (Paper No. 681).

20. S. F. Pugh, "Damage Occurring in Uranium," *ibid.*, Vol. 7, p. 441 (Paper No. 443).

21. S. H. Paine and J. H. Kittel, "Irradiation Effects in Uranium and Alloys," *ibid.*, Vol. 7, p. 445 (Paper No. 745).

22. W. K. Woods, L. P. Bupp and J. F. Fletcher, "Irradiation Damage to Artificial Graphite," *ibid.*, Vol. 7, 455 (Paper No. 746).

23. G. H. Kinchin, "Effects of Irradiation on Graphite," *ibid.*, Vol. 7, p. 472 (Paper No. 442).

24. S. T. Konobeevsky, N. F. Pravdyuk and V. I. Kutaitsev, "Irradiation of Structural Materials," *ibid.*, Vol. 7, p. 479 (Paper No. 680).

25. F. E. Faris, "Effects of Irradiation on Structural Materials," *ibid.*, Vol. 7, p. 484 (Paper No. 747).

26. G. I. Cathers, "Radiation Damage to Processing Reagents," *ibid.*, Vol. 7, p. 490 (Paper No. 743).

27. H. Brooks, "Nuclear Radiation Effects in Solids," *Annual Review of Nuclear Science* **6**, 215–276 (1956).

28. F. Seitz, "On the Disordering of Solids by Action of Fast Massive Particles," *Discussions of the Faraday Soc.* **5**, 271 (1949).

29. G. H. Vineyard, "Theory and Mechanism of Radiation Effects," IMD Special Report Series No. 3, Nuclear Metallurgy, Vol. III, AIME, N. Y., 1956, pp. 1–13.

30. D. F. Thomas, "Irradiation Effects on Physical Metallurgical Processes," IMD Special Report Series No. 3, Nuclear Metallurgy, Vol. III, AIME New York, 1956, pp. 13–31.

31. D. S. Billington, "Irradiation Effects in Reactor Materials," IMD Special Report Series No. 3, Nuclear Metallurgy, Vol. III, AIME, N. Y. 1956, pp. 31–54.

32. "Nuclear Fuels," edited by D. H. Gurinsky and G. J. Dienes, D. Van Nostrand, New York 1956. (Particularly Chapters VII–IX.)

33. "Metallurgy and Fuels," edited by H. M. Finniston and J. P. Howe, Pergamon Press, New York, 1956. (Particularly Chapter 8.)

34. J. A. Brinkman, "On the Nature of Radiation Damage in Metals," *J. Appl. Phys.* **25**, 961 (1954); "Production of Atomic Displacements by High Energy Particles," *Am. J. Phys.* **24**, 246 (1956).

35. G. H. Kinchin and R. S. Pease, "The Mechanism of the Irradiation Disordering of Alloys," *J. Nuclear Energy* **1**, 200 (1955).

36. L. B. Aronin, "Radiation Damage Effects on Order-Disorder in Nickel-Manganese Alloys," *J. Appl. Phys.* **25**, 344 (1954).

37. F. Seitz, "Source of Disordering of Alloys During Irradiation," *Bull. Am. Phys. Soc.* **30**, No. 2, 17 (1955)(A).

38. E. P. Wigner, "Theoretical Physics in the Metallurgical Laboratory of Chicago," *J. Appl. Phys.* **17**, 857 (1946); see also article by M. Burton, "Radiation Chemistry," *J. Phys. Coll. Chem.* **51**, 611 (1947).

39. W. S. Snyder and J. Neufeld, "Disordering of Solids by Neutron Radiation," *Phys. Rev.* **97**, 1636 (1955); **99**, 1326 (1955).

40. W. A. Harrison and F. Seitz, "On the Theory of Radiation Damage," *Bull. Am. Phys. Soc.* **30**, No. 2, 7 (1955)(A).

41. L. Katz and N. Penfold, "Range-Energy Relations for Electrons," *Rev. Mod. Phys.* **24**, 28 (1952).

42. H. B. Huntington, "Creation of Displacements in Radiation Damage," *Phys. Rev.* **93**, 1414 (1954).

43. W. Kohn, "Bombardment Damage of Ge Crystals by Fast Electrons," *Phys. Rev.* **94**, 1409 (1954)(A).

44. H. B. Huntington, "Mobility of Interstitial Atoms in a Face-Centered Metal," *Phys. Rev.* **91**, 1092 (1953).

45. E. E. Klontz, "Production of Lattice Defects in Germanium by Electron Bombardment," U. S. Report AECU-2664 (1952, Thesis, Purdue Univ.); see also *Phys. Rev.* **82**, 763 (1951)(A); **86**, 643 (1952)(A).

46. J. J. Loferski and P. Rappaport, "Electron Voltaic Study of Electron Bombardment Damage and Its Threshold in Ge and Si," *Phys. Rev.* **98**, 1861 (1955); **100**, 1261 (1955)(A).

47. J. B. Sampson, H. Hurwitz, Jr. and E. F. Clancy, "Sensitivity of Radiation Damage to the Displacement Probability," *Phys. Rev.* **99**, 1657 (1955)(A).

48. D. T. Eggen, Unpublished work. See: G. R. Hennig and J. E. Hove, "Interpretation of Radiation Damage to Graphite," Paper No. 751 presented at the Geneva Conference on the Peaceful Uses of Atomic Energy (1955).

49. D. T. Eggen and M. J. Laubenstein, "Displacement Energy for Radiation Damage in Copper," *Phys. Rev.* **91**, 238 (1955)(A).

50. J. M. Denney, "Radiation Damage Energy Threshold in a Face Centered Cubic Alloy," *Phys. Rev.* **92**, 531 (1953)(A); "Displacement Energy of Face Centered Cubic Iron," U. S. AEC report NAA-Sr-271 (1954).

51. R. A. Dugdale, "Recent Experiments at Harwell on Irradiation Effects in Crystalline Solids," Report of the Conference on Defects in Crystalline Solids, Bristol, 1954 (London: Physical Society) p. 246.

52. For a review see: T. Broom, "Lattice Defects and the Electrical Resistivity of Metals," *Phil. Mag. Suppl.* **3**, 26 (1954).

53. D. Bowen and G. W. Rodeback, "The Influence of Cold Work and Radiation Damage on the Debye Temperature of Copper," *Acta Met.* **1**, 649 (1953).

54. H. G. Cooper, J. S. Koehler and J. W. Marx, "Irradiation Effects in Cu, Ag and Au Near 10°K," *Phys. Rev.* **97**, 599 (1955).

55. D. L. Dexter, "Scattering of Electrons from Point Singularities in Metals," *Phys. Rev.* **87**, 768 (1952).

56. P. Jongenburger, "The Extra Resistivity Owing to Vacancies in Copper," *Phys. Rev.* **90**, 710 (1953).

57. P. Jongenburger, "The Extra Resistivity Due to Vacancies in Copper, Silver, and Gold," *Appl. Sci. Res.* **B3**, 237 (1953).

58. J. Friedel, "The Distribution of Electrons Round Impurities in Monovalent Metals," *Phil. Mag.* **43**, 153 (1952).

59. P. Jongenburger, "Extra Resistivity Due to Interstitial Atoms in Copper," *Nature* **175**, 545 (1955).

60. F. J. Blatt, "Effect of Point Imperfections on the Electrical Properties of Copper. I. Conductivity," *Phys. Rev.* **99**, 1708 (1955).

61. F. J. Blatt, "Effect of Point Imperfections on the Electrical Properties of Copper. II. Thermoelectric Power," *Phys. Rev.* **100**, 666 (1955).

62. A. W. Overhauser and R. L. Gorman, "Resistivity of Interstitial Atoms and Vacancies in Copper," *Phys. Rev.* **102**, 676 (1956).

63. J. K. Redman, T. S. Noggle, R. R. Coltman and T. H. Blewitt, "Very Low Temperature Irradiation of Metals," *Bull. Am. Phys. Soc.* **1**, 130 (1956)(A).

64. M. D. Fiske, R. M. Walker, J. W. Corbett and J. M. Denney, "Electron Irradiation of Copper Below 10°K, I," *Bull. Am. Phys. Soc. II*, **1**, 334 (1956)(A).

65. R. M. Walker, J. W. Corbett, J. M. Denney and M. D. Fiske, "Electron Irradiation of Copper Below 10°K, II," *Bull. Amer. Phys. Soc. II*, **1**, 335 (1956)(A); See also. *Phys. Rev.* **104**, 851 (1957).

66. J. M. Denney, "Resistivity of Interstitials and Vacancies in Cu," *Bull. Am. Phys. Soc. II*, **1**, 335 (1956)(A).

67. J. J. Antal, R. J. Weiss and G. J. Dienes, "Long Wavelength Neutron Transmission as an Absolute Method for Determining the Concentration of Lattice Defects in Crystals," *Phys. Rev.* **99**, 1081 (1955).

68. D. T. Keating, "X-Ray Measurments on Low-Temperature Neutron Irradiated Graphite," *Phys. Rev.* **98**, 1859 (1955).

69. G. Hennig, "The Properties of the Interstitial Compounds of Graphite I, II, III," *J. Chem. Phys.* **19**, 922 (1951); **20**, 1438 (1952); **20**, 1443 (1952).

70. G. R. Hennig and J. D. McClelland, "Magnetic Susceptibility and Free Energy of Graphite Bromide," *J. Chem. Phys.* **23**, 1431 (1955).

71. John E. Hove, "Theory of the Magnetic Susceptibility of Graphite," *Phys. Rev.* **100**, 645 (1955).

72. John E. Hove, "Magnetic Susceptibility of Neutron-Damaged Graphite," *Phys. Rev.* **100**, 106 (1955)(A).

73. D. F. Johnston, "A Calculation of the Density of Electron-Trapping Defects in Neutron-Irradiated Graphite from Measurements of the Temperature Variation of the Hall Coefficient," *J. Nuclear Energy* **1**, 311 (1955).

74. G. J. Dienes, "Mechanism for Self-Diffusion in Graphite," *J. Appl. Phys.* **23**, 1194 (1952).

75. G. R. Hennig, Private communication, 1955.

76. S. B. Austerman, "Stored Energy Release in Graphite Irradiated at Low Temperatures," *Phys. Rev.* **100**, 1867 (1955)(A).

77. J. W. Cleland, J. H. Crawford, K. Lark-Horovitz, J. C. Pigg, and F. W. Young, "The Effect of Fast Neutron Bombardment on the Electrical Properties of Germanium," *Phys. Rev.* **83**, 312 (1951).

78. The first attempt at a systematic model was given by: H. M. James and K. Lark-Horovitz, "Localized Electronic States in Bombarded Semiconductors," *Z. Phys. Chem.* **198**, 107 (1951).

79. H. Y. Fan and K. Lark-Horovitz, "Fast Particle Irradiation of Germanium Semiconductors," Report of the Bristol Conference on Defects in Crystalline Solids, The Physical Society, London, 1955, pp. 232–245.

80. E. E. Klontz, R. R. Pepper and K. Lark-Horovitz, "Electrical Properties of Electron Bombarded Ge," *Phys. Rev.* **98**, 1535 (1955)(A).

81. J. W. Cleland, J. H. Crawford, Jr., and J. C. Pigg, "Fast Neutron Bombardment of n-Type Ge," *Phys. Rev.* **98**, 1742 (1955).

82. W. L. Brown, R. C. Fletcher, and K. A. Wright, "Annealing of Bombardment Damage in Germanium: Experimental," *Phys. Rev.* **92**, 591 (1953).

83. W. H. Brattain and G. L. Pearson, "Changes in Conductivity of Germanium Induced by Alpha-Particles Bombardment," *Phys. Rev.* **80**, 846 (1950).

84. P. W. Levy and G. J. Dienes, "Colour Centers Induced in Al_2O_3 by Reactor and Gamma-Ray Irradiation," Report of the Bristol Conference on Defects in Crystalline Solids, The Physical Society, London, 1955, pp. 256–260.

85. P. W. Levy and G. J. Dienes, "Research on Radiation Effects in Insulating Materials at Brookhaven National Laboratory," Conference on Effects of Radiation on Dielectric Materials, Washington, 1954, ONR Symposium Report ACR-2.

86. F. Seitz, "The Modern Theory of Solids," (McGraw-Hill, New York, 1946) Eqn. (8), p. 664.

87. D. L. Dexter, "Absorption of Light by Atoms in Solids," *Phys. Rev.* 101, 48 (1956).

88. P. W. Levy, "Reactor and Gamma-Ray Induced Coloring in Crystalline Quartz and Corning Fused Silica," *J. Chem. Phys.* 23, 764 (1955).

89. E. W. J. Mitchell and E. G. S. Paige, "Optical Effects of Radiation Induced Atomic Damage in Quartz," *Phil. Mag.* 1, 1085 (1956).

90. L. L. Seigle and A. J. Opinsky, "Mechanism of Dimensional Instability," U. S. AEC. Report SEP-160 (1954).

91. F. R. N. Nabarro, "Deformation of Crystals by the Motion of Single Ions," Rep. Conf. Strength of Solids, Physical Society, London, 1948, p. 75.

92. C. Herring, "Surface Tension as a Motivation for Sintering," Physics of Powder Metallurgy, (edited by W. E. Kingston), McGraw-Hill Book Co., New York, 1951, p. 143.

93. C. Herring, "Diffusional Viscosity of a Polycrystalline Solid," *J. Appl. Phys.* 21, 437 (1950).

94. R. W. Cahn, "Plastic Deformation of Alpha-Uranium Twinning and Slip," *Acta Met.* 1, 49 (1953).

95. W. Primak, L. H. Fuchs and P. P. Day, "Radiation Damage in Diamond and Silicon Carbide," *Phys. Rev.* 103, 1184 (1956).

96. A. W. Overhauser, "Stored Energy Measurements in Irradiated Copper," *Phys. Rev.* 94, 1551 (1954).

97. K. Kobayashi, "Annealing of Irradiation Effects in Sodium Chloride Irradiated with High Energy Protons," *Phys. Rev.* 102, 348 (1956).

98. T. H. Blewitt, R. R. Coltman, T. S. Noggle and D. K. Holmes, "Very Low Temperature Irradiation of Metals; Energy Release at 35°K," *Bull. Am. Phys. Soc. II*, 1, 130 (1956).

99. For a review of work in the U.S.S.R. see: V. I. Klimenkov and Y. N. Aleksenko, Proceedings of the Moscow Conference on the Peaceful Uses of Atomic Energy (July 1–5, 1955); for a review of the French work see: G. Mayer, P. Perio, J. Gigon and M. Tournarie, "Modifications Produced in Non-Metallic Materials by Radiation, and the Thermal Healing of these Effects," Proceedings of the International Conference on the Peaceful Uses of Atomic Energy, United Nations, 1956, Vol. 7, p. 674 (Paper number 362).

100. G. J. Dienes, "A Theoretical Estimate of the Effect of Radiation on the Elastic Constants of Simple Metals," *Phys. Rev.* 86, 228 (1952).

101. F. R. N. Nabarro, "Effect of Radiation on Elastic Constants," *Phys. Rev.* 87, 665 (1952).

102. G. J. Dienes, "Effect of Radiation on Elastic Constants," *Phys. Rev.* 87, 666 (1952).

103. J. Friedel, "Anomaly in the Rigidity Modulus of Copper Alloys for Small Concentrations," *Phil. Mag.* 44, 444 (1953).

104. D. O. Thompson and D. K. Holmes, "Effects of Neutron Irradiation upon the Young's Modulus and Internal Friction of Copper Single Crystals," *J. Appl. Phys.* 27, 713 (1956); see also H. S. Sellers, D. A. Powell, E. C. Crittenden, Jr., and E. A. Milne, "Effects of Electron Irradiation on the Shear Modulus and Internal Friction of Copper," *Bull. Am. Phys. Soc. II*, 1, 379 (1956).

105. D. O. Thompson, D. K. Holmes and T. H. Blewitt, "Neutron Irradiation Effects upon Young's Modulus and Internal Friction of Copper," *J. Appl. Phys.* 26, 1188 (1955).

106. H. Dieckamp and A. Sosin, "Effect of Electron Irradiation on Young's Modulus," *J. App. Phys.* **27**, 1416 (1956).

107. R. Truell, L. J. Teutonico and P. W. Levy, "The Detection of Directional Neutron Damage in Silicon by Means of Ultrasonic Double Refraction Measurements," *Phys. Rev.* **105**, 1723 (1957).

108. T. H. Blewitt and R. R. Coltman, "The Effect of Pile Irradiation on the Stress-Strain Curve of Copper," *Phys. Rev.* **82**, 769 (1951).

109. R. F. Jamison and T. H. Blewitt, "Slip Lines in Pile Irradiated Copper Single Crystals," *Phys. Rev.* **86**, 641 (1952) (A).

110. R. E. Jamison and T. H. Blewitt, "Some Deformation Characteristics of Reactor Irradiated Copper Single Crystals at 78°K and 300°K," *Phys. Rev.* **91**, 237 (1953).

111. F. W. Kunz and A. N. Holden, "The Effect of Short Time Moderate Flux Neutron Irradiations on the Mechanical Properties of Some Metals," *Acta Met.* **2**, 816 (1954).

112. A. W. McReynolds, W. Augustyniak, M. McKeown and D. B. Rosenblatt, "Neutron Irradiation Effects in Cu and Al at 80°K," *Phys. Rev.* **98**, 418 (1955).

113. As discussed by D. S. Billington in "Radiation Damage in Reactor Materials," Proceedings of the International Conference on the Peaceful Uses of Atomic Energy, United Nations, 1956, Vol. 7, p. 421 (Paper No. 744).

114. As discussed by F. E. Faris, "The Effects of Irradiation on Structural Materials," Proceedings of the International Conference on the Peaceful Uses of Atomic Energy, United Nations, 1956, Vol. 7, p. 484 (Paper No. 747).

115. R. A. Meyer, "Influence of Deuteron Bombardment and Strain Hardening on Notch Sensitivity of Mild Steel," *J. Appl. Phys.* **25**, 1369 (1954).

116. C. A. Bruch, W. E. McHugh and R. W. Hockenbury, "Embrittlement of Molybdenum by Neutron Radiation," *Trans. AIME* **203**, 281 (1955).

117. For recent reviews of this topic see: F. Seitz, "Phase Transformation in Solids," John Wiley and Sons, New York, 1951, pp. 77–145, A. D. LeClaire, "Progress in Metal Physics," Pergamon Press, London, 1953, pp. 265–332.

118. M. H. Feldman and G. J. Dienes, "Silver Self-Diffusion in a Radiation Field," USAEC Document NAA-SR-Memo-22 (1951).

119. W. M. Lomer, "Diffusion Coefficients of Copper under Fast Neutron Irradiation," AERE Report 1540 (1954).

120. R. D. Johnson and A. B. Martin, "The Effect of Cyclotron Bombardment on Self-Diffusion in Silver", *J. Appl. Phys.* **23**, 1245 (1952).

121. J. Adam and R. A. Dugdale, "Some Experimental Work Carried out in Physics with the Larger Harwell Pile," *Nature* **168**, 581 (1951).

122. T. H. Blewitt and R. R. Coltman, "The Effect of Neutron Irradiation on Metallic Diffusion," *Phys. Rev.* **85**, 384 (1952).

123. T. H. Blewitt and R. R. Coltman, "Radiation Ordering in Cu₃Au," *Acta Met.* **2**, 549 (1954).

124. H. L. Glick, F. C. Brooks, W. F. Witzig and W. E. Johnson, "The Resistivity of Cu₃Au during Neutron Irradiation," *Phys. Rev.* **87**, 1074 (1952).

125. J. Adam, A. Geen and R. A. Dugdale, "An Effect of Electron Bombardment on Order in Cu₂Au Alloy," *Phil. Mag.* **43**, 1216 (1952).

126. R. A. Dugdale, "Recent Experiments at Harwell on Irradiation Effects in Crystalline Solids," Report of the Conference on Defects in Crystalline Solids, Physical Society, London, 1955, p. 246; "Some Properties of Vacancies and Interstitials in Cu₃Au," *Phil Mag.* **1**, 537 (1956).

127. R. R. Coltman and T. H. Blewitt, "The Effect of Neutron Irradiation on Metallic Diffusion," *Phys. Rev.* **86,** 641 (1952).
128. D. B. Rosenblatt, R. Smoluchowski and G. J. Dienes, "Radiation Induced Changes in the Electrical Resistivity of α-Brass," *J. Appl. Phys.* **26,** 1044 (1955).
129. A. C. Damask, "Some Resistivity Effects of Short Range Order in α-Brass," *J. Appl. Phys.* **27,** 610 (1956).
130. A. C. Damask, Private communication (1957).

Chapter 2

EXPERIMENTAL APPROACHES TO RADIATION EFFECTS

J. C. Wilson

Solid State Division, Oak Ridge National Laboratory,
Union Carbide Nuclear Company

Unfortunately there is very little information either in the unclassified or in the classified literature on the techniques, problems, and pitfalls of irradiation experiments;[1] most of the knowledge still remains in the heads of the experimenters. Thus, the newcomer has a difficult time finding out how to get started. In addition, it is impossible to understand or correlate radiation-effects data and results intelligently without some comprehension of the special experimental considerations involved.

Just why radiation-effects experimenters are so reticent about publishing their experimental techniques is not clear. Handling techniques for radioactive materials after irradiation have been well documented.[2, 3, 4] Most of the references used in this paper, however, are dated 1956 or 1957, and this may indicate increased interest in publication of experimental methods.

This chapter supplies some of the elementary knowledge needed for performing or interpreting irradiation experiments. The emphasis here will be on the use of the reactor as a radiation source; this is believed justified on the basis of the increasing importance and availability of reactors. The reactor, too, probably poses all the problems of the other radiation sources, and some additional ones.

It is impossible here to review satisfactorily all the techniques used in radiation-effects experiments because of the breadth of the problems and the paucity of reviewable, published knowledge. The author hopes to instill in the future experimenter the need for well-planned, carefully executed, and meticulously described experiments. It is hoped that a degree of well-educated skepticism can be developed in the user of the data, as well as a sympathetic understanding of the trials of those who develop even the simplest data.

The Importance of Experimental Variables

A primary precept of radiation-effects studies is: Know all the variables —with "know" meaning "measure." The high cost of irradiation experiments makes it imperative that all possible information be acquired from each experiment; furthermore, the effect of many known irradiation variables is not understood, and some probably have not yet been discovered.

The use of radiation, either as an experimental tool or a simulated service environment in research or testing, would appear to add but a single variable, that of radiation itself, to the experimental procedure. This is not the case, however. In comparing a laboratory experiment to determine the properties of a given material and one to determine the same properties during or after exposure to radiation, one finds that a multitude of extraneous variables are or need to be introduced, for example: altered specimen configuration; radiation effects on experimental equipment; inability to describe accurately the radiation dose; and gradients in the radiation field. Furthermore, irradiation effects may so drastically change the properties of a material that it may truly be said to be a new material with a new set of properties.

Thus, almost every irradiation experiment is likely to include apparent, or even hidden, variables that may influence the outcome or the interpretation of the experiment. The experimenter must be cautious and suspect all variables of conspiring against him until the contrary is proved. Further, in writing the results of his experiments he must be as explicit as possible on all aspects of the procedures so that comparison between different experiments is possible without equivocation.

Test Material. The material to be irradiated should have been well studied in all respects before irradiation. Its composition, history and state should be well known. Conventional criteria used to describe the state of the material may not always be sufficiently inclusive. The extent and even the kind of radiation effects may depend on subtle differences in composition or state that are of little importance in unirradiated materials. Presumptions based on behavior of properties in the unirradiated condition may prove inaccurate for the same materials when irradiated. The temperature dependence or strain rate dependence, for example, of some property may be completely changed by irradiation.

Large quantities of the study materials should be procured to assure an adequate supply for future experiments and often-needed supplementary studies in the unirradiated state.

Control and description of test material is particularly difficult in the case of components or assemblies. A specification for an oil, a capacitor, or a welding rod may only describe what the finished product will do; the specification may not tell *how* the product performance is achieved. Different manufacturers may use different production methods, and a presumption that articles, made to the same specification by different suppliers, are identical is likely to prove erroneous. Even articles of the same description made by the same manufacturer may not be identical, and specimens for study must be chosen from the same lot or batch.

Irradiation Temperature. Since radiation-induced defects are mobile at some temperatures, and irradiation may enhance the mobility of atoms, or give appreciable mobility to defects or atoms that they would not have in the absence of radiation, the irradiation temperature is important. In studying phenomena depending on two or more competing processes, as in ordering and disordering in a superlattice, the temperature dependence of the two may be different and thus govern which has the larger effect.

It should be emphasized that increasing the irradiation temperature does not always have the effect of decreasing the extent of radiation effects on some properties, as has been observed in beryllium-copper[5] and nickel beryllium.[6] Recently it has been observed in steels and molybdenum that the changes in some mechanical properties were greater after irradiation at 600°F than after irradiation at room temperature.[7] Thus, in evaluating a specific property, one should not assume that irradiation at the next higher temperature will result in less effect. In uranium or boron-containing materials, especially, it has frequently been observed that greater effects of irradiation are observed at higher temperature of irradiation than at lower. Sometimes post-irradiation annealing will intensify, rather than decrease, the effects of irradiation.

Since simpler irradiation studies are often performed in a relatively inexpensive way by calculating the temperature in the irradiation device, the experimenter should be warned of the errors that may be introduced. In the irradiation of samples where fission heat is generated, or in high flux reactors where the gamma heating is great, calculations of such temperature can be in error by as much as 200°–600°F.

In the cyclotron the temperature problem is particularly severe because a very large fraction of the beam energy produces heat rather than displaced atoms. Also in the cyclotron the thermocouples tend to approach the size of the specimens, and severe temperature gradients can be created.

Irradiation Rate and Dosage. The problems of flux measurement will be dealt with later, but it should be pointed out that the flux is seldom as well known or constant in time and space as may be represented, and certainly less constant than is desired. Some properties do not change monotonically with dose, and, indeed, it is not too unusual to observe a property undergo a monotonic change with dose and then at some higher dose the direction of the change may reverse. Accordingly there is some advantage in using a series of dosages or fluxes (or better still, continuous in-pile measurements) for thoroughly understanding radiation effects. The effect of dose rate has been little studied, but the possibility of dose-rate dependence certainly should not be overlooked.

Environment. Radiation may cause the experimental environment in which a test is performed to have rather different properties than one might suppose. The production of ozone in irradiated air in the reactors has been observed.[8] In moist air nitrogen fixation occurs,[9] and materials attacked by nitric acid are susceptible to corrosion. In fact, in a fast flux of 10^{12} neutrons/cm²/sec, small nickel wires have corroded and split in two in a few weeks. Apparently nitrogen fixation can occur in the relatively weak radiation field resulting from radioactive decay of experimental apparatus after irradiation, followed by accelerated corrosion. Therefore it may be necessary to keep specimens in an inert atmosphere until they are removed from the apparatus for test.

In some instances even "inert" atmospheres (helium or argon) have given trouble. Most of the difficulties have arisen from decomposition, radiolysis, or pyrolysis of organic materials under the combined, or possibly separate, effects of heat and irradiation. For instance, the organic binder in electrical or thermal insulation has been suspected of contaminating inert atmospheres although the effects in air are negligible or may have been masked. Inert atmospheres are not a cure-all.

Charged-Particle Accelerators

The cyclotron was enlisted as a tool for the study of irradiation effects at a time when reactors were few, and neutron fluxes were not adequate for the studies to be undertaken. The cyclotrons, or other charged-particle machines, have the potential of causing much higher rates of displacement than the best of projected reactors, but this potential can be realized only within a limited area. Much of the cyclotron work has been done with alpha-, proton-, and deuteron-particles of 10 to 40 Mev energy with currents of a few microamperes over an area of a few square centimeters; Van de Graaff accelerators have been used mainly with electron energies of about 1 Mev. The heating rates in the specimen under these conditions, with currents of a few microamperes per cm², are on the order of several hundred watts per cm³, and disposing of this heat is one of the major experimental problems. On the order of 10 to 50 times more heat per displacement will be produced in charged-particle experiments as in fast neutron experiments.

The action range of the charged particles in solids is on the order of a few one-hundredths of an inch. The specimens must be very small for uniform dosage, and the size may be further limited by heat transfer considerations and temperature gradients. Rapidly varying oscillations of the beam also cause temperature control problems. Heat transfer considerations prevent the use of much higher beam currents to increase the rate of displacements.

There is some non-uniformity along the range of the particles in the specimen if its thickness is equal to or greater than the particle range. For uniform damage the specimen thickness is chosen to be about half the range of the particles, but this results in an even higher ratio of heating to displacements. Part of the reason for the high rate of heating in charged-particle experiments has been the high energy of the particles used (dictated in part by what was available in the cyclotrons at the time). Use of machines that provided particles of energies much lower than the 10 to 40 Mev particles that have most commonly been used would alleviate the heating problem somewhat, as would use of heavier charged ions. In both cases, however, the usable range of the particles in the specimen would be reduced.

Besides the limitation on space and size, the charged-particle machines are not generally capable of sustained operation for long periods. Using charged particles, where the end of the particle range is in the specimens, one must be concerned with the effect of the particles trapped in the specimen at the end of their range (for example, hydrogen from proton bombardment).[10]

Some advantages of the cyclotron are: The particle energy can be held constant and dosimetry is relatively simple. Specific areas of the sample may be chosen for bombardment at will. The radioactivity of the irradiated specimens is usually low. And the experimental apparatus may be placed in a very much weaker radiation field than the specimen, even when located close to it. The apparatus cost may therefore be much less than in a reactor. It is possible to use different particles in successive irradiations of the same specimens for certain purposes.[11]

The experimental techniques of using the cyclotron have been very well documented by the experimenters at the Atomics International Division of North American Aviation, Inc., and the several reports on techniques should be consulted for an appreciation of the problems involved.[12, 13]

Most charged-particle work has been done on electrical resistivity specimens, but many other properties have been measured. Experiments for measurement (in the irradiation source during irradiation) of creep, stored energy, dimensional stability, and solution stability have been performed. The cyclotron is mainly used today for fundamental research on metals and graphite.

Electron accelerators are frequently used for studying ionization effects (particularly in organics) as well as relatively simple displacement effects.

Direct measurements of displacement energies in metals have been made.[14] Typically the Van de Graaff accelerators operate at about 1 Mev with currents up to the order of 1 milliampere. The relatively long range of electrons gives them a distinct advantage over other charged particles.

Gamma-Ray Sources

The increasing availability of reactor by-products has brought the cost of high-intensity, gamma-irradiation sources down to rather modest levels, and the experimental work of radiation chemistry predominantly takes place in these facilities. Professor Burton's chapter should be consulted for the experimental details. A number of typical gamma-irradiation facilities have been recently described.[15, 16, 17] Most often cobalt-60 sources are used (5.3-yr half-life). Eventually cesium-137 (33-yr half-life) may become available in higher specific activities than cobalt, but at present the output is reserved for teletherapy units. The cost of an irradiation unit capable of dose rates of the order of 10^6 r/hr with cobalt-60 is about \$30,000. (There has been a reduction in the price of cobalt-60 recently.)

With gamma sources such as cobalt or cesium, the energy of the photon is well known and the reduction in source strength with time can easily be calculated. With spent fuel elements now available on rental from the Atomic Energy Commission, gamma rays over a whole range of energies are produced and the spectrum and intensity change with time. As the number of high power reactors in operation increases, larger numbers of spent fuel elements can be made available for rental purposes.

The gamma-ray sources are notably free of contamination from other radiation, but, in high-energy fuel-element sources in a water medium, it is possible to have photoneutron fluxes as high as $10^4/cm^2/sec$ [18] and precautions must be taken if high-cross-section materials, such as cadmium, are irradiated in them.

There have been a number of recent experiments[19, 20] in which the gamma sources have been used for producing displaced atoms in solids by the electrons produced in the Compton process. This is the equivalent of electron irradiation except that the source of the energetic electrons is in the sample itself and more uniform damage can be produced than with an accelerator but at much lower rates.

Very large gamma-ray sources of high intensity are a possibility in conjunction with a reactor. A food-irradiation reactor has been proposed[21] in which an indium sulfate solution would be circulated continuously between a reactor and an irradiation facility. Uncontaminated gamma rays would be available from the radioactive decay of the indium activated in the reactor. Such a scheme might be feasible on a smaller scale at other operating reactors.[95]

Dosimetry in gamma-ray sources is fairly well developed and of relatively high accuracy. Several typical reviews should be consulted for details.[22, 23] In addition, the dose can be computed fairly accurately once the source is calibrated if the experiment geometry is simple.

Reactors

Properties of Radiation in the Reactor. Compared to the charged particle machines or the gamma-ray sources, the reactor produces radiation of three different sorts that are of importance in producing radiation effects.

Fast Neutrons. First let us consider the properties of the fast neutrons produced in the fission process. The energy of fast neutrons is sufficient to transfer large amounts of energy to atoms with which they collide (and these knock-ons will then displace other atoms); relatively little of the neutron energy transferred to the specimen will be dissipated in ionization to cause specimen heating; the range of fast neutrons is long, so homogeneous damage in the specimen will result; and all these factors, as will be seen, contribute to simplicity of the experiment in which displacement of atoms is required. The fast neutron indirectly causes ionization effects: A knocked-on atom will dissipate the energy received from the neutron by ionization until a certain threshold energy is reached, but thereafter elastic collisions will predominate. The ionization effects are greater, the lower the mass of the knocked-on atom, and, whether fast neutrons (again indirectly) ultimately cause more ionization or knock-on effects, depends on the material being studied and the energy of the neutrons.

Difficulties with respect to the fast neutron are: The reactor supplies fast neutrons with a spectrum of energies, and measurement of this spectrum is apparently neither easy nor accurate. Reactor-fast-neutrons are contaminated by gamma rays and thermal neutrons that, respectively, cause ionization damage (heating) and activation of specimens. In experimental reactors the fast neutrons can be found in quantity only in the core and gradients in the fast neutron flux will be steep. All these factors contribute to experimental difficulties.

The fast neutrons from the fission process are slowed down (degraded in energy) by the moderator atoms and eventually become thermal neutrons with an energy of about 0.025 ev.

Thermal Neutrons. Thermal neutrons can indirectly cause radiation effects in three ways:

(1) by causing fission in fissile materials such as U-235

(2) by causing (n, α) reactions as in boron-10

(3) by being captured to form unstable nuclei that emit (upon decay) particles of sufficient energy to cause energetic recoils.

The fission process is of the greatest interest in studying the effects of radiation on fuel materials, but fissionable materials can be incorporated in non-fissile materials for the study of radiation effects. Fission in U-235 results in formation of two fission nuclei (average mass number about 100) with energies of about 80 Mev each. Most of the energy of these energetic fission nuclei (fission fragments) is given up in electronic excitation and but a few per cent—a very considerable several Mev of energy—will cause displacements. The energy transferred by a single, fast neutron will be on the order of one-tenth this much. The fission fragment has a range of only a few microns in solids so the energy is dissipated in a region very close to the fission. Thus, uniform fission fragment damage requires fine, uniform dispersion of the fissionable materials. The total energy (about 180 Mev) evolved in the fission process is tremendous, and since most of the energy appears as heat, cooling of samples can be a difficult problem. Each fission results in two atoms in the sample where only one was present before; in studying solids the effect of the extra atoms must be considered.

The (n, α) reaction in boron is unique because of the large, thermal neutron cross-section of the boron-10 and the helium atoms produced. Here the energy of the helium and lithium formed must be considered as well as the effect of two atoms replacing one.

The effect of recoils resulting from radioactive decay does not appear to be an important factor in most reactor irradiations.[24]

Gamma Rays. In the reactor gamma rays are produced by fission (about 5 Mev of gamma rays per fission) over a wide range of energies, and fission products as well as capture gammas make substantial contributions to the gamma field. In making use of gamma rays for irradiation experiments, there is inevitable contamination from thermal and fast neutrons although it is possible to reduce the contamination somewhat.[21] In reactors of high-power density, the gamma flux in a fast or thermal neutron experiment gives rise to experimental difficulties because of the intense heating produced by gamma-ray absorption in specimen and apparatus.

Considerations. One's first impression upon evaluating the available reactors for use in radiation-effects experiments is that they are not very well suited to the task. This is generally true for several reasons. Until recently interest in radiation-effects experiments has not been great, and little attention was given to design of reactors particularly suited for this class of experiments. Great interest in neutron physics experiments antedated attention to radiation effects, and the reactors were designed with penetrations in the reactor shielding to let neutron beams out, not experiments in. (The penetrations are still called "beam holes".) Even the swimming-pool type reactor and its many variations, regarded by many as the best all-round reactor for radiation-effects studies, is an accidental godsend: it was first built for shielding studies although the radiation-effects experimenter had long shouted in vain for something like it.

Another difficulty has been that usually a physicist-engineer team is given the task of reactor design and the physicist usually thinks of the reactor in terms of physics, not radiation-effects, experiments. However, it should be realized that design of general purpose reactors to satisfy fully the desires of neutron physicist, radiation-effects experimenter, and the test engineer must involve a great deal of compromise. Nevertheless, it appears to the author that there has been a lack of ingenuity, under-standing, and imagination in most designs.

It has only recently been fully realized that experiments that require the highest flux (fast or thermal) must be located *in* the reactor core, not adjacent to it. The impact of this is seen in the ETR[25] and WTR[26] designs and that of projected reactors with even higher fluxes.

The following are rough generalizations about the experimental reactors usable for radiation-effects studies. Perhaps power density is the best index to the characteristic types. With high power densities (thermal watts generated per unit volume) the flux will be high for a given power, the gamma-ray heating will be high, flux gradients will be steep, the reactor is usually relatively small and the amount of useful experimental space is limited by the flux gradients and the small surface area. Fast fluxes of the same order of magnitude as the thermal flux will be obtained, and experiments containing large amounts of fuel will not cause severe flux depressions. The period of operation of these reactors tends to be short, control is a problem, and experiments must be designed with a great deal of concern for reactor safety. The constant flux problem is aggravated by the large number and severe influence of the control rods; their motion has an appreciable effect on the flux, and in the higher power reactors consider-able motion (and thus flux change) will occur during a reactor cycle of a few weeks. The small size of the reactor also increases the influence of adjacent experiments on each other.

Typical of the high power density reactors are the MTR[27] and others of similar core arrangement (light water moderated and cooled) with core volumes of the order of 4 cubic feet (Table 1). This class includes the various swimming-pool and tank-type reactors that make up the majority of experimental reactors being built today in the United States.

The reactors of intermediate power density are generally the D_2O-moderated reactors. High unperturbed thermal fluxes are achieved per unit power in considerably larger volumes than in the high-power-density class. Using enriched fuel, the core volume is of the order of 8 or more cubic feet with an even greater volume adjacent to the core usable for

Table 1. Experimental Facilities in Research and Test Reactors

	Heat power (megawatts)	Neutron flux (neutrons/cm²/sec)		Experimental facilities			Core size	
		Thermal	Fast	Number	Cross section (inches)	Length* (inches)	Cross section	Height
Swimming Pool (ORNL BSF)	0.1	1×10^{12}	4×10^{11}	12	3 × 3 sq.	18 V	15 in. dia.	24 in.
Brookhaven (BNL) Graphite Reactor	30	6×10^{12}	4×10^{11}	30	4 × 4 sq.	120 H	25 ft. cube	
Argonne (CP-5) Heavy Water Reactor	1	2×10^{13}	10^{12} est	10	1 to 4 dia.	18 V	2 ft. cube	
				2	4 dia.	12 H		
				2	12 dia.	12 H		
Chalk River (NRX) Heavy Water Reactor	40	6×10^{13}	3×10^{12} est	1	5½ dia.	80 V	9 ft. dia.	10 ft.
				large	4 dia.	12 H		
				large	12 dia.	12 H		
					2½ dia.	80 V		
Materials Testing Reactor (MTR)	40	4×10^{14}	2×10^{14}	3	5½ dia.	12 H	9 × 27 in.	24 in.
				15	3 sq.	18 V	32 in. dia.	36 in.
Engineering Test Reactor (ETR)	175	4×10^{14}	3×10^{14}	1	9 × 9 sq.	24 V		
				1	6 × 9 sq.	24 V		
				3	6 × 6 sq.	24 V		
				4	3 × 3 sq.	24 V		

Note: The fluxes, numbers and sizes of the experimental holes are for comparison purposes only.
* Typical length without severe fast flux gradients. (H indicates horizontal and V indicates vertical.)

thermal neutron experiments. The MIT reactor,[28] CP-5 at Argonne,[29] and DIDO[30] and Pluto[31] in England, are typical. With natural uranium or only slightly enriched fuel, criticality requires a larger reactor with a core volume on the order of 500 cubic feet. NRX[32] and NRU[33] in Canada are representative of this type. All these reactors make available large amounts of experimental volume for thermal neutron experiments, but the ratio of fast to thermal flux is not high except next to, or inside, the fuel elements. Flux depression tends to be rather high, but the gamma-ray heating levels are much lower than in a high-power-density reactor of equivalent thermal flux.

In the reactors of low-power density—the graphite moderated reactors at ORNL[34] and Brookhaven[35]—the neutron fluxes are not high enough

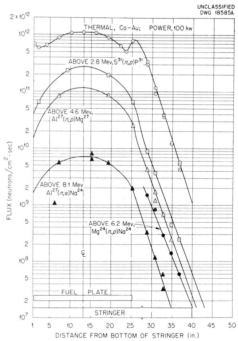

Figure 2.1. The vertical flux distribution in the lattice of the Bulk Shielding Facility at ORNL (Swimming Pool Reactor).[63] Note the peaking in thermal flux in the water at the end of the fuel plates. By extrapolation it can be seen that the fast flux, above 1 Mev, is about 60 per cent of the thermal flux in the center of the reactor. In a graphite reactor the fast flux would be about 10 per cent of the thermal. The thermal flux at the end of the fuel elements is about one-half the maximum, but the fast flux above 2.8 Mev at the end of the fuel plates is only about $\frac{1}{7}$ the maximum. It can be seen why monitors were included in the experiment in Fig. 2.5 over the full length of the irradiation tube.

for radiation-effects studies except on the more sensitive materials (semiconductors, organics, pure metals, et cetera) unless long exposures can be tolerated. The thermal fluxes will only be of the order of that found in a 100 KW swimming-pool reactor and the fast flux much lower; but flux gradients are low, the experimental holes are numerous, and the reactor shields are large enough for a great deal of equipment to be located outside the shield but adjacent to the reactor, although it is often still crowded. The large size of the cores of these reactors permits relatively complex equipment to be placed in the reactors, even though the geometry is restricted, and the gamma heating is at such low levels that low-temperature facilities can be economically operated inside them.

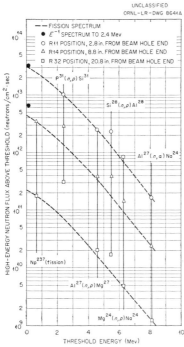

Figure 2.2. The high energy neutron flux versus threshold energy is shown for several positions in HB-3 of the MTR.[64] By inspection of the upper two curves it may be seen that the position of specimen in a beam hole is very important: a difference of 6 inches in specimen position means a difference of a factor of 6 in fast flux. The thermal flux at two points the same distance apart would be different by a factor of 3.[60] There is a severe penalty in flux if the specimen in a beam-hole experiment, such as in Fig. 2.7, is any farther from the lattice than necessary. It can be seen that the usable length of a beam hole is not very long if one expects all specimens in it to receive comparable doses. The fast flux, above 1 Mev, in HB-3 is about $\frac{1}{10}$ the thermal. Compare this ratio and the gradients with a location in the lattice of a similar reactor, Fig. 2.1.

The choice of a reactor for a specific experiment is intimately tied up with a large number of factors:[1]

1. Required flux level
2. Type of flux—fast or thermal
3. Permissible gradients in the flux and variations with time
4. Permissible gamma-ray heating
5. Cost of experiment and cost of reactor space
6. Handling facilities available or required for removal and post-irradiation work

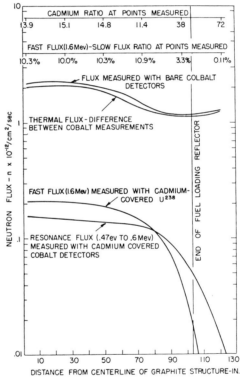

Figure 2.3. In the graphite reactors, where the active lattice is about a 20-ft cube, the flux gradients are not very steep compared to the high power density reactors in Figs. 2.1 and 2.2. The flux distribution above is for hole E-13 at Brookhaven.[80] The flux in this hole is about ⅓ the maximum in the reactor. Although the experimental holes are only about 4 in. square, the usable length for fast or thermal flux experiments is at least 15 ft. The rental cost of such a hole is $4000 to $7000 per month. The cost of neutrons (on the basis of the product of volume of the facility times neutrons/cm²) is about the same as the MTR (Fig. 2.5). If the specimens do not use the greater part of the volume of the hole, the cost of neutrons is much less in the MTR. Cost of the experimental equipment is not included in this comparison.

7. Permissible flux depression (in large, fuel-containing experiments)
8. Experimental space outside reactor for auxiliary equipment
9. Hot, off-gas, handling facilities at reactor
10. Excess reactivity to handle high cross-section experiments
11. Distance from originating laboratory and convenience.

The following sections show in more detail the problems associated with the design and operation of an experiment. The point of view of the experimenter will be presented here; the views of the reactor operator should be studied also.[36, 37, 38]

Accessibility of Reactors for Experiments. Very often the experimental apparatus itself represents but a small part of the effort and cost of an irradiation experiment. The equipment necessary to gain access to,

Figure 2.4. A view of the Bulk Shielding Facility Reactor at ORNL through the shielding water. Although not used as a source for radiation-effects experiments, this illustrates the relatively uncluttered nature of this type reactor. The box to the left was used for experiments to determine the effects of voids on reactivity,[46] but it might as easily be a housing for almost any type of experiment. The greatest advantage of this type of reactor is easy access for the experiment and experimental leads. Another significant advantage is that the geometry of the experimental apparatus is not restricted to the shape of existing beam holes or lattice opening as long as the specimen proper is close to the reactor. With a hot cell for preliminary disassembly located above the same pool, as in the ORR,[90] (with the provision for bringing the experiment into the cell from the water), the experiment may be moved from reactor to hot cell without the use of expensive casks or withdrawal shields.

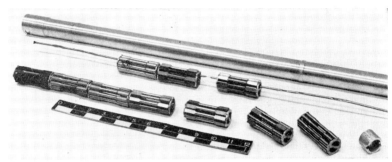

Figure 2.5. Utilizing the lattice irradiation facilities in the MTR, the tube in the rear fits into one of the beryllium pieces adjacent to the lattice. An orifice in the end of the tube is experimentally adjusted to give the correct water flow and pressure drop. The specimens are tied to spacers in close-spaced groups, and cooling water flows directly over them. The small tube with crimped sections contains the fast and thermal flux monitors. No connections go to out-of-pile instrumentation. Space for such an experiment costs \$55.00 per 10^{20} neutrons/cm^2 (thermal neutrons) per linear inch of space occupied by the above tube. The fast flux varies by a factor of 7 from the center to the end of the tube. The thermal flux varies by a factor of 3.

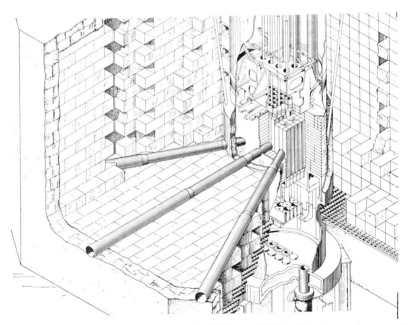

Figure 2.6. A cut-away drawing of the LITR at ORNL. This shows the essential features of the beam-hole type reactor. Except for shielding details the MTR looks the same. Compare the limited and geometrically constrained access with that of the swimming-pool type (Fig. 2.4). The clutter of mechanical supports and guides above the active lattice has been eliminated in many later reactors where the control rod drive mechanisms enter from the bottom of the reactor (as in the ORR[90]).

or effect communication with, the experiment in the reactor is often the most costly item.

Pool-Type Reactors. The situation is least complicated in the swimming-pool type reactor.[39] The equipment must generally be sealed against a head of water equal to the pool depth, and communication with the experiment by wires or tubes is accomplished with the leads inside a piece of tubing brought to a terminal strip at the surface of the pool. The experiment will usually be required to be non-buoyant, immovable during reactor operation, and, if it contains a large volume of voids, these must be of sufficient watertight integrity that rapid flooding cannot occur to upset the reactivity of the reactor (see Fig. 2.4). For moderate heat dissipation in the experiment, the pool water can furnish convection cooling.

Tank-Type Reactors. In a tank-type reactor (such as the MTR[27]), there are essentially two different means of placing experiments. First, the beam holes may be used. These are stepped, tubular holes in the reactor shielding that go, in some cases, to a thin plate separating them from the active lattice. "Dummy plugs" provide shielding (and cooling in the higher-

Figure 2.7. An assembled beam-hole experiment for use in HB-3 of the MTR. The apparatus is resting on carefully aligned V-blocks that must be used to keep the apparatus straight during assembly; otherwise the experiment would not meet the MTR straightness requirements, and it would not be permitted to be placed in the reactor. The near end of the plug contains the experimental apparatus (see Fig. 2.8 and 2.9) for irradiation. The step in the plug conforms with the shape of the inside of the experimental hole in the reactor. At the outer or far end of the plug is a pressurized terminal strip housing equipped with bulkhead fittings to carry electrical leads to the instrumentation. Any gaseous activity is thus confined to the housing where an off-gas line goes to the radioactive, off-gas system of the reactor. The slot in the side of the plug is a keyway to assure alignment in the reactor. In reactors not provided with such keyways, it is necessary to build tilt registering mechanisms into the experiment where the orientation is critical. The plug is about 13 feet long. A special crate must be used for shipment to prevent bending. (R. G. Berggren, ORNL).

powered reactors) when the holes are not occupied by experiments. The
experimenter must normally supply the plug to fill the hole for his experiment. The plug must furnish adequate neutron and gamma shielding while
allowing penetration of such connections to the experiment as are required
(see Fig. 2.7).

Beam holes are on the order of 12 feet long and 4 to 12 in. in diameter.
The materials of construction of the shielding plug may be required to be
the same as the adjacent materials in the permanent reactor shield (in
the MTR, for instance, 4 ft of graphite and 8 ft of concrete). Construction
of such a shield with numerous penetrations through the concrete and
graphite is extremely expensive since the plugs are not normally reusable.
More recently it has been possible to make the shielding plugs hollow and
fill them with water when in place. This is much less expensive and the
plugs are lighter and easier to handle. Depending on the reactor power, it
may be necessary to include a small amount of boral in the apparatus for
thermal neutron shielding, and auxiliary gamma shielding outside the
reactor may also be required. All connections to the experiment (in tubing

Figure 2.8. View of MTR beam-hole plug during assembly. To the right is the
specimen chamber with a large number of metallic specimens strapped to four square
tubes. The long round central tube supplies water to the square tubes in contact
with the specimens. The specimen chamber will be enclosed by a tube and welded.
The outer shell (seen in Fig. 2.7) will then be put in place. The cooling water returns
in the annulus between specimen chamber and outer shell.

White strips in specimen chamber are ceramic thermocouple insulation. The
thermocouple lead wires exit through the two undulating tubes.

Except for the boral discs at the midpoint on the tubes, water filling the outer shell
is the neutron- and gamma-ray-shielding.

of suitable size) then pass through the water filling the plug. Tubing, if of large size, must usually follow a spiral or serpentine path to prevent streaming of radiation, Fig. 2.8.

The second way of irradiating experiments in the tank-type reactor is in the active lattice inside the tank. Experiments in the reactor tank, are required to be machined to rather close dimensional tolerances to fit into the lattice without binding or upsetting the water flow pattern. In the case of corrosion-resistant specimens irradiation directly in the cooling water stream is possible. Materials that might be corroded by the reactor stream are usually canned in corrosion-resistant materials (aluminum, zirconium or stainless steel).

Where specimens in the reactor tank require connection going outside the tank (thermocouple leads, etc.), the engineering problems become more complex. Usually the tube or pipe communicating with the experiment must go through a sealed, flanged nozzle in the top of the reactor tank. This makes for very long experiments that are difficult to build and transport. The small diameter of the tank of most reactors prevents use of the tank top for experiment penetrations. Rather close tolerances are required to

Figure 2.9. Here the gamma heating in a beam-hole experiment in the MTR is put to good use. The tensile and impact specimens on the face of the wedge-shaped block are arranged to operate at a series of three temperatures during irradiation. Although the outer specimens are in spring-loaded contact with the aluminum water jacket, the inner specimens (against the wedge) reached temperatures as high as 1000°F. Intermediate temperatures were reached by the middle row. The angle of the wedge is dictated by the gradients in the gamma-ray heating. Auxiliary holes in the block were needed because the thermal impedance of the two types of specimens was different. Note large number of wires in thermocouple cable so that temperature pattern was well recorded. Flux monitors are in quartz ampoules. This unit fits in shell in Fig. 2.7. (R. G. Berggren, ORNL).

get the experiment to fit the lattice correctly and line up with the tank nozzles. In older reactors, gridwork above the lattice further complicates access to core or active lattice; often it is necessary to remove the experiment at each shutdown for refueling. In the higher-powered reactors, turbulence from the high rate of coolant flow may develop vibration in the experiment or connecting tubes.

In general, penetration into the reactor tank requires considerable amounts of careful engineering, close tolerances, and a great concern with safety. But where high thermal or fast fluxes are needed, the experiment must be in the lattice and thus in the tank. The cost and complexity of the experiments is part of the price for the high flux. In the ETR[25] for instance, there are no beam holes; all experiments are in the reactor tank, either in the lattice or in the surrounding reflector.

Mechanical Considerations in Experiment Design

Ingenuity, miniaturization, and reliability are the most important requirements of mechanical design of an experiment. The best way to visualize the reliability and ruggedness problem is to ask yourself: "Can I design a laboratory experiment that can be compressed to one-tenth its normal size, welded into the box, shipped 1,000 miles by common carrier, and then operated (without opening the box) when it gets back?"

One of the first considerations in mechanical design of irradiation apparatus is whether it can be gotten out of the reactor again, and, if so, can the data contained therein be extracted at reasonable cost and no danger to personnel. Unfortunately many experiments have been designed with little thought to these considerations. During mechanical design and assembly of any apparatus that is to be handled after irradiation, the personnel designated to do the disassembly should have a strong voice in the design and methods. Disassembly in a hot cell is difficult at best; a great deal of good data from irradiations has been lost because the design was such that it was impossible to open the irradiated apparatus economically or without great damage to the contents.

Materials of construction for in-pile and irradiation experiments are generally aluminum alloys or stainless steels. The aluminum alloys are generally preferred where temperatures and stresses allow them because of the light weight (important from a handling standpoint) and relatively low neutron activation. There is a superstition among most reactor operators that 2S aluminum, now called 1100, is pure aluminum and therefore it is most suitable. In many cases the low strength of 1100 results in excessively thick sections, and other alloys have comparable or lower induced activity for the same strength. Even on an activity per unit weight basis the 5052 alloys may show to advantage over 1100. The importance of induced radioactivity in materials of construction depends on the circumstances. If the activity of the specimens is high, the activity of the apparatus or irradiation container may be unimportant. Where experiments are to be handled with a minimum of shielding very soon after withdrawal from the reactor, high-purity magnesium alloys have been used. Calculation of induced activities is relatively simple *if* the composition is well known. Otherwise it is best to use actual data, because of the importance of trace elements.[40, 75]

In a fast flux experiment there is little concern with self-shielding since the cross section of materials for neutrons of high energies is almost uniformly low. However, light materials that are capable of efficient moderation of the high-energy neutrons can reduce the energy of the neutrons reaching the inside of the experiment. Accordingly, excessive thicknesses of water (for example in the cooling-water jacket) may reduce the fast neutron flux. However, in reactors with the highest fast neutron flux, the fast flux gradients are often much steeper than the thermal flux gradients, and there is or may be considerable penalty in placing the important part of a specimen any farther from the active lattice of the reactor than is absolutely necessary. In an MTR beam hole for instance, there is a difference of a factor of 6 in the fast flux (above 1 Mev) in the first 6 inches of the experimental hole.[41] Thus the usable length of such a facility is in great part determined by the allowable flux gradients in the experiment.

In thermal flux experiments, one is most concerned with interposition of any high cross-section materials between the active lattice and the specimen. For instance, the thermal flux has been calculated to be higher by a factor of 1.7 inside a Zircaloy experiment tube than in a similar tube of equal mechanical strength made of relatively high cross-section stainless steel.[42] The amount of high cross-section materials in the specimen itself will cause flux depressions.

One of the more difficult problems in design is calculation or estimation of heat transfer of small objects in complex geometries—small irregular test specimens in a helium atmosphere inside a water jacket, for instance. Frequently, such problems are best solved with mockups employing electrical heat. Where fission heat is generated or a high level of gamma heat, it may not be possible to duplicate the heat fluxes in the laboratory. In this case the experiment must be designed with some possible auxiliary heating or cooling means to correct errors in estimation of heat transfer. In beam-hole experiments, it may be possible to move the experiment with respect to the reactor lattice to adjust heat transfer errors or variation in the neutron flux.

If the experiment is water cooled, or in the cooling stream of the reactor, the corrosion resistance of the apparatus per se and as a couple with the

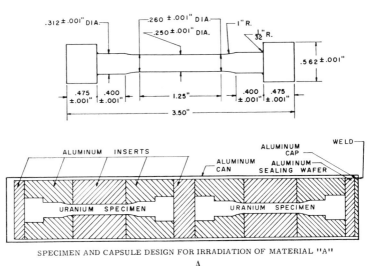

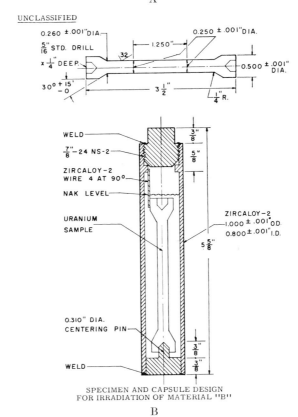

SPECIMEN AND CAPSULE DESIGN FOR IRRADIATION OF MATERIAL "A"

A

SPECIMEN AND CAPSULE DESIGN
FOR IRRADIATION OF MATERIAL "B"

B

Figure 2.10. Shown are two schemes for irradiated specimens that may be corroded in a cooling medium.[43] An additional advantage often accruing from such methods is that the effective heat transfer surface is much larger than the specimen itself.

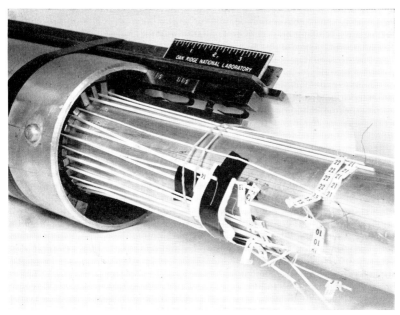

Figure 2.11. Irradiation of large numbers of specimens is possible with careful design. Here over 400 impact specimens of two sizes are contained in the first 13 inches of an MTR beam hole (as in Fig. 2.8). Water flows inside the inner tube and outside the outer tube for cooling. The inner tube accommodates a separate unit carrying 70 tensile specimens. The U-shaped springs, seen between the specimens not yet inserted, exert a force to keep good contact between specimens and container. In spite of proximity of water cooling, the springs are expected to reach a temperature of 1000°F. The heavier specimens will reach about 500°F. Hence there are numerous thermocouples on specimens. Thermocouples are located on springs also to verify design temperature calculations and make certain future experiments can follow this design with assurance. (R. G. Berggren, ORNL).

reactor components must be good. For instance, graphite has adequate corrosion resistance in water, but coupled to the aluminum in a reactor it increases the corrosion in the aluminum. Zirconium, the aluminum alloys, stainless steels, nickel and molybdenum have been used in contact with the aluminum and cooling water in the MTR or LITR.

Figure 2.10.—*Continued*.

On the left metal blocks machined to fit the shape of the specimen are sealed in a tight-fitting can. Any dimensional changes will in part be restrained by the can.

On the right may be seen the frequently used system of canning the specimen in sodium or NaK. The sample is free to change shape without constraint; this is a most important advantage in irradiating fissile materials. Obviously the integrity of the welds is most critical. Opening these capsules after irradiation is easy in a properly equipped hot cell with trained personnel, but not otherwise. Temperature monitoring in the NaK rig has been possible with deep thin thermowells in the end caps.

Generally speaking, apparatus that is intended to effect containment of an experiment uses welded construction. Accordingly, design must be on this basis. The use of gaskets and 0-rings of non-metallic materials is generally not feasible because of radiation effects in the high flux end of the experiments. Metallic gaskets and 0-rings have been used, but gasketed joints often require flanges that will not fit in the limited experiment space available. Also, bolted and gasketed joints may be susceptible to leakage upon the thermal cycling that occurs in most experiments in high flux reactors.

Designing for welded construction follows normal practices, but careful

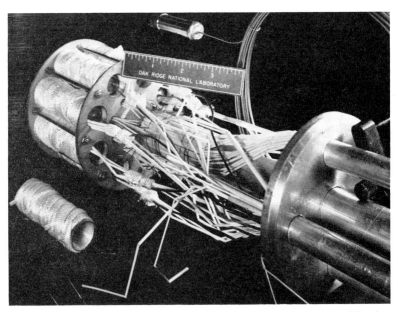

Figure 2.12. This experiment is used to measure the creep and rupture life of metal specimens in an MTR beam hole. The specimens are short lengths of tubing with a reduced center section to localize the creep deformation under the influence of stress applied by internal gas pressure through the capillary tubing (specimen and tubing in background). The gradient in the gamma heating causes one end of the specimen to be hotter than the other; the eight furnaces have three separate windings each so that the gradients in temperature may be adjusted out with external resistors. The furnaces, one of which is shown in the foreground, are of resistance wire interwound with flexible quartz sleeving on a fused quartz tube. Only about $\frac{1}{8}$ of an inch of insulation surrounds each furnace otherwise the specimens will overheat—control temperature 800°C—before the furnaces are turned on in spite of the fact that the unit is helium-filled and operates in a water jacket as in Fig. 2.7. There are about 24 heater leads and 35 thermocouples in this apparatus. Assembly is tedious because of the limited space and the need for logging all the wires accurately. (N. E. Hinkle et al., ORNL).

Positioning Facility

Figure 2.13. Temperature control of specimens that are self-heated by gamma-ray absorption or fission is always difficult because the amount of heat evolved from a small specimen may be much greater than a furnace of comparable size can furnish. The apparatus pictured above is simply a positioning device, actuated through a rack and pinion drive from an electric motor, that permits the specimen location to be varied to keep it at constant temperature as the neutron flux varies during the reactor cycle. The unit is mounted on the top head of the LITR. In this case daily adjustment by the operator is sufficient to keep the temperature constant, once the reactor operation has settled down after startup. It could of course be adapted to servodrive. Depending on the reactor and the kind and amount of material in the apparatus, the reactor operators may place limitations on the rate of insertion or withdrawal. The fact that the experimenters went to this much trouble to get constant temperatures should be a warning that capsule experiments where the temperature is calculated, not measured, are subject to wide temperature fluctuations during operation. (J. G. Morgan, ORNL).

consideration must be given to the effects of the heat of welding on specimens that are often only a few inches from the weld. Continuous monitoring of the temperature inside the experimental apparatus during welding is often a wise precaution.

Joining tubing, in the order of 1 inch, and smaller, special mechanical fittings such as Swagloks may be permitted in reactors. Caution must be used in welding near the mechanical fittings: thermal stresses may cause them to leak. This is particularly true where tubing and fitting are of dissimilar metals.

The assembly of any in-pile apparatus must be carefully sequenced and scheduled; with the all-welded construction, backtracking to cure a mistake may be expensive or impossible. Accordingly checking of all components before assembly, after assembly, and after closure is necessary.

Leakage tolerances, say between the water jacket and inside of a high temperature experiment, are very strict and careful welding is required. Generally no indication of leakage on a helium leak detector test is permitted.

Materials that are subject to corrosion in the reactor coolant stream must be canned in non-corrosive materials. With fuel-bearing materials, canning in a metal jacket may be advisable because the surface-to-volume ratio of small specimens may not permit sufficient heat transfer, or possible growth of the specimen may rupture the can. In such cases, it is customary to can the specimen loosely in an environment of NaK or sodium, Fig. 2.10, so that both good heat transfer and lack of constraint of the specimen are achieved.

Where highly stressed members upon which the safety of an experiment and the reactor may depend, such as the can enclosing a pressurized experiment, are exposed to high rates of gamma-ray heating (in the order of several watts per gram), the resulting cyclic and thermal stresses in the member often greatly exceed the yield stress of available materials. This problem arises in pressurized loops in the MTR and ETR.[44] Gamma-ray heating of the order of 5 to 25 watts per gram may be found in the core of these reactors. The problem cannot be solved by thickening the stressed sections because this may both increase the thermal stresses and cause even greater thermal neutron attenuation. Separately cooled, multiple-wall tubes may be one solution but the problem still confronts the experimenter. Simulating high gamma heat in the laboratory to develop test data is extremely difficult, and it may yet be necessary to use the reactors as heat sources to solve the problems the reactors themselves pose. In addition, the effects of radiation on the properties of the materials of construction is a concern.[45]

There may be on the order of 100 critical components in an in-pile engineering experiment; 99 per cent reliability for each component gives a system reliability of about 35 per cent. Accordingly, each idea for a component or a method must prove reliable, and it is often truly difficult to reconcile the bold ingenuity needed to get some apparatus into the small space provided and yet be sure that the bold idea is sufficiently reliable.

Effect of the Experiment on Reactor Operations and Safety

The mutual interactions of the reactor, experiments, and experimenters' manipulation can seriously compromise the safety of a high power reactor or markedly decrease the efficiency of the reactor in providing efficient service to other experimenters. In some experimental reactors, the reactor period (that is the time required for the power to change by a factor of e) may be on the order of $1/30$ second. The operation of such a reactor puts severe demands on the control system in normal operation, and any experiments that can abruptly alter the reactivity during operation cannot be tolerated.

Experiments containing large amounts of high cross-section material can be undesirable in several ways. If the reactor does not have sufficient excess reactivity, it may be impossible to go critical. Reactor operators insist on knowing the amounts and cross section of all materials in any irradiation. At the MTR and the future ETR reactivity measuring facilities, in the form of actual zero or low power reactors, are used to measure the effect of experiments on reactivity. Experiments, in which it is possible for the position of apparatus containing high cross-section materials to change or be changed, must be safeguarded so that it is not possible to suddenly increase the reactivity of the reactor by shifting the material in or out of the reactor.

Any changes in the density of the moderating medium cannot be tolerated, because the control system may not be able to respond rapidly enough. For this reason water-cooled experiments must be designed so that no boiling occurs. Where a void is surrounded by water, the size of the void must be controlled within limits[46] so that in case of collapse of the void the control system can handle the transient. Obviously the reactor operators will wish to be assured of the structural integrity of any apparatus surrounding a void. Air bubbles in a coolant stream cannot be tolerated for the same reason.

In cases where experiments have the capability of directly or indirectly causing a hazard to personnel or the reactor, the designer will be required to equip the experiment with safeguards that will forestall any credible accident.

In experiments dissipating large amounts of heat, failure of the coolant could cause a meltdown of the experiment and possibly part of the reactor.

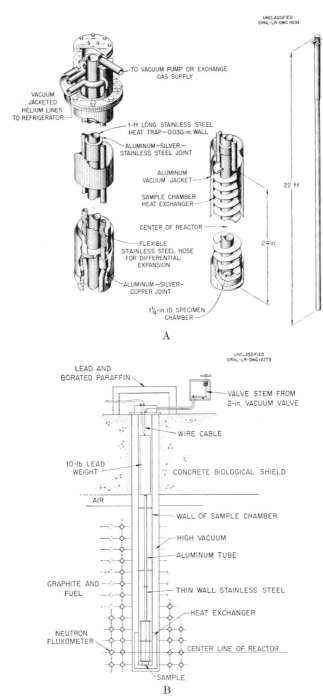

TO VACUUM PUMP OR EXCHANGE
GAS SUPPLY

VACUUM
JACKETED
HELIUM LINES
TO REFRIGERATOR

1-ft LONG STAINLESS STEEL
HEAT TRAP—0.030-in. WALL

ALUMINUM—SILVER—
STAINLESS STEEL JOINT

ALUMINUM
VACUUM JACKET

SAMPLE CHAMBER
HEAT EXCHANGER

CENTER OF REACTOR

FLEXIBLE
STAINLESS STEEL HOSE
FOR DIFFERENTIAL
EXPANSION

ALUMINUM—SILVER—
COPPER JOINT

$1\frac{1}{4}$-in. ID SPECIMEN
CHAMBER

22 ft

24 in.

A

LEAD AND
BORATED PARAFFIN

VALVE STEM FROM
2-in. VACUUM VALVE

WIRE CABLE

10-lb LEAD
WEIGHT

CONCRETE BIOLOGICAL SHIELD

AIR

WALL OF SAMPLE CHAMBER

HIGH VACUUM

ALUMINUM TUBE

GRAPHITE AND
FUEL

THIN WALL STAINLESS STEEL

HEAT EXCHANGER

NEUTRON
FLUXOMETER

CENTER LINE OF REACTOR

SAMPLE

B

Figure 2.14. Schematic diagram and drawing of hole No. 12 cryostat in the ORNL Graphite Reactor. This facility constitutes a rather complete in-pile, low-tempera-

Experiments with a large heat production capacity are usually instrumented so that loss of, or diminished, coolant flow (or higher than normal coolant temperature) will automatically cause a decrease of reactor power. Other situations that may call for automatic reduction of reactor power are excessive radioactivity of the exit coolant or off-gas stream, excessive experiment temperature, failure of some instrument that is vital in guarding the safety of the reactor, or high radiation levels dangerous to personnel outside the reactor.

Most reactor operators have specific standards set up for safety circuit design construction and operation.[47] Even the type of instruments to be used may be specified because the operators have judged them to be most reliable or easiest to maintain. The shutdown of a busy reactor containing millions of dollars worth of engineering experiments is a serious matter because of the loss of time to experimenters sharing the reactor. Accordingly, the reliability of the safety circuits is of paramount importance as is the requirement that they be "fail-safe"; i.e., failure of a component in an important circuit will cause the same signal as though the process it monitored had become dangerous. Design of a good safety circuit, and selection of the quantities that will signal troubles is a ticklish task.[48] On one hand is the tendency to provide the maximum of safety, but counterbalancing this is the necessity for keeping the reactor operating as much of the time as possible without interruption.

It must be remembered that high flux reactors are not turned on and off like light bulbs.[48] Start up may require half an hour and the build up of xenon-135 after a shutdown may prevent the reactor from starting up for several days (unless refueled), unless power is regained in a matter of minutes after a shutdown. The slower the rate at which the power of a reactor is reduced by some unusual or hazardous indication from an experiment, the more rapidly may full power be regained upon elimination of the trouble. Accordingly, each potential hazard from each experiment

Figure 2.14.—*Continued.*

ture laboratory for performing irradiations and experiments at temperatures as low as 15°K.[8] Electrical resistivity[49] and Young's modulus (Fig. 2.15) have been measured at low temperatures during irradiation. Furthermore, annealing experiments can be conducted with the apparatus in place. For measurement of stored energy, the sample chamber was used as a calorimeter with heat supplied by gamma radiation from the reactor at carefully controlled power levels. Note that a fluxmeter was included close to the apparatus for close control of reactor power during calorimetric experiments; control by neutron-sensing elements at another location in the reactor leads to variable flux at the experiment location.

Some of the mechanical and engineering problems may be deduced from the schematic diagram and the sectioned drawing of the cryostat proper. (R. R. Coltman, T. H. Blewitt, and T. S. Noggle, ORNL).

must be evaluated and the safety circuit connected to reduce reactor power at a rate commensurate with the hazard presented. In the case of a severe hazard, a scram will be signaled; this drops all the shim rods in the reactor and the power is reduced by at least a factor of 100 in the first second. The terms scram, junior scram, fast setback, and reverse are the jargon of the reactor operators denoting successively slower rates of insertion of the control rods.

Radiation Effects in Experimental Apparatus

In experiments containing more than just the specimen under irradiation, radiation effects in a number of components can cause errors or failure of the experiment. Although there is very little information published on this subject, there is some knowledge, particularly in the important area of electrical components. A compendium of experience with many varied components already tested would be of immense value to future experimenters.

The performance of the electrical lead wires from thermocouple circuits is particularly important since errors will normally result in a higher temperature of irradiation than the thermocouple voltages may indicate.

The electrical resistance of metals is changed relatively little by irradiation at room temperature and above. (Quite large changes may be observed at low temperatures.[49]) Even at neutron exposures over $10^{20}/cm^2$ the resistivity of copper changes only about 10 per cent.[24] Molybdenum may change as much as about 25 per cent and other metals commonly used for electrical conductors much less. The usual techniques for eliminating the effects of lead wire resistance change may be employed if the resistance of the wire is critical.

The resistance of electrical insulation may decrease several orders of magnitude,[51, 52] but the importance of the change depends on whether the wires are used in high-impedance circuits (studies of semiconductors, high-impedance transducers, etc.), or in low-impedance circuits such as furnaces and thermocouples. The various plastics and elastomers do not appear usable for high-impedance circuits in high fluxes because of the deterioration of the electrical properties. Also in high-impedance circuits, non-ohmic behavior, polarization effects and photovoltages may result during irradiation. These effects in organic materials at low doses have been reported by Pigg and Robinson,[50] but it should be noted that the criterion of failure used by them was rather stringent (because they worked with high-impedance circuits). Some of the materials might be used at higher doses where the electrical resistivity is not so critical, although deterioration of mechanical properties might result.

At high flux levels inorganic insulating materials must be employed. At

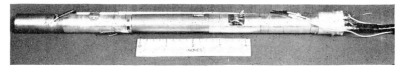

Figure 2.15. A device for measurement of Young's modulus and internal friction during pile irradiation. A resonant bar technique was used with eddy current drive.[69] To eliminate the effects of radiation and other variables on lead capacity in the reactor, a 100 Mc transmitter was frequency-modulated by capacity variations between the vibrating specimen and a circuit element. The FM output, telemetered to an out-of-pile receiver, gives the vibration amplitude. The transmitter tank coil can be seen in the opening in the apparatus. Operation under irradiation has taken place in the hole No. 12 cryostat of the ORNL Graphite Reactor (Fig. 2.14) for periods as long as two weeks at temperatures from 20° to 370°K. (D. O. Thompson, ORNL).

UNCLASSIFIED
SSD-C-1097
ORNL-LR-DWG-4407

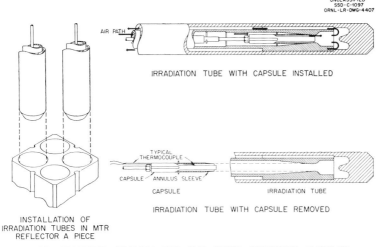

AIR PATH

IRRADIATION TUBE WITH CAPSULE INSTALLED

TYPICAL THERMOCOUPLE

CAPSULE   ANNULUS SLEEVE

CAPSULE   IRRADIATION TUBE

IRRADIATION TUBE WITH CAPSULE REMOVED

INSTALLATION OF IRRADIATION TUBES IN MTR REFLECTOR A PIECE

MTR IRRADIATION FACILITY FOR ANP STATIC CORROSION CAPSULES

Figure 2.16. The above apparatus has been used for capsule irradiation of very high-power-density fuels at high temperatures. The specimen is sealed in a heavy wall capsule. Air cooling was necessary because of the high capsule temperature and space limitations. The overall diameter of the apparatus is about $1\frac{1}{4}$ in. Temperature control is achieved by an automatic controller that varies the air flow. The apparatus is reusable and the capsules are easily loaded and unloaded. Studies of thermocouple welding techniques and thermocouple calibration were necessary to assure accurate temperature readings in the 700 fps air stream. (J. G. Morgan and W. E. Browning, ORNL).

present, wrapped or braided glass and ceramic insulators are most frequently used.[52] The commercially made, glass-insulated thermocouple pairs are much used for temperature measurements and other low-impedance circuits. The behavior of the glass insulation appears to depend

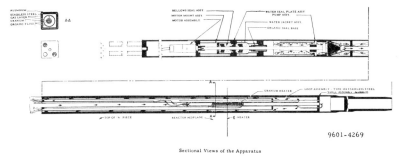

9601-4269

Sectional Views of the Apparatus

Figure 2.17. Another approach to the in-pile loop is to make the loop a small package that can be wholly inserted in the reactor. The loop above was used to study the effect of temperature and irradiation on the properties of organic coolants.[92] The complete loop unit is 3 in. square and 101 in. long. Operation was carried out in an "A" position in the MTR tank. Heat was supplied by fission in a uranium section, and the heat rejected to the reactor coolant water. The problems of designing, building, and proving operational reliability of miniature air motors, pumps, and seals are great. Obtaining the correct heat transfer rates from the fluid to the cooling water must have been difficult; the heat transfer path is from fluid to stainless steel tube, to a gas space, to the aluminum can, to the thin film of water flowing outside the can. Prior to the reactor experiment, information on radiation effects in the fluid had been obtained by electron irradiation in the Van de Graaff machine,[93] and the results of the two irradiations showed good agreement.

upon the type of impregnant (usually an organic material) used to hold the fibers together, the atmosphere, and the changes in manufacturing processes. In an inert atmosphere some of the organic impregnants carbonize at room temperature under irradiation and short out the thermocouples; in air the same materials may behave satisfactorily. It is possible to burn out the impregnant with a flame and obtain some improvement, but the glass fibers then tend to become fluffy and the resulting insulation is delicate, fragile, and easily abraded. No rules can be given on selecting the best wire; apparently different manufacturers—or the same manufacturer at different times—use impregnants that vary in their resistance to irradiation. It is best to test each lot of wire before depending upon it in an experiment.

Although some glass-insulated wire is available in unimpregnated form, it has been found that some volatile materials may be driven off at high temperatures and use in inert atmospheres, where contamination cannot be tolerated, should be preceded by tests.

In addition to long time or static changes, radiation may cause a dynamic change in the resistivity of the insulator as a function of the flux. The insulation resistance between two wires in a glass-insulated, braided-glass-covered pair may be changed from one to three orders of magnitude by irradiation.

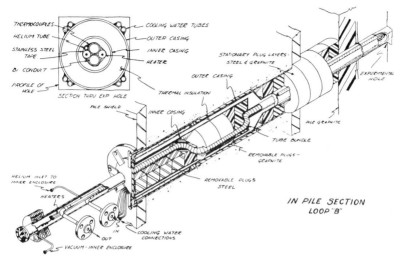

Figure 2.18. A section of the Brookhaven (LMFR) in-pile loop is shown.[91] The loop circulates a solution of uranium in bismuth into the BNL reactor at temperatures over 500°C. In this loop the pumping equipment is located outside the reactor because it was necessary to process the bismuth-uranium solution to obtain information on continuous extraction of volatile and non-volatile fission products. In essence the experiment not only gives corrosion data and tests the reliability of components at this high temperature, but is also a chemical pilot plant for fission product extraction. The authors state that about 60 man-years of development went into this project up to this point; this gives a good idea of the cost of performing these difficult but very necessary experiments.

The figure shows the complexities of getting water, helium, bismuth and electrical lines through the shielding. Fortunately the holes in the shielding at BNL are much larger than the experimental holes in the graphite so there is more room for the necessary leads going into and out of the pile than in most reactors. The cross section shows the necessarily compact construction. Also shown is the paradoxical situation existing in most all loops: the need for providing both cooling (to protect the reactor) and heating (to keep the loop molten and remove fission heat). The original paper must be consulted to appreciate the difficulties that must be solved in such an experiment.

Part of the lowered leakage resistance will be recovered when the reactor is off; for this reason, leakage-resistance measurements must be made while the experiment is in the reactor. Proprietary forms of asbestos insulation are suitable for electrical insulation in some instances.

Where there may be a question about the reliability of the glass-insulated wire, ceramic insulators are strung on the wires in the high flux section of the experiments. This practice is tedious, but has had the advantage of higher leakage resistance at high temperatures and complete freedom from contamination of inert atmospheres in high-temperature experiments. It is wise to include spare, open wires in all in-pile experiments so that the leakage resistance of these wires can be checked with a megohm meter during the course of the experiment to detect signs of deterioration.

Thermocouples themselves appear to be affected but little by radiation,[8, 53, 54] but there have been no tests at high flux levels or for long times. There is indirect evidence (from numerous engineering experiments such as loops), however, to indicate that the accuracy is adequate for engineering purposes. There have been sporadic rumors that the radiation caused thermocouples to become unwelded or open. Experience among several different groups at Oak Ridge National Laboratory using different methods of welding has indicated that a properly welded couple, no matter by which method, will withstand irradiations without becoming detached.

In radiation experiments, thermocouples may be subjected to rough handling during assembly of compact apparatus, shocks in shipment, steep gradients, and rigorous thermal cycling during irradiation. Well-tested methods of attachment should be used. Welding of each wire to the specimen independently (in close proximity to each other) is useful because the couple will become open if a weld fails, which failure may be confirmed by a continuity check.

For displacement or force transducers, pneumatic gaging with spring elements (bellows or bourdon tubes) appears to be one of the best possibilities. There is some suspicion that highly stressed springs may relax under irradiation, but this may have been the result of unmeasured, elevated irradiation temperatures.

In complex experiments such as loops, in which some parts of the apparatus may be in much weaker radiation fields than the specimens proper, one must be on the lookout for situations where leakage in the shields or circulating, radioactive fluids may cause gamma fields high enough to cause damage to organics in such diverse components as motors, V-belts, lubricants, hydraulic fluids, valve packing, 0-rings, etc.

Electrical devices such as motors, transducers, etc., suffer from the effects of irradiation on the electrical insulation. It appears that ceramic insulated wire could be used if these devices are to operate at high fluxes. Monitoring of leakage resistance or resistance to ground is often useful to give warning of impending failure. Bonded strain gages have been used at low fluxes,[85] and use up to 10^{19} nvt appears possible.[86] Some development work on high-temperature, radiation-resistant transducers is in progress.[87]

The problem of lubricating moving parts may be solved under static conditions or slow speeds by standard inorganic lubricants. Organic lubricants that one might use for ball bearings, for instance, quickly deteriorate under relatively small amounts of radiation.[82]

Monitoring and Instrumentation

A distinguishing feature of a well-designed, in-pile experiment is the copious use of automatic, continuous, recording of every possible experimental variable. Instrument costs may be a substantial percentage of the initial cost of an irradiation experiment. Not only are more quantities recorded than in out-of-pile experiments, but also provisions should be made for occasional measurement of quantities that may foretell breakdown of critical components. For instance, in experiments in which the temperature of irradiation is important, continuous recording of temperature is well advised; temperature excursions in the reactor may be brief. In addition to the continuous monitoring, thermocouple circuits should be brought to a central switch or patch panel from which continuity, resistance, grounding, and leakage resistances may be periodically measured to determine whether the measuring circuits are in good order. Such an arrangement is also useful for calibrating instruments in place.

It is most important that the reliability over long times of all instruments used with the experiment be checked during extensive bench tests. At NRX[32] all instrumentation of types not approved by the reactor operators must undergo long-time reliability tests before their use is allowed. Another important feature of the instrumentation design is to utilize, in

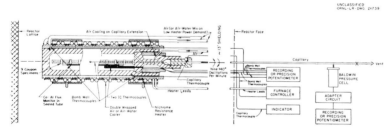

IN-REACTOR ROCKING AUTOCLAVE EXPERIMENT TYPE III (HB-5 June 1957 to Date)

Figure 2.19. Cross section drawing and instrumentation diagram of an in-pile autoclave used for solution stability and corrosion studies on homogeneous reactor fuel solutions.[94] The inside of the autoclave is only 3 in. long, but note the attention to important details: The thermocouples are well distributed and numerous; a flux monitor is present over the length of the specimens, and the pertinent experimental quantities are recorded. In place of the usual laboratory furnace, the in-pile experiment must have provisions for cooling (to remove fission heat during irradiation) as well as heating to control the temperature during operations and supply all the heat during reactor shutdowns. The heater-cooler unit is often needed in in-pile experiments; the unit here contains resistance wires for heating and coolant tubes for cooling. An air-water mix is used as a coolant when the electrical heater power demand is low, but only air is used when the heater demand is high. Typical operating conditions for the autoclave would be 300°C and 2000 psi in the LITR.

so far as possible, standard instruments that can be readily serviced at the reactor site.

In general, modern, commercially available instrumentation for control or recording of such variables as temperature, pressure, etc., is suitable for in-pile experiments. In control instruments very much faster response times are required than for simple laboratory experiments. A simple on-off temperature controller may be suitable in the laboratory; the in-pile experiment may require a control instrument capable of continually varying the power to the heater circuit. Because of the long leads to the in-pile experiment (and often small wire size), potentiometer-type instruments are preferred because the effect of leadwire resistance is at a minimum. Pyrometers that draw current from a thermocouple circuit are nearly always unsuitable, because sensitivity is lost with the relatively high resistance leads and recalibration is required with each new installation.

The number and location of thermocouples are extremely important. It is often wise during construction of an apparatus to apply a greater number of thermocouples to the specimens in an apparatus than will eventually be used. Then, if some thermocouples are injured during subsequent assembly operations, spares will be available to take their place. It is desirable to have important thermocouples duplicated, and provisions should be made in the external instrumentation for rapid switching of thermocouple-recorder connections on a patch panel.

In locating the positions of thermocouples on specimens of test apparatus, it should be remembered that very high temperature gradients are possible in high-power reactors. Accordingly sufficient thermocouples must be used

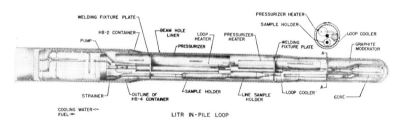

Figure 2.20. The uranyl sulfate loops used in the study of homogeneous reactor corrosion are engineered to fit within the confines of a beam hole in the LITR (Fig. 2.6). The above drawing[95] illustrates the elements of the loop more clearly than an engineering drawing, but does not show the crowded arrangement of tubes, heaters, thermocouples, etc. Again limited space and geometry require the experimenter to conform to a layout that would never occur but for these limitations. In this loop the pump is within the beam hole to hold the solution volume to reasonable levels and keep the bulk of the radioactive materials within the reactor shielding. With water loops, the pump is often located in a shield outside the reactor.

to make certain that any temperature gradient, if important, is measured and not estimated.

For compactness and ease of manipulation in confined spaces, thermocouple wires of relatively small size (24 to 30 gauge) are most often used. Small wires have the additional advantage that they are relatively flexible and will be subjected to less stress at the junction than larger stiffer wires.

Alternating current pickup frequently gives trouble with the electronic null-balance potentiometer instruments. Part of the difficulty is the long leads; another, the effect of radiation on insulation resistance; and often it is necessary to run power leads (to a heater for instance) in the same conduit with thermocouple wires or leads from in-pile transducers. Occasionally it is worthwhile to use d.c. for heaters. Often it is helpful to use isolation transformers on power leads into the reactor; this makes it possible to ground or isolate leads to minimize a.c. pickup and gives some flexibility in rearranging leads in case of an accidental ground.

Figure 2.21. The operating area in front of one of the beam holes at the LITR where the homogeneous reactor loops (Fig. 2.20) are tested. In the foreground is a complete loop ready for insertion. To the left may be seen a portion of the instrument console. At the right of center in the rear is the shield enclosure for the many gas and sampling lines. A 3 ml sample from the loop requires 6 in. of lead for shielding. The original paper gives in detail the method of disconnecting the loop and removing it from the reactor.[96]

Variations in the Neutron Flux

Variations in the neutron and gamma-ray fluxes in a reactor may be large in magnitude and strongly influence design and operation of the experiment. These variations are important to the experimenter particularly when fissionable materials are used, where the irradiation conditions (such as temperature) may depend on the flux. In experiments where only the integrated flux is of importance, the variations in flux will, in large measure, be averaged out by using flux monitors of reasonable half-life. The greatest variations in flux are observed in the high-power density reactors with small cores.

Apparently the greatest variations at a given point will be observed in the thermal flux rather than in the fast. However, it is often found that the gradients in the fast flux are much steeper than the thermal flux gradients (see Fig. 2.1), and variations in fast flux with position in the reactor will require close attention in locating or positioning the experiment in the reactor to obtain consistent results in successive experiments.

The loading of the reactor will strongly influence the flux in a given location. The cautious experimenter checks the loading pattern at every shutdown to determine whether a different configuration of fuel elements or adjacent experiments is likely to change the flux in his experiment. Some of the situations that will change the flux are rearrangment of fuel elements or moderator in the vicinity of the experiment, replacement of a partially used fuel element with a new one or vice versa, and change in content of an adjacent experiment or one between the fuel and one's own experiment.

During reactor operation the flux may vary, even at constant reactor power. The flux may not be at all constant during a reactor cycle, from shutdown to shutdown. The flux distribution in a reactor will change as fuel is burned out and the poison sections of the shim rods are replaced by a fuel section. During a startup after a shutdown without refueling, the shim rods may have to be withdrawn a large amount until the xenon-135 is burned out, and then reinserted to continue their normal, slow withdrawal during the cycle. The variations in the thermal flux may be seen from the vertical flux traverses performed in several reactors.[56, 57] Varying shim rod position during the first few hours of operation in the LITR (with a fuel-containing specimen) has resulted in temperature variations as high as 400°F although the reactor power was constant.

The experiment itself may cause variation in the flux realizable in the specimen. Superimposed on the reactor variation in flux are self-shielding (sometimes called self-protection) and flux depression. These are of great importance in irradiation of fuel and control rod materials. Self-shielding results when relatively thick sections of high cross-section materials are irradiated; the outer layers of the specimen will strongly absorb neutrons, and the neutron flux in the center of the specimen will be less than on the surface. Thus inhomogeneous distribution of damage will result and the heat evolution will be less than calculated from the amount of fuel and the neutron flux. Consequently, the geometry of the sample will affect the amount of heat evolved and the homogeneity of the damage. To a lesser but very appreciable extent, the thickness and materials of construction of the apparatus will attenuate the flux.

Flux depression is the local depression of the flux because of the presence of strong neutron absorbers. In effect any neutron sink will lower the flux about it. Depression may be caused by adjacent experiments as well as one's own. The effect depends on the amount of high cross-section material and appears to depend upon the power density of the reactor; that is, in a high-power-density reactor loaded with a fuel sample, the flux depression will be less than in a reactor of lower power density although the unperturbed neutron fluxes may be the same. Hughes[58] gives an example in Brookhaven where the self-shielding and flux depression together result in only 47 per cent as much activation in a small cobalt specimen as would be expected from the unperturbed flux and neutron capture cross section. A method of calculating flux depression has been given by Lewis,[59] and Trice has described actual measurement of flux depression in the MTR.[60]

Intentional Modification of the Flux. To some extent the fast, thermal or gamma flux may be enhanced or reduced.

The fast flux may be increased at the expense of the thermal flux by introducing "converters" or "transformers" around the specimen. The converter is usually enriched uranium (with proper cooling). Thermal flux causes fission, and the specimen is then exposed to a predominantly fission spectrum. The efficiency of these devices is not well known. Primak has obtained figures for CP-3'.[66] It appears that their usefulness would be restricted to reactors of lower power density (graphite- and D_2O-moderated) where the average thermal flux is much greater than the fast flux.

The thermal flux may be increased by moderating the fast flux in an efficient moderator: This requires a fast flux comparable to the thermal for appreciable gains, and such a ratio of fluxes is found in rather limited areas. The peaking of the thermal flux curve in water may be seen in Fig. 2.13. The effects of flux depression should be measured before counting on a gain in thermal flux in this way.

For the purpose of reducing activation in samples, a shield of cadmium on the order of 0.03 in. thick is used. The cadmium may require cooling, and the gamma flux in the specimen may be increased several fold. Bopp and Sisman[61] have used cadmium to increase the gamma flux during irradiation of plastics and elastomers. Some calculations on the use of thermal neutrons for production of gamma rays have been made.[81]

Measurement of Flux and Dose. One of the least quantitative and most tedious phases of radiation experimentation is that of determining the effective dosage of radiation. The experimental techniques are not well established, the flux measurements often require more effort than the experiment proper, and our knowledge of radiation effects is not sufficient to assign quantitative weight to the contributions of different types or energies of radiation even if these should be known.

Often an experimenter, using a single facility in a reactor whose loading pattern is stable for a series of experiments, need not know the flux accurately because the relative exposure can be fairly accurately measured by exposure time and power of the reactor. Very often the experimenter will have devised a phenomenological flux monitor wherein the reproducible property change in one of the materials of study is used to monitor the consistency of exposure. The experiments run under such conditions will be self-consistent, but there may be difficulty when attempting to compare results with other sources. In experiments seeking to determine the quantitative mechanisms of the action of radiation, it is obviously an absolute, rather than a relative, measure of the radiation that is necessary.

In applying data from radiation experiments to the prediction of properties of components of reactors or reactor systems, the inability to express quantitatively, in simple form, the dosage resulting from various types and energies of radiation is most serious. For example, testing of pressure vessel steel for a reactor may be carried out in or near the core of a high-power-density reactor in a fission spectrum. In service the same materials may be separated from the core by iron thermal shields and water so that the fast neutron distribution departs from the fission spectrum. Development of methods for expressing the effective radiation dose in a consistent manner would greatly increase the confidence with which radiation-effects data could be applied.

Thermal Flux. The measurement of thermal flux can be done in a consistent manner. Activation of a material with a high thermal neutron cross section and counting of the radioactivity of the daughter product is the usual procedure.[58] Indium and gold are very frequently used for these measurements, but for longer reactor exposures cobalt (with a 5.3-year half-life) is more often used for convenience since there is less need for counting immediately or at a well-known time interval after exposure. Another advantage of a long, half-life material is that the monitor will tend to average out the flux for the whole exposure and serve more nearly as an integrated flux monitor. The variations and vagaries of the thermal flux have been pointed out above, and for accurate measurement in the presence of high cross-section materials it is necessary that the monitoring foil be placed at the exact point where the flux is required, not some distance away.

The exact physical form of the monitor will depend on the experiment. Thin cobalt foils are frequently used, but in high fluxes the foil must weigh only a few milligrams (for convenient handling and counting). For this reason aluminum-5 per cent cobalt alloys have been used to secure a more manageable sample. Structural members containing nickel, such as stainless steels, often have sufficient residual cobalt to be used as flux monitors. For high temperature measurements, cobalt-containing ceramics have been tried.

Continuous monitoring of the thermal flux is desirable in some experiments that contain large amounts of fissionable materials, such as fuel loops, where flux changes require adjustment of loop operating parameters. The sensing devices are usually of the same type as used for reactor control.

The monitoring of the integrated thermal flux in fissile materials is often accomplished by mass spectrometer or chemical analysis of the fission products after irradiation. Cesium-137 is frequently used. This system is particularly applicable to analysis of the burnup in different regions of the same specimens.

Fast Neutrons. It is most important to realize that the "fast flux" or the "time-integrated fast flux" are meaningless terms unless a definition of what is meant by "fast" is supplied. To some—notably physicist and reactor operators—fast neutrons mean all neutrons that are *not* thermal neutrons. To others fast neutrons are epithermal (cadmium) neutrons; and, finally, some use a convention of specifying fast neutrons as those neutrons above a certain threshold energy (0.1 and 1.0 Mev thresholds are common). Occasionally "fast neutrons" mean those with energies above the resonance region, 10 Kev.[58]

The problem of fast neutron dosimetry is twofold. First, the number and energy of all neutrons capable of causing radiation effects are necessary; and, second the relative effects of each energy group of neutrons in causing the property change under study must be known. In both cases our knowledge is sketchy.

Measurement of the numbers of neutrons of the various energies is readily done in the thermal and resonance regions up to about 8 Kev.[58] But for displacement effects, we are most interested in energies above this. The most success in measuring the high-energy neutron fluxes has been with threshold detectors. The cross section of some materials is quite low until some threshold energy is reached. Then, the cross section rises with neutron energy and often remains constant from this point to higher

TABLE 2. THRESHOLD DETECTOR REACTIONS[64]

Reaction	Threshold energy Mev.	Saturation cross section barns	Half-life of product
$P^{31}(n, p)Si^{31}$	2.4	0.075[a]	2.62 hr
$S^{32}(n, p)P^{32}$	2.9	0.300[b]	14.3 days
$Al^{27}(n, p)Mg^{27}$	4.6	0.039[c]	9.8 days
$Ni^{58}(n, p)Co^{58}$	5.0	1.23[c]	72 days
$Si^{28}(n, p)Al^{28}$	5.5	0.080[c]	2.3 min
$Mg^{24}(n, p)Na^{24}$	6.3	0.048[c]	14.9 hr
$Al^{27}(n, \alpha)Na^{24}$	8.1	0.111[c]	14.9 hr

[a] D. J. Hughes and J. A. Harvey, *Neutron Cross Sections*, BNL-325, p. 105.
[b] D. J. Hughes and J. A. Harvey, *Neutron Cross Sections*, BNL-325, p. 108 (0.0 Mev to 3.5 Mev). E. D. Klema and A. O. Hanson, *Phys. Rev.* **70**, 106 (3.0 Mev to 6.0 Mev).
[c] N. Goldstein et al., ANL Quar. Prog. Rep., CF-3574, July 26, 1946, p. 29.

energies. There are few reliable threshold detectors and the thresholds are not always as sharp as is desired. Table 2 lists some of the detectors and their properties. It will be noted that range of neutron energies is rather narrow (0.7 to about 8 Mev) and there is a big gap downward to the resonance region.

A number of the threshold detectors have short half-lives, and some require chemical separations; accordingly, complete spectral measurements are a major undertaking.[62, 63, 64, 65] The use of sulfur is becoming widespread. The cross section is well known, which is not true for many of the other detectors, and beta counting—used after relatively simple chemical treatment—is quite accurate. The 14-day half-life permits several weeks' delay before counting. About 1 gm of elemental sulfur is an adequate monitor for fast fluxes of 10^{11} to 10^{14} neutrons/cm²/sec. Sulfur is particularly useful for periodic checking of the fast flux where the spectrum has previously been measured.

Another unit of neutron exposure is the "Megawatt days per adjacent ton" (Mwd/at), which corresponds to the exposure of neutrons in a specimen during liberation of one megawatt of heat in one ton of nearby uranium.[63] This unit may be roughly converted to thermal neutrons per square centimeter by multiplying by 5×10^{17}.

The term Megawatt days (Mwd) for exposure is also used, but the meaning is ambiguous since the actual neutron dosage will depend on the reactor and the position in the reactor. Mainly it is a way of specifying time-integrated power of the reactor.

The use of phenomenological monitors for estimating fast-flux dosage is in fairly widespread use although the fact is seldom mentioned. Most such monitors utilize an easily measured, reproducible property change in some materials (similar in radiation-effects characteristics to the material under study) as an index of integrated fast neutron exposure. The idea is far from new; the earliest radiation-effects data were reported in "loki" units, based on a 25 per cent elastic modulus change in a certain type of graphite.[66] In a number of cases phenomenological monitors have been calibrated against measured, estimated or calculated neutron fluxes (often of unknown accuracy), and the results are expressed or published in terms of neutron flux. Thus, it is not easy to assess the absolute accuracy of the measurements, but the relative accuracy will usually be quite good. Phenomenological monitoring may be done in the following ways: carrier concentration in n-type germanium measured by the electrical resistivity,[83] the lattice expansion in diamonds, fused (not crystalline) quartz, electrical resistivity of graphite.[66, 67, 68]

The number of possibilities is of course very large, but most of the monitors used or proposed for use are rather sensitive to temperature of irradiation so that it may be difficult to use them in high flux reactors. Much more study is needed to establish the sensitivity to temperature of irradiation. Bruch has suggested the use of the electrical resistivity of molybdenum as a monitor;[70] changes of the order of 25 per cent take place at about 10^{20} fast neutrons/cm².[24] The sensitivity to irradiation temperature is unknown, but it is an interesting possibility because of the large changes that take place. If the resistivity of the molybdenum were continuously monitored during irradiation, and the specimen periodically annealed in place, the monitor could be used over and over again and very high doses could be measured. Such an apparatus could probably be built in less than one cubic inch of space.

The obvious difficulty with the phenomenological monitors is that they would not be equally suitable for all materials; the validity of results should depend on the mass of the atoms in the specimen.

Primak has developed a linear, fast-flux dosage measuring system that can be used where the rate of change of a property during irradiation declines from the start of irradiation.[66, 68]

Although phenomenological monitors have been used almost exclusively for fast-neutron effects, there is no reason why they should be so restricted.

Ionizing and Mixed Radiation. In fast and thermal neutron experiments, the reactor gamma flux is usually unimportant unless it is high enough to cause undesirable gamma heating or thermal stresses resulting from gamma heating. The accuracy required is not high, in view of the many other variables, and simple calorimetric measurements will suffice. Often temperature rise or heat loss in a previous experiment will give enough information to calculate the gamma heating with the accuracy required.

In studying materials such as plastics and elastomers, where a substantial fraction of the total damage may be caused by ionizing radiation, monitoring of the gamma flux becomes more important. Good calorimetric measurements have been performed in the reactor[71] and chemical dosimetry has been applied in reactors of relatively low flux.[72] Ionization chambers may also be used.

The use of dosage units that represent a measure of energy absorption of radiation in the sample has become widespread. In this way one can express the combined effects of fast neutrons and gamma rays by expressing the dosage in terms of the sum of the energies dissipated in the specimen by the two types of radiation. Chapter 10 should be consulted for more information on energy absorption dosimetry.

Future Experimental Reactors

For radiation-effects purposes at modest fluxes, it appears that the pool-type reactors offer an unbeatable combination of low original cost, versatility, and low cost for experimental use. These reactors have sufficient flexibility to do almost anything within the range of fluxes available, and this is a tremendous advantage where—as one often suspects—reactors are acquired before firm and realistic plans for their use take shape. It appears that powers of several megawatts are possible in the pool reactors without excessive cost, and this brings the flux to within a factor of ten of the best experimental reactors we have today (MTR and ETR). Since the pool reactor is so flexible, it is relatively easy to incorporate experiments in the active lattice and gain a large factor in fast flux over a similar experiment in a beam hole in a reactor with a power as much as ten times higher. The large number of pool-type reactors being built is an indication that at least some of their advantages are recognized, and undoubtedly the techniques for performing experiments in them will become well developed.

Between the pool reactor and the tank-type (MTR) is the ORR concept, which, if it proves successful, will make available an almost continuous series of powers from a few hundred kw to perhaps 30 Mw at costs very nearly proportional to power.

The only other experimental reactor presently being built in appreciable numbers is the CP-5 type. In Europe quite a large number of this general type are built or being built. As these reactors are presently designed, they are not the best tools for radiation-effects studies with either fast or thermal neutrons. It appears possible to increase the fast flux facilities by making provision for insertion of specimens in the fuel elements or immediately adjacent thereto, but to date this has not been done. For high thermal fluxes, when testing fuel materials, it is believed the flux depression will be severe. There is insufficient information available to evaluate the NRX and NRU reactors for radiation-damage experiments.

If additional high-flux experimental or test reactors are built in the very near future, it is most likely that they will be somewhat similar to the MTR or ETR, with increased emphasis on experimental facilities in the active lattice, as in the ETR. The realization that the highest usable fast and thermal fluxes can only be found in the active lattice of a high-power-density reactor will dictate to a very great extent the direction of reactor types of the near future. In Europe this realization has apparently not come about or has been ignored because the neutron flux level required for fuel-element testing in unenriched or slightly enriched systems is not as great as in the United States. One great improvement that could be made in the newer reactors for component and engineering tests, and one hears little of it, would be to design the reactors with a greater concern for the experimenter and experiment in view. In general, little regard for this facet of the problem has been shown by reactor designers. Since, as has been pointed out, much of the cost of an experiment is in hardware that must be built in order to effect communication with the experiment in the reactor, a substantial reduction in the manpower required to perform experiments seems possible by minimizing the design difficulties (for the experiments) that are built into almost every reactor. There are many factors here that cannot be dealt with at length. One of the easiest improvements to make would be to design all openings in the reactor to receive standard sizes of pipe or tubing. Presently most reactors are built of standard size pipe or tubing and the experimenter who is required to work inside these (as in a beam hole) must have specially made or machined, non-standard size tubes in order to make the most efficient use of the small penetrations in the reactor shield.

There are a number of compelling reasons why advanced test reactors with substantially higher neutron fluxes than are available today are needed to further power-reactor technology. First, the neutron-flux level in projected power reactors may equal or even exceed the highest virgin fluxes now available in our test reactors. Since the maximum flux in the test reactor is not usually available to experiments, because of flux depression and the self-shielding of the materials of construction of the experiment, an advanced test reactor should offer considerably higher fluxes. In this way irradiation of power reactor components under service conditions could be achieved. Even higher fluxes would be desirable to aid in accelerating irradiation programs, studying the effect of rate of irradiation, and studying possible flux-dependent processes (such as creep) in structural materials. Huffman has outlined some of the needs for advanced reactors in terms of space, flux, and usage.[73] Another feature of advanced test reactors might well be the operation of reactors at conditions of temperature and pressure that would be suitable for research or development on a particular type or class of reactors. For instance, for research on pressurized-water-reactor technology, a special test reactor might be operated at 600°F and 2000 psi pressure, so that the numerous and expensive features of the experimental apparatus that are now required when test reactor coolants, temperatures, and pressures differ from those in the experiment, could be eliminated.

Advanced reactors with thermal neutron flux (and perhaps fast flux) levels of the order of 10^{15} to 10^{16} neutrons/cm^2/sec or greater are being studied. It is apparent from the proposals already made that some of the characteristics of such advanced reactors would be: high power, 200 to 600 Mw; limited experimental facilities in the highest flux (perhaps room for only one experiment); high cost (Grout has estimated operating costs of $3,000,000 per year);[74] and thus an astronomic cost per experiment. Although at least three proposals are available (see below) with neutron fluxes in excess of 10^{15}/cm^2/sec, many questions have not been answered from the experimenters' viewpoint. First, what will be the effect of flux perturbations? How much of the flux will be available at the experiment? And, will engineering realities (of reactor design and construction) produce a reactor that is usable from the experimenters' standpoint without exorbitant experiment cost? The answers to the questions, rather than the unperturbed maximum flux, should be the basis of evaluation by the experimenter.

Argonne has proposed the "Mighty Mouse"[75] reactor for achieving high fluxes for research purposes. The reactor is not designed to withstand perturbation by high cross-section experiments, and it is designed primarily as a research tool, rather than for engineering experiments. An annular heterogeneous core surrounds a small central cavity for experiments in the highest flux. Cooling and moderation would be supplied by D$_2$O. Some of the important characteristics would be a power of 250 Mw; reflector moderated and cooled by D$_2$O; and plate-type fuel elements in an annulus surrounding a two inch diameter central cavity for high flux experiments. Beam holes and other experimental facilities would be included.

Phillips[76] is working on conceptual design of advanced reactors that might be built with present technology. Annular cores, power in the hundreds of megawatt range, and a single high flux facility in the center of the core are envisioned.

The feasibility of a homogeneous research reactor has been studied at ORNL.[77] A single region reactor with a diameter of about 10 feet was investigated. Unperturbed thermal fluxes of the order of 5×10^{15} neutrons/ cm^2/sec should be realized at a power of 600 Mw. Experimental facilities would be beam holes penetrating well into the core. The significant advantage of the homogeneous reactor, continuous operation without shutdowns for refueling—heterogeneous reactors will probably operate on a 5 to 10 day cycle—is counterbalanced by a relatively low fast flux, experiment complexity, and flux depression in engineering experiments.

Just before this manuscript was finished, a report on an advanced test reactor concept by the Internuclear Company was reported.[78] Instead of a single, Jack-of-all-trades reactor, a complex of six independent, single-purpose reactors (possibly in the same shield) is proposed. Each reactor would consist of a water-cooled annular core about a foot in diameter. Moderation would take place in the surrounding D_2O reflector, and control would be relatively uniformly achieved in a D_2O-poison region outside the reflector. The central cavity inside the fuel would accommodate experiments up to the size of engineering loops, and provision for other experimental facilities could be made. The reactors would operate at relatively high pressure to minimize the pressure differential between loop and reactor. Advantages claimed for the system are: less reactor power required than for a lesser number of reactors with the same facilities, reduction of interaction between different experiments, or experiments and controls system, continuity of operation in each experiment independent of others, and location of experiments where fluxes of well over 10^{14} n/cm^2/sec can be achieved *in* the experiment. This report represents the most realistic thinking to date on future test reactors that has yet been presented. Safonov[79] has recently proposed another unusual configuration for a test reactor. Two other proposals have just been published.[88, 89]

Specific Experiments

The figures following the text demonstrate some of the principles discussed above by illustrating actual experiments and pointing out in the captions some of their features or peculiarities.

Some emphasis has been given to the problem in developing loop experiments. Loops are necessary to study corrosion and the radiation chemistry of liquid fuels, coolants and moderators. In studies on fuel materials, loops may be required to get sufficient cooling on large specimens or actual test-fuel elements. The need for reactors that will accommodate loops of several types is the most pressing of experimental reactor problems and the most difficult to fulfill.

Summary

Operation of successful and economical radiation-effects experiments that give clean-cut results is extremely difficult. The breadth of the problems involved is tremendous; the scientist has to be a good engineer and the engineer a good scientist for success. The experimenter is (once again) admonished to take nothing for granted and measure everything possible; he should not only measure everything reported but report everything measured.

Acknowledgments

Based as this chapter is on unwritten lore, not history, it has not been possible to give personal credit for most of the ideas and suggestions included herein. To these anonymous contributors the author expresses his gratitude, as well as to a large number of people at various AEC installations who were kind enough to furnish material, suggestions or criticism. The author's colleagues at ORNL were also most generous in supplying information, much of it heretofore unpublished.

References

1. Berggren, R. G. et al., "The Mechanics of Testing Irradiated Materials," ASTM S.T.P. 208 (1957).
2. ——, "Hot Labs," *Nucleonics* **12**, No. 11, 35–100 (1954).
3. ——, Fourth Annual Symposium on Hot Laboratories and Equipment, TID-5280 and TID-5280 Supplement 1 (1955).
4. ——, Fifth Hot Laboratories and Equipment Conference, 1957 Nuclear Congress, Philadelphia.
5. Cleland, J. W. et al., "Low-Temperature, Fast-Neutron Bombardment of Cu-Be Alloy," *Phys. Rev.* **91**, 238 (1953).
6. Kernohan, R. H. et al., "Effect of Neutron Irradiation on the Precipitation-Hardening Reaction in Alloys Containing Beryllium," *J. Appl. Phys.* **27**, 40 (1956).
7. Wilson, J. C. and Berggren, R. G., "Effects of Neutron Irradiation in Steel," *Trans.* ASTM **55**, 689 (1955).
8. Coltman, R. R., Blewitt, T. H., and Noggle, T. S., "Techniques and Equipment Utilized in Low-Temperature Reactor Irradiations," *Rev. Sci. Inst.* **28**, 375 (1957).
9. Primak, W. and Fuchs, L. H., "Nitrogen Fixation in a Nuclear Reactor," *Nucleonics* **13**, No. 3, 38 (1955).
10. Heckman, R. A., "The Fate of Deuterons in Solid Aluminum Targets," LRL-83.
11. "Effects of Fission Fragments on Radiation Damaged Metals," NAA-SR-262 (1953).
12. Yockey, H. P. et al., "The Use of Cyclotron Irradiation in the Study of Radiation Effects on Materials," NAA-SR-186 (1952).
13. Gilbert, W. S. et al., "The Use of Cyclotron Irradiation in the Study of Radiation Effects on Materials; Techniques Developed Since 1952," NAA-SR-1477 (1956).
14. Kenworthy, H. M. and Neely, H. H., "Threshold Displacement Energy in Nickel," NAA-SR-1580 (1956).
15. Deutsch, A., "Designing a High Gamma Radiation Facility," 5th Hot Lab and Equipment Conference, Philadelphia, Pa., 159 (1957).
16. Colichman, E. L., Mallon, P. J., and Jarrett, A. A., "A Laboratory Facility for Irradiation at Elevated Temperatures," NAA-SR-1704.

17. Black, J. F., Kunc, J. F., Jr. and Clark, G. B., "A Laboratory for Studying the Chemical Effects of Gamma Rays," *Intl. Jnl. of Appl. Rad. and Isotopes* **1**, No. 4, 256–269 (1957).
18. ——, "Research Reactors," Selected Reference Material, USAEC Program, TID-5275, p. 250.
19. Dugdale, R. A., "Recent Experiments at Harwell in Irradiation Effects in Crystalline Solids," *Report on Conference on Defects in Crystalline Solids*, The Physical Society, London, 246 (1955).
20. Thompson, D. O. and Holmes, D. K., "The Effect of Gamma Irradiation on the Young's Modulus of Copper," *J. Phys. Chem. Solids* **1**, 275 (1957).
21. Arnold, E. D., "Selection of a Food Irradiation Reactor Type," AECU-3319 (1956).
22. Miller, N. and Wilkinson, J., "II. Actinometry and Radiolysis of Pure Liquids, Actinometry of Ionizing Radiation," Radiation Chemistry, Discussions of the Faraday Society, No. 12, 50 (1952).
23. Hine, G. J. and Brownell, G. L., "Radiation Dosimetry," Academic Press (1956).
24. Bruch, C. A., McHugh, W. E., Hockenbury, R. W., "Variations in Radiation Damage to Metals," Trans. *AIME* **206**, 1362 (1956).
25. Dempsey, R. H. et al., "ETR-Core and Facilities," *Nucleonics* **15**, No. 3, 45 (1957).
26. Schultz, M. A., "Westinghouse Testing Reactor," *Nucleonics* **14**, No. 11, 138–144 (1956).
27. ——, "Research Reactors," Selected Reference Material, USAEC Program, TID-5275, p 153.
28. ——, "MITR," *Nucleonics* **14**, No. 8, 51 (1956).
29. ——, "The World's Reactors — CP-5," *Nucl. Eng.* **1**, No. 2 following p 62.
30. ——, "The World's Reactors — No. 8 DIDO," *Nucl. Eng.* **2**, No. 2, following p 14 (1957).
31. ——, "Dounreay Pt. 2," *Nucl. Eng.* **2**, No. 16, 286. (On DMTR which is similar to Pluto: both resemble DIDO except for enlarged facilities for engineering tests.)
32. ——, "The World's Reactors — NRX," *Nucl. Eng.* **1**, No. 3, following p 106. NRX Reactor Staff, "NRX Reactor Research Facilities," AECL No. 215, Atomic Energy of Canada Limited.
33. Lewis, W. B., "The Canadian Reactors and Their Uses," *Brit. J. Appl. Phys.* Suppl. No. 5, 96–100 (1956).
34. Cagle, C. D., "The Oak Ridge National Laboratory Graphite Reactor," ORNL-CF-53-12-126 (1953).
35. ——, "Research Reactors," Selected Reference Material, USAEC Program, TID-5275, p 383.
36. Cox, J. A., "Administrative Control of a Research Reactor," ORNL-2085 (1956).
37. duBoisblanc, D. R., "History and Operating Practice of the MTR Reactor Safeguard Committee," IDO-16284.
38. Ramsey, M. E. and Cagle, C. D., "Research Program and Operating Experience on ORNL Reactors," Paper No. 486, International Conference on the Peaceful Uses of Atomic Energy, Geneva, 1955.
39. Mesler, R. B., Luckow, W. K., and Gomberg, H. J., "The Ford Nuclear Reactor and Phoenix Memorial Laboratory," Nuclear Engineering Pt. IV, *Chem. Eng. Progress Symp.*, Series No. 19, **52**, 9 (1956).
40. Bopp, C. D. and Sisman, O., "How to Calculate Gamma Radiation Induced in Reactor Materials," *Nucleonics* **14**, No. 1, 46 (1956).

41. Trice, J. B., Solid State Division, *Semiannual Progress Report for Period Ending August 30, 1955*, ORNL-1945, following p 46.
42. Westfall, G. C., "Zircaloy Thimble for KAPL-120 Loop," KAPL-M-GOW-1 (1956).
43. Hueschen, R. E., Kemper, R. S., and Kelly, W. S., "The Effect of Irradiation on the Tensile Properties of Uranium," Paper No. 57-NESC-13, Philadelphia, Pa., (March 1957).
44. Fromm, L. W., "Design Evaluation of In-Reactor Tube for Argonne Water Loop at MTR (ANL-2)," ANL-5403.
45. Robinson, M. S., "Radiation Damage Studies Program — ETR Loop Materials Progress Report," IDO-16337 (1957).
46. Johnson, E. B., Henry, K. M., and Flynn, J. D., "The Reactivity Effect of an Air Tank Against One Face of the Bulk Shielding Reactor," ORNL-2179 (1957).
47. Jones, L. H. (editor), "Notes on Design of MTR and ETR Safety Circuits," Project Engineering Staff, Phillips Petroleum Company.
48. ——, "Research Reactors," Selected Reference Materials, USAEC Program, TID-5275, following p 269.
49. Blewitt, T. H. et al., "Mechanism of Annealing in Neutron Irradiated Metals," *Creep and Recovery*, ASM, 84 (1957).
50. Pigg, J. C., Bopp, C. D., Sisman, O., and Robinson, C. C., "The Effect of Reactor Irradiation on Electrical Insulation," *Communication and Electronics* (January 1956).
51. Mechlin, G. F., "WAPD-1 Experiments in the Materials Testing Reactor; II. Bellows Extensometer Test-WAPD-1-2," WAPD-76, (March 12, 1953).
52. Zukas, J. C., Davis, W. W., and Wilson, J. C., (ORNL) Unpublished data.
53. Boorman, C., "The Effect of Neutron Flux on the Thermoelectric Power of Thermocouples and on the Resistivity of Platinum and Nickel," AERE-E/R-572 (1950).
54. Madsen, P. E., "The Calibration of Thermocouples Under Irradiation," AERE-M/R-649 (1951).
55. Mannal, C., "Testing Electrical Insulation for Use in Gamma-Ray Fields," *Nucleonics* **12**, No. 6, 49 (1954).
56. Bright, G. O. and Schroeder, F., "Neutron Flux Distributions in the Materials Testing Reactor, Part I," IDO-16047 (1953).
57. Huffman, J. R., "The MTR Reactor Operational Behavior," *Nucl. Eng. Pt. IV, Chem. Eng. Prog. Symp. Series No. 19*, **52**, 25 (1956).
58. Hughes, D. J., "Pile Neutron Research," Addison-Wesley (1953).
59. Lewis, W. B., "Flux Perturbations by Material Under Irradiation," *Nucleonics* **13**, No. 10, 82 (1955).
60. Trice, J. B., "A Flux Depression Experiment," ORNL-2164 (1956).
61. Bopp, C. D. and Sisman, O., "Radiation Stability of Plastics and Elastomers," ORNL-1373 (1954).
62. Bopp, C. D. and Sisman, O., "The Neutron Flux Spectrum and Fast and Thermal Flux in Hole 19 of the ORNL Reactor," ORNL-525 (1950).
63. Trice, J. B. et al., "Two Neutron Energy Measurements in the Bulk Shielding Facility Using Radioactivants," ORNL-CF-53-5-139 (1953).
64. Trice, J. B., et al., "A series of Thermal, Epithermal and Fast Neutron Measurements in the MTR," ORNL-CF-55-10-140 (1955).
65. Uthe, P. M., "Attainment of Neutron Flux Spectra from Foil Activations," WADC-TR-57-3 (1957).

66. Primak, W., "Fast Neutron Damaging in Nuclear Reactors. I. Radiation Damage Monitoring with the Electrical Conductivity of Graphite," *Nuclear Science and Engineering* **2**, 49–56 (1957).

67. Primak, W., "Fast Neutron Damaging in Nuclear Reactors. II. The Radiation Damage Function of Graphite," *Nuclear Science and Engineering* **2**, 117–125 (1957).

68. Primak, W., "Fast Neutron Damaging in Nuclear Reactors. III. The Radiation Damage Dosage," *Nuclear Science and Engineering* **2**, 320–333 (1957).

69. Thompson, D. O. and Holmes, D. K., "Effects of Neutron Irradiation Upon the Young's Modulus and Internal Friction of Copper Single Crystals," *J. of Appl. Phys.* **27**, 713 (1956).

70. Bruch, C. A., (Knolls Atomic Power Lab.) Private Communication.

71. Richardson, D. M., Allen, A. O., and Boyle, J. W., "Dosimetry of Reactor Irradiations by Calorimetric Measurement," Paper No. 154, International Conference on Peaceful Uses of Atomic Energy, Vol. XIV, United Nations (1956).

72. Wright, J., "The Problem of Dosimetry in the Pile," "Radiation Chemistry," *Discussions of the Faraday Society*, No. 12, 60 (1952).

73. ——, "Test Reactors — The Larger View," *Nucleonics* **15**, No. 3, 42 (1957).

74. Grout, H. J., "The Use of Research Reactors in Nuclear Power Development," *J. of the British Nuclear Energy Conference* **1**, 35–51 (January 1, 1956).

75. Schuman, R. P., and McWherter, A. C., "Pile Induced Threshold Reactions in Stainless Steel," KAPL-1779.

76. McMurray, H. L., "MTR Technical Branch Quarterly Report," IDO-16331, following p 32 (March 26, 1957).

77. Kasten, P. R., Ludin, M. I., and Segaser, C. L., "Aqueous Homogeneous Research Reactor-Feasibility Report," ORNL-2256.

78. Elgert, O. J., Leyse, C. F., and Ott, D. G., "Preliminary Investigations for an Advanced Engineering Test Reactor," AECU-3427.

79. Safonov, G., "Engineering Test Reactors with Large Central Irradiation Cavities," Letter to Editor, *Nuclear Science and Engineering* **2**, 527 (1957).

80. ——, "Research Reactor Facility, Irradiation Services and Radioisotopes," Brookhaven National Laboratory (August 1956).

81. Mittleman, P. S. and Liedtice, R. A., "Gamma Rays from Thermal Neutron Capture," *Nucleonics* **13**, No. 5, 50 (1955).

82. Carroll, J. C. and Calish, S. R., "Some Effects of Gamma Radiation on Commercial Lubricants," *Lubrication Engineering* **13**, No. 7, 389 (1957).

83. Crawford, J. H., and Lark-Horovitz, K., "Fast Neutron Bombardment Effects in Germanium," *Phys. Rev.* **78**, No. 6, 815 (1950).

84. Link, L. E. and Cook, W. H., "The Mighty Mouse Research Reactor," ANL-5688.

85. Binder, D. and Sturm, W. J., "Expansion of LiF Under Neutron Irradiation," *Phys. Rev.* **107**, 106 (1957).

86. Berggren, R. G. and Wilson, J. C., (ORNL) Unpublished data.

87. Toomb, D. S., et al., "Liquid Level Transmitters," *Homogeneous Reactor Project Quarterly Progress Report for Period Ending July 31, 1957*, ORNL-2379, p 21.

88. Mallen, R. G., Saldick, J., and Gibbons, R. E., "Conceptual Design of an Advanced Engineering Test Reactor," NYO-4848 (1957).

89. Aeroneutronic Systems Inc., "A Selection Study for an Advanced, Engineering Test Reactor," AECU-3478 (1951).

90. Cole, T. E. and Gill, J. P., "The ORNL Research Reactor (ORR) — A General Description," ORNL-2240 (1957).

91. Raseman, C. J., Susskind, H., and Waide, C. H., "Liquid Metal Fuel Reactor (LMFR), In-pile Fuel Processing Loop (Loop B) — Construction, Operation, and Experimental Results," Paper No. 57-NESC-27, Philadelphia, Pa. (March 1957).
92. Nakazato, S. and Gercke, R. H. J., "Organic In-Pile Loop, NAA-18," NAA-SR-1592 (1956).
93. Colichman, E. L. and Gercke, R. H. J., "Radiation Stability of Terphyls and Other Polyphenyl Materials as Measured by Gas Evolution," NAA-SR-1288 (1956).
94. Warren, K. S. and Davis, J. R., "In-Reactor Autoclave Corrosion Studies — LITR, Outline of Methods and Procedures," ORNL-CF-57-5-110 (1957).
95. Evans, J. E. (Ed.), "Quarterly Progress Report for MTR Technical Branches (2nd Quarter 1957)" IDO-16394, following p 35 (1957).
96. Jenks, G. H., Jones, D. T., and Savage, H. C., "Circulating In-Reactor Loops," 5th Hot Lab and Equipment Conference, 1957 Nuclear Congress, p 321.

The following are not referenced in the text, but may be useful: Martens, John H. and Minuth, F. G., "Neutrons and Gamma Irradiations Facilities," U.S.G.P.O. (1957); ——, "Nuclear Reactor Data," Raytheon Mfg. Co. (1956); Mueller, W. D., Die Reaktoren der Welt," Verlag Handelsblatt GMBH, Duesseldorf (1956).

Chapter 3

RADIATION EFFECTS IN METALS
AND ALLOYS

D. S. Billington

Solid State Division, Oak Ridge National Laboratory
Oak Ridge, Tennessee

It is of some advantage to discuss radiation damage in metals and alloys
in terms of some of the variables that appear to be important to this field
of endeavor as well as those that metallurgists usually employ in considering metals and alloys. It is hoped that such a presentation will provide a
convenient introduction and guide for sorting the information into reasonable arrays of knowledge for those who may not be familiar with the
field. It should already be apparent, however, from the discussions in
the preceding chapters that our ignorance about the behavior of metals
under irradiation far exceeds our knowledge in this field, particularly with
regard to the basic theory of the radiation damage process. This is not
surprising when we consider that a basic understanding of the behavior
of metals and alloys, in the absence of radiation, also is lacking in many
areas. The promising side of the picture is that radiation damage experiments may help clarify our knowledge of the unirradiated state.

The previous chapters have summarized well the current status of our
knowledge in regard to the fundamental interactions between energetic
particles and solids and, also, the vast array of experimental difficulties
that confront the experimenter in the field of radiation effects. Therefore,
no attempt will be made to enlarge upon these matters other than to
emphasize that they must be borne clearly in mind when one wishes to work
in this field.

It is fortunate, indeed, that metals and alloys are more resistant to
radiation damage than many other classes of solids since this makes them
of more general use in reactor technology. This relatively high radiation
resistance is probably the result of certain characteristics of the metallic
state; for example, plasticity and high thermal and electrical conductivity.
However, the radiation resistance of metals and alloys does create certain
difficulties for the experimenter since he must now become concerned with
very subtle effects. Thus, creep tests run under typical service conditions

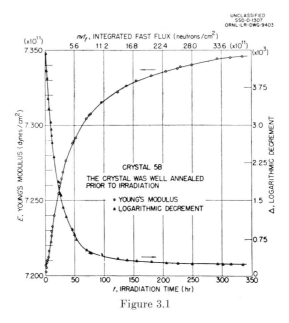

Figure 3.1

are difficult and tedious so that the determination of a small rate change in a process that normally proceeds at a low rate is fraught with many problems. Still, such experiments are of importance because time can ultimately make the effect sufficiently large to become of engineering significance.

Not all properties of a metal are equally insensitive to radiation. In general, metals and alloys differ widely in their response to irradiation and their behavior is dependent on a number of factors involving both the properties of the metal and the conditions of irradiation. D. O. Thompson and D. K. Holmes[1] have shown that the internal friction and apparent elastic modulus of high-purity, copper single crystals are extremely sensitive to neutron irradiation. Figure 1 indicates that large effects can be produced by low radiation exposure. Barnes and Hancock[2] at Harwell have made similar observations.

The nuclear fission reaction that takes place in uranium is the source of radiation damage in nuclear reactors because of (1) the high energy of the fission fragments and (2) the fact that several energetic neutrons are born during the fissioning of uranium atoms. The fission fragments are chiefly responsible for the damage to metallic uranium and other uranium-containing nuclear fuels because they are so energetic and because this energy is given up to its surroundings in the space of only a few microns. The damage sustained by the fuel can be severe and the study of this problem has engaged the attention of many scientists. This subject will be reviewed in subsequent chapters, and consequently will not be discussed here.*

The major emphasis in this chapter is placed on the damage originating from the energetic neutrons whose range in contrast to that of the fission fragments is very great—extending throughout the entire structure of the reactor. Our attention, therefore, becomes focussed upon radiation effects in all types of metals and alloys that may form a part of the reactor structure. The rate of damage originating from the neutrons is much lower than that caused by fission fragments. However, when we consider that most of the structural components of a reactor are required to withstand radiation indefinitely, while the fuel is often removed periodically for reprocessing, we find that ultimately the total damage sustained by the structure will be comparable to and in some cases greater than that sustained by the fuel.

The lower rate of damage from neutrons poses a particularly difficult problem in reactor design since we are now confronted with the problem of deriving, from low flux, short time irradiation experiments, in which the effects are of little immediate consequence, what the damage will be after long time, high flux service conditions—a problem that may be a determining factor in evaluating the probable lifetime of power reactors.

Over the past several years an imposing amount of neutron irradiation data has been reported in the open literature by several experimental groups† both in applied and basic areas of study. No attempt will be made here to review the literature in a comprehensive fashion but rather typical examples will be chosen to illustrate basic principles.

There are, of course, many controversial areas in the field, and some discussion of those areas of disagreement will be included as appropriate. In any event, a sufficient number of references[3] are included to enable the reader to consult the original work for the many details that must of necessity be omitted during this presentation.

Types of Radiation Effects

Radiation effects in metals and alloys arbitrarily may be classified in several different ways, but for present purposes it may be considered that such radiation effects fall into two main classes. First, there are those effects which result directly from the production of defects in the metal or alloy by the radiation field. The second class of effects arises from the subsequent motion and interaction of these radiation-induced defects

* Ed. note: See paper by Weber for discussion of radiation damage in uranium and other nuclear fuels.

† In the U. S., the National Laboratories of the Atomic Energy Commission and several AEC contractors have been active in this field.

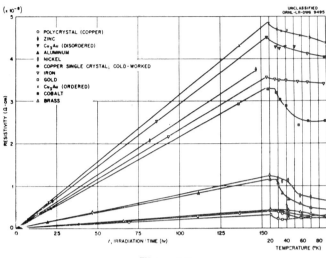

Figure 3.2

with pre-existing lattice imperfections. This implies that the defects
produced by the radiation may not give rise to significant changes in the
metallic lattice until they acquire sufficient mobility, as, for example,
under the influence of a subsequent rise in temperature. This is perhaps
only another way of saying that defects can be stored and their influence
will not be felt until the temperature is raised, whether the sample is
now in or out of the radiation field. This second class of effects is particularly
important in alloys; in pure metals, effects of the second type usually are
apparent as an annealing or recovery of the direct effects produced by
the radiation.

Thus, if a pure metal is irradiated at 20°K or lower, substantial increases
in the electrical resistivity during irradiation can be observed.[4, 5, 6] When
the temperature is allowed to rise to room temperature, subsequent to
irradiation, an appreciable portion of the resistivity increase produced
by the irradiation will gradually anneal out (Fig. 2). With pure aluminum,
for example, the pre-irradiated resistivity value is recovered by the time
the temperature reaches −30°C.[7] For a simple alloy such as alpha brass,
irradiation below 20°K also results in a resistivity increase just as in the
case of the pure metal.[6] However, when the temperature of the irradiated
sample is increased to room temperature, it is observed that the resistivity
is now actually lower than it was before irradiation,[8] indicating that some
solid state process has taken place under the influence of the subsequent
temperature rise. This subsequent decrease in resistivity has been attributed
to the development of short range order.[9] However, if the temperature of

the irradiated brass sample is raised to 100° to 200°C above room temperature, the original resistivity will be recovered.

In summary then, the above examples illustrate the direct effect of the defects introduced by irradiation of a pure metal; in the case of a simple alloy, the defects possess a latent capacity for inducing property changes, e.g., resistivity decrease, which do not become evident until the defects gain mobility as a result of a post-irradiation temperature increase. Numerous examples of these two types of effects are in the literature and many of these will be referred to in later discussion.

Factors Determining the Extent of Radiation Effects

With reference to the above two types of radiation effects, it is convenient to discuss radiation effects in metals and alloys in terms of a number of variables which reflect the conditions of irradiation, the pre-irradiation state and the properties of the metal or alloy under consideration.

It can be immediately deduced from the above discussion that one of the most important factors governing the behavior of the metals under irradiation is the *temperature of irradiation*. Other important variables are: *melting point, crystal structure, prior thermal and mechanical history, radiation environment, neutrons flux,* and *the property being studied.*

The temperature of irradiation is important because, as has already been noted, it determines whether the radiation induced defects will have sufficient mobility to cause secondary effects. The melting point of the metal being irradiated is closely related to the temperature of irradiation because the melting point gives a rough measure of the temperature required for appreciable mobility of defects. As a rough approximation, it may be stated that at temperatures somewhat above half of the absolute melting point many solid state reactions will proceed at an appreciable rate. Thus, a modest room temperature irradiation of pure aluminum will result in little change in mechanical strength. However, when copper, iron, molybdenum and other high melting point metals and alloys are irradiated at room temperature, pronounced changes in mechanical properties are observed. Furthermore, relatively high annealing temperatures are required to bring about any noticeable recovery. The total exposure may have an important role in this regard as will become evident later.

A knowledge of the crystal structure of the metal or alloy being irradiated may provide some indication of the possible structure sensitivity of the material to radiation. Thus, iron and carbon steels, which at room temperature are body-centered cubic, exhibit a high degree of sensitivity to notch embrittlement and relatively low impact strength, and show increased weaknesses in regard to these properties under neutron irradiation. Molybdenum and tungsten exhibit similar behavior. On the other hand, face-centered cubic metals, while they may suffer a loss in ductility under irradiation, do not become brittle. Metallic uranium[10, 11] has a very anisotropic structure and undergoes exaggerated dimensional changes and brittleness under irradiation. This behavior of uranium is perhaps the best example of the relationship between anisotropy in crystal structure and radiation effects, though graphite runs it a close second.[12, 13] Unfortunately, the relationship between crystal structure and these properties in the absence of radiation is not well enough understood to permit broad generalizations in regard to radiation behavior, but it is recognized as being a factor of some importance.

The prior thermal and mechanical history of the metal or alloy can be of importance in determining subsequent behavior for the following reasons: Preferred orientation may cause enhanced anisotropic effects similar to the radiation-induced growth in uranium, but on a much smaller scale. Severe cold working of a sample will influence its subsequent radiation behavior because of the large number of dislocations which are introduced during deformation. This high density of dislocations may mask the effects of the irradiation for appreciable irradiation periods. Thus, a different rate of radiation damage between annealed and cold-worked metals or alloys is observed

The metastability of an alloy may be important because locally enhanced diffusion resulting from irradiation may cause the breakdown of a metastable solid solution at temperatures which, in the absence of radiation, would normally be so low that any measurable changes could not be observed even after several years. Supersaturated solid solutions of beryllium in copper and nickel[14, 15] and many of the stainless steels fall within this category.[16] The net result of the irradiation process appears to be toward the promotion of thermodynamic equilibrium. Apparent important exceptions to this generalization have been found in U-Mo[17] alloys and in ZrO_2,[18] in which radiation-induced stabilization of high temperature phases has been observed.

The purity of the metal may have a strong influence on the post-irradiation annealing kinetics, particularly at low temperature[6] (Figs. 3 and 4); it also may influence radiation-induced changes in such properties as internal friction and apparent elastic constants.[1] The magnitude of room temperature radiation effects in aluminum appear to be dependent upon the purity. High-purity aluminum shows little effect after short periods of irradiation, while impure aluminum, after long irradiation, shows significant changes.[19]

Normally, metals and alloys are not subject to damage by ionizing radiation, at least not to a significant degree. However, if a metal or alloy is irradiated in the presence of gases, liquids or solids which are sensitive to

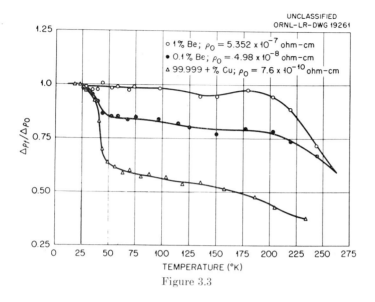

Figure 3.3

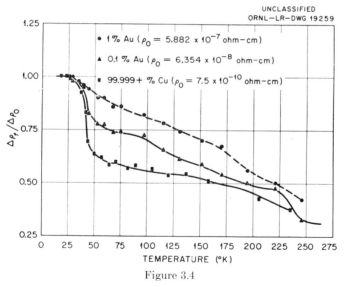

Figure 3.4

ionization, the increased chemical activity of the environment, resulting from the formation of ions and free radicals, may cause chemical interaction with the surface of the metal or alloy. One therefore might be led to expect increased reaction, e.g., oxidation, nitriding, etc., or corrosion rates under appropriate conditions. A detailed discussion of these and similar problems is beyond the scope of this presentation and is considered elsewhere in this monograph.*

The neutron flux would appear to be an important variable and this has been demonstrated in a few instances. However, suitable reactor conditions have not been sufficiently available to enable comprehensive studies to be carried out in all areas of interest. Preliminary experiments have indicated that aluminum and beryllium are sensitive to high flux only.[19] It is to be hoped that, in the near future, the flux dependence of properties such as creep and various solid state reactions of metallurgical interest will be better understood. The central question to be resolved is whether the total dose of radiation or the rate of irradiation is the more important factor.

The last important variable is the physical or mechanical property, per se, which is being studied. It is becoming increasingly apparent that certain properties are affected more than others and, furthermore, a knowledge of the unirradiated state is often not a good criterion for estimating the relative behavior of various properties under nuclear irradiation. This matter is not well understood and must form the basis for much of our future study in the field. However, changes in various properties are the primary index of the damage process and the defects introduced by radiation. In subsequent paragraphs, those properties which have been studied extensively after various conditions of irradiation will be treated in some detail.

Property Changes After Neutron Irradiation

Density

To a first approximation it may be stated that density changes in metals and alloys caused by reactor irradiation are trivial. Although in certain nonmetals density changes may be very large, it has been observed by several investigators that the room-temperature changes in density of metals seldom exceed 0.1–0.2 per cent. Many materials have been studied, including copper, iron, nickel, molybdenum, tungsten, tantalum, stainless steel, carbon steels, brasses, and aluminum alloys.[20] The observed changes always indicate a decrease in density.

McDowell and Kierstad[21] have reported that, for copper, the density decrease, resulting from deuteron bombardment, can be accounted for within a factor of two by assuming the formation of vacancy-interstitial pairs, the number formed being calculated by Seitz' method.[22] Similar agreement between theory and experiment has not been obtained in regard to other property changes.

*Ed. note: See chapter by Simnad.

Presumably, similar considerations should apply to neutron-irradiated metals and alloys, but no attempt has been made to correlate the change in density. Below temperatures at which any annealing could occur, i.e., 20°K or below, it would be expected that prolonged irradiation would lead to a greater density change; such data, however, are still lacking. Although the likelihood of metals being required to withstand extremely low temperatures and high neutron fluxes is not presently considered as a problem, it should be pointed out that these small changes are of considerable interest to the researcher who is concerned with the detailed mechanisms of the production of defects by neutron irradiation. The correlation of lattice parameter changes with density changes should yield information of fundamental interest. R. O. Simmons has recently begun studies of this sort.[23]

Occasionally dimensional changes of metals after irradiation have been reported. These have been shown to be caused by the radiation annealing of residual stresses which were present in the metal prior to irradiation, since the temperature of irradiation was sufficiently high to provide a stress-relieving anneal. Slight dimensional changes also can originate in metals or alloys with highly preferred orientation. Precipitation hardening alloys also will exhibit dimensional changes under irradiation. For such alloys, the effects are attributed to the dimensional changes associated with the precipitation effect induced by the irradiation and not to the production of vacancy-interstitial pairs.

Thermal Properties

The introduction, upon irradiation, of substantial numbers of defects in the form of vacancies and interstitials would be expected to result in significant amounts of stored energy which might be of particular importance if the energy so stored was released in a narrow temperature range. That energy can be stored by neutron irradiation has been well documented in the case of graphite.[13] Only limited experiments have been conducted with metals and alloys, but it may be concluded that the stored energy must be liberated over a wide range of temperature. One experimental study by the Oak Ridge National Laboratory indicates that vacancy-interstitial annihilation may not be an important factor in the low temperature annealing process in metals, thereby explaining why a sudden burst of energy is not observed[5] (Fig. 5). There is an obvious need for more extended experiments in this area; however, the difficulty of conducting such experiments precludes any immediate resolution. The problem of low-temperature annealing of radiation effects will be discussed in some detail under electrical properties.

The thermal conductivity of metals is not affected appreciably by radia-

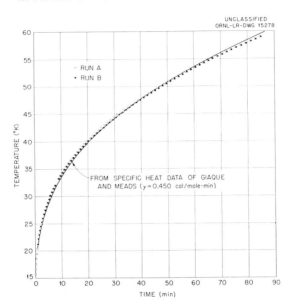

Run No.13. Copper Single Crystal Bombarded at 21.7 °K. Integrated
Flux = ~ 4 x 10^{17} nvt. Time = ~ 150 hr. Exchange Gas = ~ 30 μ.

Figure 3.5

tion at room temperature or above. Below temperatures of 20°K, however,
conduction becomes much more sensitive to the presence of impurity
atoms and defects, in general, so appreciable decreases in the low temperature conductivity after irradiation might be anticipated. To date, such
studies at low temperature have been made only with nonmetals.[24] In
any event, there do not appear to be immediate technological reasons for
becoming concerned with thermal conductivity of metals or alloys at
low temperatures in the presence of appreciable neutron fluxes.

No studies have been made of the possible changes in thermal expansion
coefficients. For isotropic metals and alloys, this is not of concern, since
the elastic constants, except under specialized conditions, do not undergo
significant change. Nor has it been shown that the Debye characteristic
temperature changes* under irradiation. Thus, it is highly likely that the
coefficient of thermal expansion will not exhibit any significant change
upon irradiation.

Magnetic Properties

Although a number of magnetic measurements have been made, they
have been used for the primary purpose of following the course of certain

* Heavy deuteron bombardment experiments may provide an exception.[6]

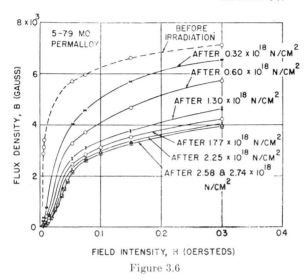

Figure 3.6

solid state reactions and not for examining the effect of radiation on the magnetic properties, per se.[14, 16] It is to be expected that those magnetic properties which are structure sensitive, such as permeability, would be affected by irradiation, while such non-structure-sensitive properties as the saturation magnetization would not be affected. Recently Sery, Fischell and Gordon[25] have studied certain high permeability alloys, e.g., 5–79 molybdenum permalloy, and found that after an exposure of approximately 3×10^{17} nvt the maximum permeability dropped from about 540×10^3 to less than 60×10^3, a ninefold decrease. Further irradiation produced a continuing decrease in permeability, but at an extremely low rate. Figure 6 illustrates the influence of neutron irradiation on the d.c. magnetization curve. Studies also have been made on 3.5 per cent silicon-iron and other magnetic materials. Much of the data are preliminary in nature and a full analysis has not been completed.

Electrical Resistivity

The electrical resistivity is a convenient property to measure on irradiated material and, as a consequence, the number of experiments for which resistivity measurements are reported is far greater than the relative importance of the changes observed. The changes in resistivity of some metals which have been observed after extensive irradiation at room temperature are indeed quite small and of little technological significance. For example, pure aluminum displays no measurable change, and copper shows a resis-

TABLE 1. CHANGES IN ELECTRICAL RESISTIVITY AND BRINELL HARDNESS OF VARIOUS METALS AFTER IRRADIATION AT 90°C ON 5-6 × 10^{20} NVT*

	% increase in resistance	BHN (500 Kg load) ΔH	% increase in hardness
Copper	7.3	56	128
Nickel	2.4	42	69
Titanium - commercial	7.0	36	20
High purity zirconium	5.9	20	29
High purity iron	8.3	41	78
Molybdenum - commercial	22	23	22
Stainless steel	1.8	44	27

* C. A Bruch, W. E. McHugh and R. W. Hockenbury, Trans. AIME 206, 1362 (1956).

tivity increase of only 0.1–0.4 per cent. Whether an appreciable effect will be observed at room temperature is somewhat dependent, as pointed out earlier, on the melting point of the metal. High melting point metals, such as zirconium, titanium, iron and molybdenum, exhibit substantial resistivity increases after room temperature bombardment. Bruch, McHugh and Hockenbury[26] have reported resistivity changes for a number of metals (Table I), but again such resistivity increases would not have occurred or would have been much less if the temperature of irradiation had been 100° to 300°C higher. The large change observed in copper may have been due to a high impurity content.

Much of the resistivity measurements have been made after irradiation below room temperature, because low temperature resistivity changes afford the means of determining the rate of defect production. The concentration of defects calculated from resistivity measurements are valid only if the temperature of irradiation is low enough to prevent any annealing, and if the types of defects produced and the resistivity change associated with each defect is known. With respect to the first proviso, it has been found that temperatures of irradiation of 20°K or less are required to avoid annealing. Analysis of the available data leads to the conclusion that either defects other than simple vacancy-interstitial pairs are formed or the value of resistivity increase assumed to be associated with either type of defect is in error. This latter point is a subject of controversy at the present time, and the reader is referred to the literature on this matter. Briefly, it must be concluded that either the present calculated values of defect concentration (based upon resistivity measurements) are not correct, or the theoretical predictions concerning the rate of production of defects are in error, since theory predicts a fivefold larger increase in resistivity than is observed experimentally.

Another factor contributing to the controversy is the lack of knowledge about the kind of defects produced. Annealing experiments on metals, previously irradiated below 20°K, indicate that the kinetics of the annealing process are not simple, and are not consistent with the behavior to be expected from the annealing of simple vacancy-interstitial pairs. Thus, the post-irradiation changes in resistivity upon annealing at higher temperatures do not correlate with the stored energy measurements (previously discussed), made within the same temperature range.[5]

In any event, a substantial increase in resistivity is observed for all metals and alloys after irradiation at low temperature ($<20°$K), as is evident from Figure 2.

To complicate the matter still further, it has long been believed that bombardment by electrons, particularly at low temperatures, results only in the formation of the simplest types of defects, presumably simple vacancy-interstitial pairs, which from energy considerations is not an unreasonable assumption. Nevertheless, there is a strong resemblance between the annealing kinetics in electron-irradiated and neutron-irradiated copper.[19] Thus, another question may be posed: Are the electron irradiation effects more complicated than originally supposed, or are the neutron and heavy charged-particle effects simpler than now are believed?

The data obtained by the Oak Ridge National Laboratory have shown that the increase in resistivity, at 20°K, is linear with radiation exposure time, which would be anticipated in the absence of annealing. The results of an equivalent cyclotron experiment by the Illinois group,[4] involving deuterons instead of neutrons, revealed a slight bending over in the latter part of the resistivity vs. exposure curve, implying that some annealing during irradiation had occurred. The total irradiation in the cyclotron experiment was considerably higher than in the reactor experiment, so it is possible that in high-flux, long-time neutron irradiation experiments a similar effect will be noted.

The cause of the so-called radiation annealing is not altogether clear. It may be connected with thermal spikes which could annneal out (reunite) the vacancy-interstitial pairs formed by the "billiard ball" collisions. Such annihilation of close vacancy-interstitial pairs would, in itself, cause some "annealing" departure from linearity of the resistivity-exposure curve. An adequate explanation of radiation annealing must be closely coupled with the proper identification of the defects introduced by irradiation which, as noted above, is not possible at this time.

Blewitt, Coltman, Klabunde and Noggle,[5] in the above-mentioned series of experiments, have shown that impurity content may have a pronounced effect upon the annealing characteristics of copper single crystals. They investigated copper alloyed with 0.1 and 1.0 atomic per cent gold and beryllium and found that the addition of 0.1 atomic per cent of impurity did not change the resistivity annealing curve sensibly from that observed for the pure metal. On the other hand, the annealing characteristics of the 1.0 per cent alloy were different from that of the pure metal, the effect of the beryllium addition being more pronounced than that of gold. These findings strongly imply that the crowdion[27, 28] may indeed be an important aspect of the mechanism of the annealing of electrical resistivity in pure copper. Regardless, the purity of the metal is certainly important, as can be seen in Figures 3 and 4.

Microstructure

From the earliest days of reactor technology, metallurgists have been interested in the possibility of alteration of the microstructure of a metal or alloy by irradiation; consequently, numerous observations have been made on this point by different groups. The present consensus would indicate that the "grain size" is unaltered by irradiation, but important exceptions exist. For example, Konobeevsky[29] has reported substantial increases in the grain size of both copper and nickel after irradiation at temperatures of 250–300°C, and also noted the appearance of deformation twins in zirconium. Unfortunately, the prior history of these samples was not well documented nor was the possible effect of thermal cycling during reactor operation considered (i.e., strains induced by temperature gradients might well lead to enhanced grain growth).

Recently, Bruch, McHugh and Doig[30] irradiated samples of copper, nickel, titanium, zirconium, iron and molybdenum for exposures ranging from 2 to 7 × 10[19] nvt (above 1 Mev). Examination, both after irradiation and after annealing (to remove the radiation-induced hardness increase), failed to reveal any increase in the grain size of the metals. They concluded that the grain size increase observed by Konobeevsky[29] could not be caused by neutron irradiation.

All metallographers involved in "hot" metallography are well aware of the effect of irradiation upon the etching characteristics of metals and alloys. Radiation decomposition of etchants by radioactive samples results in abnormal reaction rates and causes considerable trouble to the metallographer. A proper consideration of this problem lies in the province of the radiation chemist and those concerned with liquid-metal interfaces and will not be further considered here.

The deformation characteristics of copper are altered appreciably during irradiation and the altered slip-line structure is readily revealed by microscopic examination.

This matter is considered below in more detail.

Important microstructural changes have been observed in uranium and uranium alloys[11] but these will be discussed in a subsequent chapter.

Crystal Structure

The white to grey transformation in tin has been shown by Dienes[31] to be accelerated under irradiation. Warren, Dienes and Chipman[32] have reported the appearance of red phosphorous diffraction lines in x-ray diffraction patterns of irradiated black phosphorous. These, plus the possibility of structural changes in zirconium as noted by Konobeevsky,[29] seem to constitute the whole of the observations of crystal structure changes in elemental solids induced by irradiation.

The more interesting aspects of this problem are to be found in uranium alloys, Mo-U and Nb-U,[17] and in nonmetals such as ZrO_2[18] and $BaTiO_3$[33] in which neutron irradiation tends to stabilize the high temperature phases.

Mechanical Properties

All metals and alloys thus far examined show substantial increases in hardness and other strength properties under appropriate conditions of irradiation. The amount of change is a sensitive function of the total fast neutron exposure and the temperature of irradiation. Thus, short exposures at room temperature yield slight, if any, changes in low melting alloys, such as aluminum, magnesium[1, 10] and lead.[34] On the other hand, if the temperature of irradiation is lowered or if the exposure is increased, then significant changes are observed.[19] Also, if the metal is only slightly alloyed, more pronounced effects are produced, even for a room temperature irradiation.[35, 36] A large number of metals and alloys have been studied, including aluminum, beryllium, copper, iron, lead, magnesium, molybdenum, nickel, titanium, tungsten, zinc, zirconium, carbon steels, stainless steels, copper base and aluminum base alloys, but nevertheless the study cannot be considered to be complete. In addition it is often difficult to compare the results obtained by different investigators because of widely varying conditions of irradiation and the lack of knowledge of the exact neutron flux existing in the reactor at the time of irradiation.

It has been shown that the initial condition[14, 34] of the metal or alloy may determine the extent of the irradiation effect. Annealed metals exhibit significantly larger property changes than those in the initially cold-worked state. Makin and Minter[37] have actually observed a decrease in yield strength of irradiated, heavily cold-worked zirconium. It has not been found possible thus far to harden or strengthen metals or alloys to a greater extent than is possible by conventional means. The yield strength appears to be very sensitive to irradiation. Blewitt and Coltman[5] have observed a thirty-fold increase in the critical shear stress of copper single crystals upon irradiation. Makin[38] has also noted the sensitivity of the critical shear stress of copper to irradiation but observed a lower rate of increase,

TABLE 2. TYPICAL INCREASES IN PLASTIC PROPERTIES OF METALS AND
ALLOYS AFTER NEUTRON IRRADIATION*

Materials	Yield Strength (psi)	Tensile Strength (psi)	YS/TS	
			Pre	Post
2 S H14 aluminum	+5,000	+7,000	.9	.85
2SO aluminum	+10,000	+9,000	.51	.65
High Purity Iron	+13,000	+1,000	.5	.84
Normalized Carbon Steel	+43,000	+22,000	.67	.96
Hardened and Tempered Alloy Steel	+43,000	+34,000	.93	.99
Austenitic Stainless Steel	+60,000	+17,000	.38	.84
Titanium-commercial 75A	+42,000	+23,000	.75	.99
High Purity Zirconium	+18,000	+3,000	.33	.73

* Adapted from:
Bruch, McHugh and Hockenbury, Trans. AIME, 206, 1362 (1956).
J. C. Wilson and D. S. Billington, J. of Metals 8, 665 (1956).
R. V. Steele and W. P. Wallace, Met. Prog. 68, No. 1, 114 (1955).
E. R. W. Jones, W. Munro, N. H. Hancock, J. Nuc. Energy 1, 76 (1954).

possibly because of higher temperatures of irradiation. The ultimate
tensile strength[20] is increased by neutron irradiation too, but to a lesser
degree than the yield strength. Figure 7 shows the effects of irradiation
upon the mechanical properties of a carbon steel and Table 2 contains
additional data. Many metals such as high purity iron, aluminum, nickel,
zirconium and face centered cubic metals in general develop a yield point
upon irradiation while the pre-existing yield point in steels and molybdenum is erased by irradiation. Stainless steels show a strain rate dependent
yield point upon irradiation.

The irradiation induced change in the critical shear stress[5] of copper has
been shown to be temperature dependent, varying as the square root of the
testing temperature subsequent to irradiation at room temperature, and
also displays square root dependence upon integrated flux, with saturation
apparently setting in at about 5×10^{20} nvt. Steele and Wallace[35] and
Klein[36] observed similar saturation effects in alloys of aluminum, at an
approximate flux of 10^{20} nvt.

The yield strength effects in steels appear to be more sensitive to the
temperature of irradiation than the changes in ultimate tensile strength.[39]
The difference in rates of increase of the yield strength and the ultimate
tensile strength for room temperature irradiations leads to the inference
that irradiation should result in a loss in ductility and in general a loss in
ductility does occur after substantial irradiation. In most cases the loss in
ductility is not severe except for low carbon steels (refer to Figure 7) and
for beryllium.[19] In the case of steel the major loss in ductility occurs in the

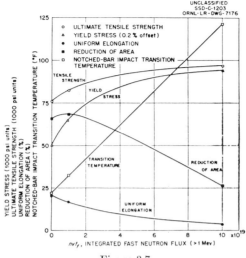

Figure 3.7

uniform elongation, prior to necking, in tension tests. Unfortunately, a serious reduction in the impact strength of low carbon steels is also observed, which begins to be significant after exposures as short as 5×10^{18} nvt. Accompanying the decrease in impact strength is an increase in the temperature for the transition from brittle to ductile fracture; thus it is apparent that the use of pressure vessel steels in fields of high fast neutron flux may present a serious problem. The effects of irradiation upon both the impact strength and the brittle to ductile transition temperature of these steels, as well as on their yield strength, are strongly influenced by the temperature of irradiation. Thus, the selection of appropriate irradiation temperatures may alleviate the serious loss in room temperature properties.

The elastic constants usually are insensitive to irradiation,[34] though it might be expected that long-time, high fast-flux irradiations at low temperatures would lead to changes greater than one percent. In the special case of ultra-high purity metals such as copper, in which little opportunity for dislocation pinning exists, it has been shown by Thompson and Holmes[1] that irradiation will cause dislocation pinning and, consequently, the dislocation motion detraction from Young's Modulus will be wiped out, leading to as much as a 10% increase in the apparent Young's Modulus.

It has been observed generally that recovery of neutron irradiation induced changes in hardness and strength occur within approximately the same temperature range as recovery of more conventional cold working effects; i.e., the temperature region of self-diffusion (usually the annealing

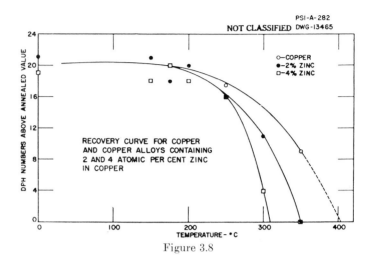

Figure 3.8

temperature for radiation effects) is slightly lower. Mechanical property changes are more thermally stable than the changes in electrical properties produced by irradiation. Figure 8 illustrates the annealing behavior of the hardness changes in irradiated copper base alloys and should be contrasted with Figures 2–4 inclusive.

Several creep experiments in radiation fields have been performed.[36, 39] The effect is usually a negative one; that is, decreases in the creep rate are observed because of the general strengthening introduced by irradiation. Fillnow, Cook and Johnson[23] have shown an unusually large decrease in the creep rate of zirconium at 260°C and an exposure of 3×10^{12} neutrons/ cm². Wilson[40] points out, however, that under the proper conditions of high stress and temperature plus high flux a slight increase in creep rates might be expected. A. H. Cottrell also has made a similar observation.[3] The loss of ductility upon irradiation as observed in tensile tests may limit the useful extension under creep conditions; that is, rupture might occur during the steady state region of creep.

No experiments on 'in-pile' fatigue have been performed to date, nor can possible changes be predicted with any assurance since one might argue equally strong for an increase in fatigue strength as for a decrease.

In summary, metals and alloys after exposure to radiation fields become harder, stronger and less ductile. These changes are not unduly great, except for certain metals and alloys such as carbon steels, which are subject to embrittlement even in the absence of irradiation. All of the changes in mechanical properties induced by irradiation can be eliminated by an appropriate anneal at temperatures that approximate the annealing temperatures for the removal of cold working effects.

Radiation Hardening

A satisfactory explanation for radiation hardening has not been derived as yet. However, some general ideas are beginning to evolve. It does not appear likely that isolated vacancies and interstitials are capable of providing the requisite hardening because of their inability to anchor dislocations strongly enough; furthermore, it appears evident that vacancies and interstitials can be annealed out at temperatures below which mechanical property changes are still stable. On the other hand, it does appear necessary to postulate the formation of clusters of defects which are sufficiently large to impede dislocation motion. Kunz and Holden[34] were the first to postulate the formation of interstitial platelets. These platelets form on close-packed planes and may be considered to be similar to stacking faults, but compressed in an interstitial layer. It is believed that these platelets form by diffusion of interstitials to appropriate sites. Kunz and Holden believe that irradiation at low temperature (below 78°K) would not produce any measurable hardening, until the temperature was increased and the interstitials given an opportunity to agglomerate. Recent experiments by Blewitt and his co-workers[5] have shown that the critical shear stress of copper is increased by irradiation at 20°K, even when measurement is made at 20°K, before the metal is allowed to warm up. Furthermore, when the sample was allowed to reach room temperature and again measured at 20°K, no subsequent increase in critical shear stress was observed. This experiment indicates that subsequent migration of defects is not essential to the hardening process. Blewitt and Holmes are of the opinion, therefore, that the agglomerates necessary for the thermal stability of the irradiation effect are created directly from the debris along the wake of a knocked-on atom, the composition of the agglomerate presently being unspecified with its size perhaps approaching the order of 10–20 angstroms in diameter. In any event, the size will be such as to permit the dislocation to move with the aid of thermal fluctuations, thus producing the observed temperature dependence of the critical shear stress.

The results of the low temperature internal friction experiments of Thompson, Holmes and Blewitt[41] performed at very low fluxes, indicate a wider dispersal of defects than would be possible in the case of the creation and subsequent motion of vacancy-interstitial pairs formed either by a direct knock-on or by a thermal spike mechanism. The replacement mechanism of Kinchin and Pease[42] in regard to interstitials may have an important bearing on the matter.

The shape of the post-irradiated stress-strain curve of pure copper bears a strong resemblance to that of alpha brass, suggesting strongly that the direct introduction of dislocations by irradiation does not take place.

The combined effects of irradiation and cold work are not additive, which should not be the case if dislocations had been introduced.

The role of the crowdion concept, discussed by Lomer and Cottrell[28] and Blewitt, Holmes, Coltman and Noggle[5] with reference to low temperature resistivity effects, has not been adequately evaluated in regard to mechanical property changes, nor has the effect of impurity content been adequately studied, though conceivably both of these factors could be important to our understanding of radiation hardening.

Friedel[43] has argued that the rapid accumulation of vacancies near dislocations might result in spherical voids which would impede dislocation motion, but the hardening obtained at low temperature and the pinning observed at low fluxes appear to negate such a mechanism.

Cottrell[3] points out that many of the jogs formed in dislocation lines by the absorption of defects can be annealed at low temperature. A stable dislocation network is built up because the nodes, connecting a dislocation line with the main network, now lie in different slip planes. That is, the dislocation line will straighten out as much as possible but will necessarily retain some jogs in order to bridge the two nodes. An elevated temperature anneal will be required to transform this metastable network to one characteristic of the fully annealed state.

One may hope to gain additional insight into the hardening mechanism by appropriate experiments involving electron bombardment since it is generally believed that because of the simple nature of the defects introduced by electron bombardment hardening at elevated temperatures will not persist. Preliminary experiments[44] indicate some hardening; however, further experimentation is required before the nature and extent of the hardening are understood.

Effects of Irradiation Upon Solid State Metallurgical Reactions

Many reactions in metals and alloys which occur in the solid state can be strongly influenced by irradiation, particularly when the process is diffusion controlled and proceeds by a vacancy mechanism. While the observations are not completely explainable by a simple model, it does seem clear that the large number of defects introduced into solids by irradiation are responsible for the increased reaction rates.

Siegel[45] was the first to show that Cu_3Au, in the ordered condition, when irradiated at room temperature exhibits a progressive increase in electrical resistivity, indicating an increasing degree of disorder (Figure 9). This was subsequently verified by x-ray diffraction studies. Other alloys, such as beta brass,[46] $CuAu$,[47] Ni_3Mn,[48] and Ni_3Cr[49] have been studied and similar results have been reported. The resulting disorder appears to be caused by the direct "billiard-ball" type collisions or the replacement

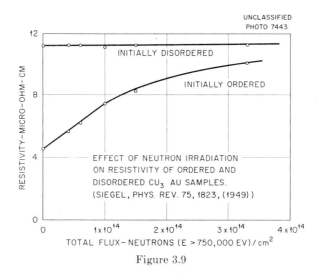

Figure 3.9

mechanism of Kinchin and Pease,[42] the latter being favored even over a thermal spike mechanism, because of the temperature dependence of the effects as discussed below.

Effects of irradiation upon initially disordered alloys is even more interesting. A sample of Cu_3Au in the disordered state, when irradiated at room temperature, does not show any resistivity change. However, if the temperature of irradiation is increased to 150–200°C, a temperature low enough to insure no thermal ordering but still sufficiently high to increase the mobility of vacancies introduced by irradiation, the disordered alloy becomes progressively more ordered as indicated by the decrease in resistivity.[50] (Figure 10) The rate of increase of ordering is flux dependent. The group at WAPD have shown substantial changes at temperatures as low as 80°C.[51, 52] These alloys have been studied as simple examples of order-disorder reactions, but in reactor materials research a real concern exists over the possibility of changing the metastable state of many alloys by a change in the degree of order under irradiation.

Several simple types of precipitation-hardening alloys also have been studied[14, 15, 53, 54] in order to provide some insight into the behavior of more complex alloys. It originally was hoped that a general model for the effect of neutron irradiation on this class of alloys could be established, however, at the present stage of research, it appears that the peculiarities of each alloy are such that each is uniquely influenced by irradiation. Despite this divergence, several interesting observations may be noted:

1. Hardness and resistivity increases almost always are observed for room temperature irradiated copper-beryllium alloys regardless of prior

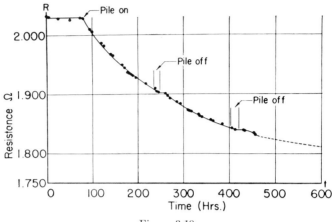

Figure 3.10

heat treatment, except for the fully hardened state in which no further increase in hardness occurs.

2. There is a strong analogy between the properties of room temperature irradiated copper-beryllium and a solution-quenched alloy heat treated at 100–150°C.

3. The radiation effects in copper-beryllium and nickel-beryllium alloys are temperature dependent. No radiation induced precipitation takes place in Ni-Be alloys at room temperature but does so at elevated temperatures, while conversely, Cu-Be alloys show precipitation effects at room temperature but not at 80°K.

4. Neutron irradiation increases the amount of precipitation in Ni-Be alloys over that produced by conventional heat-treatments.

5. When aluminum-silver precipitation hardening alloys are neutron-irradiated, then heat treated out-of-pile, the "Guinier-Preston zones" grow at a slower rate than they would in the unirradiated case.

6. The neutron irradiation effects in the Cu-Fe system are particle size dependent and prior-history dependent. Boltax[54] has shown that small particles tend to redissolve while large particles tend to grow (similar to Ni-Be and Cu-Be); also, when the precipitate is still coherent with the parent matrix, resolution is more probable than when such coherency is lost.

7. The ferromagnetic form of the precipitate in Cu-Fe alloy is produced during irradiation. In the unirradiated case this phase appears only by cold working the alloy subsequent to the precipitation heat treatment.

8. The temperature dependence of the effects in all precipitation hardening alloys appears to be closely related to the temperature required for appreciable motion of vacancies.

The exact mechanism of behavior under irradiation is far from being understood, but it does appear safe to say that the introduction of excess vacancies is an important aspect. We therefore may draw the conclusion that any reaction which appears to be vacancy diffusion controlled will be sensitive to irradiation at an appropriate temperature. The enhanced diffusion effects caused by the excess vacancies occurs only on a microscale and it is not safe to assume that macroscopic diffusion effects will be observed. In fact, all experiments designed to show enhanced diffusion or self diffusion on a gross scale have, to date, given negative results. It thus appears that the rates of various reactions can be speeded up but the ease with which the reaction takes place is unaltered.

Stable Solid Solutions

Most alloys, whether stable or metastable, show appreciable radiation-induced increases in hardness and strength and slight increases in resistivity. Interesting exceptions to this behavior are exhibited by some of the copper base alloys, such as Cu-Zn, Cu-Al, and Cu-Ga. These alloys, interestingly enough, show resistivity decreases when irradiated at room temperature, the resistivity going through a minimum and, if irradiated long enough, eventually showing a resistivity increase. If the irradiation is carried out at or below liquid-nitrogen temperatures, no decrease in resistivity is observed. However, if the temperature is allowed to approach room temperature after irradiation, then the decrease in resistivity becomes apparent. The critical temperature for this process appears to be approximately $-30°C$.

The resistivity decreases which are of the order of 1–2 per cent have been explained by Rosenblatt et al.,[9] as being caused by radiation-induced short-range order. However, certain aspects of the problem need to be examined further before this can be accepted. Dependence of the effect on the solute concentration and the purity of the alloy require additional study. In any event the irradiation appears capable of inducing a reaction to take place which normally could not occur because either the temperature is too low for migration of defects, or the short-range order is too unstable to be maintained at elevated temperature.

Important Analogies

The metallurgist might hope that an understanding of radiation effects might be gained in terms of the common variables with which he concerns himself in studying metals and alloys in the absence of irradiation. The usual methods of altering the properties of metals and alloys are (1) cold working, (2) alloying, and (3) heat treatment; and many attempts have been made to fit the explanation of radiation effects completely within one

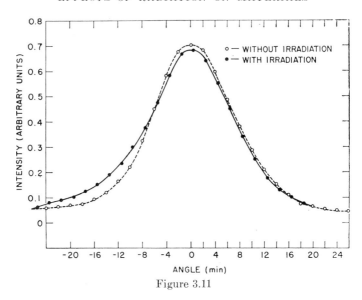

Figure 3.11

of these areas. To date, however, there has been too little success for such analogies to be used even for rough engineering purposes. It may be argued that radiation effects bear some resemblance to each of the above factors, but not sufficiently so for each case to warrant an exact comparison. The following tabulation summarizes arguments for and against the various analogies:

PRO	CON

Cold Working

a. Increase in hardness and strength

b. Decrease in ductility

c. Slight density decreases

d. Similarity of annealing temperatures

a. No introduced preferred orientation

b. No asterism in x-ray patterns

c. No dislocations introduced

d. No recrystallization

e. No line broadening (See Fig. 11)

f. Cold working and radiation effects not additive

Alloying

a. Increase in critical shear stress

b. Shape of stress strain curve

c. Slip line appearance (coarse)

a. Radiation effects completely removable

Heat Treatment

a. Low temperature aging in Cu-Be and Ni-Be
b. Ordering effects in Cu_3Au
c. Cold working effects-annealed partially

a. No apparent effect in pure metals
b. Temperature dependence of effects in alloys

Summary

It is now clear that neutron irradiation of metals and alloys may result in pronounced changes in many properties. The properties which are most sensitive to change are those which are structure sensitive. The magnitude of the effect is a sensitive function of a number of variables of the materials before irradiation, such as:

        a. Melting point
        b. Crystal Structure
        c. Prior thermal history
        d. Prior mechanical history

In addition the following factors can influence the effects of irradiation:

        a. Flux
        b Total exposure
        c. Temperature of irradiation
        d. Chemical environment during irradiation
        e. Stress level
        f. Impurity content and composition

Conclusion

Many new experiments and theoretical studies are necessary before we can hope to understand completely radiation effects. The importance of radiation effects as a factor in high-flux, long-service, power reactors may be grave in certain materials. On the other hand, neutron bombardment is revealed as an important new technique for the manipulation and study of metals and alloys as well as other solids. Two important advantages of this technique are: (1) dislocations presumably are not introduced by neutron irradiation and (2) the property changes induced by neutron irradiation are completely removable.

References

1. D. O. Thompson and D. K. Holmes, *J. Appl. Phys.*, **27**, 713 (1956).
2. to be published
3. A. H. Cottrell, Met. *Reviews*, **1**, 479 (1956).
   G. H. Kinchin and R. S. Pease, *Rep. Prog. in Phys.*, **18**, 1 (1955).
   J. W. Glen, *Adv. in Phys.*, **4**, 381 (1955).
   G. H. Vineyard, D. Thomas and D. S. Billington, AIME Symp. Vol. III (1956).
   F. Seitz and J. S. Koehler, Solid State Phys. Vol. III.

4. H. G. Cooper, J. S. Koehler and J. W. Marx, *Phys. Rev.*, **94**, 496 (1956).
5. T. H. Blewitt, R. R. Coltman, D. K. Holmes and T. S. Noggle, "Creep and Recovery" ASM—published 1956, p. 84, Lake Placid Conf. on Dislocations (to be published by John Wiley and Sons).
6. T. H. Blewitt, R. R. Coltman, C. E. Klabunde, and T. S. Noggle, *J. Appl. Phys.*, **28**, 639 (1957).
7. A. W. McReynolds, W. Augusymiak, Marilyn McKeown and D. B. Rosenblatt, *Phys. Rev.*, **98**, 418 (1955).
8. R. H. Kernohan and D. S. Billington, ORNL 324, Feb. 1949.
9. D. B. Rosenblatt, G. J. Dienes and R. Smoluchowski, *J. Appl. Phys.*, **26**, 1044 (1955).
10. F. G. Foote, Proc. Geneva Conf. **9**, 33 (1956); H. H. Chiswick and L. R. Kilman **9**, 147 (1956).
11. S. T. Konobeevsky et. al. Proc. Geneva Conf., **7**, 433 (1956); S. F. Pugh ibid., **7**, 441 (1956); S. H. Paine and J. H. Kittel, ibid., **7**, 445 (1956).
12. W. K. Woods, L. P. Bupp and J. G. Fletcher, Proc. Geneva Conf. **7**, 455 (1956).
13. G. H. Kinchin, Proc. Geneva Conf. **7**, 472 (1956).
14. D. S. Billington and S. Siegel, *Met. Prog.*, **58**, 847 (1950); R. H. Kernohan, D. S. Billington and A. B. Lewis, *J. Appl. Phys.*, **27**, 40 (1956).
15. G. T. Murray and W. E. Taylor, *Acta Met.*, **2**, 52 (1954).
16. M. B. Reynolds, J. R. Low and L. O. Sullivan, *Journal Met.*, **7**, 555 (1955).
17. M. L. Bleiberg, L. J. Jones and B. Lustman; WAPD-T-300; *J. Appl. Phys.* **27**, 1270 (1956).
18. M. C. Wittels and F. A. Sherrill, *J. Appl. Phys.*, **27**, 643 (1956).
19. M. H. Bartz, TID-7515, Part I, p. 19 (1956).
20. S. H. Paine (ANL); D. O. Leeser, *Materials and Methods*, **40**, 115 (1954).
21. W. R. McDonnell and H. A. Kierstad, *Phys. Rev.*, **93**, 247 (1954); H. A. Kierstad, *Phys. Rev.* **98**, 245 (1955).
22. F. Seitz and J. S. Koehler, Solid State Physics, Vol. III, Academic Press (1957).
23. R. O. Simmons, Thesis, Dept. of Phys., U. of Ill. (1957).
24. R. Berman, *Proc. Roy. Soc.*, **A208**, 90 (1951).
25. R. S. Sery, R. E. Fischell and D. E. Gordon, Naval Ordance Lab. Report No. 4381 (1956).
26. C. A. Bruch, W. E. McHugh and R. W. Hockenbury, Trans. *AIME*, **206**, 1362 (1956).
27. H. Paneth, *Phys. Rev.*, **80**, 708 (1950).
28. W. M. Lomer and A. H. Cottrell, *Phil. Mag.*, **46**, 711 (1955).
29. S. T. Konobeevsky, N. F. Provdyuk and U. T. Kutaitser, Proc. Geneva Conf. **7**, 479 (1956).
30. C. A. Bruch, W. E. McHugh and L. J. Doig, Paper 57-NESC-15 2nd Nuclear Engineering and Science Conf., March 11–14, 1957, Philadelphia, Pa.
31. J. Fleeman and G. J. Dienes, *J. Appl. Phys.* **26**, 652 (1955).
32. D. L. Chipman, B. E. Warren and G. J. Dienes, *J. Appl. Phys.* **24**, 1251 (1953).
33. M. C. Wittels and F. A. Sherrill, *J. Appl. Phys.*, **28**, 606 (1957).
34. F. W. Kunz and A. N. Holden, *Acta Met.*, **2**, 816 (1954).
35. R. V. Steele and W. P. Wallace, *Met. Prog.*, **68**, (1), 114 (1955).
36. F. E. Faris, Proc. Geneva Conf., Paper 747 (1955).
37. M. J. Makin and F. J. Minter, *Journal Inst. Metals*, **24**, 399 (1957).
38. Personal Communication.
39. W. F. Witzig, 23, 1263 (1952).

40. J. C. Wilson and R. G. Berggren, Pacific Coast Mtg. ASTM, Sept. 1956.
41. D. O. Thompson, D. K. Holmes and T. H. Blewitt, *J. Appl. Phys.*, **28**, 742 (1957).
42. G. H. Kinchin and R. S. Pease, *Nuclear Mec. Energy*, **7**, 200 (1955).
43. J. Friedel, "Creep and Recovery" ASM—published 1956, p. 84, Lake Placid Conf.
    on Dislocations (to be published by John Wiley and Sons).
44. C. E. Dixon and C. J. Meechan, *Phys. Rev.*, **91**, 237 (1953).
45. S. Siegel, *Phys. Rev.*, **75**, 1823 (1949).
46. R. R. Eggleston and F. E. Bowman, *J. Appl. Phys.*, **24**, 229 (1953).
47. A. B. Martin, S. B. Austerman, R. R. Eggleston, J. F. McGee and M. Torpinian,
    Phys. Rev., **81**, 664 (1951).
48. L. R. Aronin, *J. Appl. Phys.*, **25**, 344 (1954).
49. J. C. Wilson, private communication.
50. T. H. Blewitt and R. R. Coltman, *Phys. Rev.*, **85**, 384 (1952); *Acta Met.*, **2**, (1954).
51. H. L. Glick and W. F. Witzig, *Phys. Rev.*, **91**, 236 (1953).
52. R. H. Fillnow, E. K. Halteman and G. F. Mechlin, *Phys. Rev.*, **91**, 236 (1953).
53. R. E. Jamison, *Bull. Am. Phys. Soc.*, V, Phil. (1957).
54. A. Boltax, Pacific Coast Mtg. ASTM Fall 1956.

Chapter 4

INFLUENCE OF RADIATION UPON CORROSION AND SURFACE REACTIONS OF METALS AND ALLOYS

M. T. SIMNAD

John Jay Hopkins Laboratory for Pure and Applied Science
General Atomic Division

General Dynamics Corp., San Diego, California

Nuclear irradiation may influence the corrosion and surface reactions of metals by altering the properties of the metals and/or by changing the composition of the ambient environment. The effects of radiation upon solids have been reviewed adequately[1]* and these will be considered only briefly insofar as they pertain to corrosion behavior. The radiation chemistry of solutions and gases has been studied quite extensively, and a more detailed discussion of this subject may be obtained from several recent reviews.[2]

Radiation effects in metals are caused by neutrons and charged heavy particles which may displace atoms for their lattice sites, produce vacancies and interstitial atoms in excess of the number that are in thermal equilibrium, create impurity effects, produce ionization, or give rise to thermal pulses in small regions in the metals where vacancy-interstitial pairs and thermal or displacement spikes form. The composition of the material may be altered by the introduction of impurity atoms from fission fragments or by transmutations caused by thermal neutrons. The extent of the damage depends not only on the energy, the flux and the type of the bombarding particle, but also on the nature and temperature of the material. Most of the damage is due to recoil atoms or recoil ions. The effects of radiation sometimes may be beneficial, e.g. as a substitute for cold-work to increase the hardness and strength or as a means of producing age-hardening in certain alloys.[3] Atomic displacements also can be produced by energetic

* Ed. note. See also papers by G. J. Dienes and D. S. Billington.

gamma radiation by Compton collisons and the photoelectric effect. For example, cobalt gamma radiation can disorder Cu_3Au alloys.[4] Although there has been little work published on the chemical reactivity of irradiated metals, the marked effects observed in connection with other properties of solids suggests that significant changes may take place in the rates of surface reactions.

In aqueous solutions the mechanism of energy transfer from the radiation flux or charged particles is complex and imperfectly understood. The action of radiation on water is to produce molecular or ionic species capable of either oxidation or reduction of certain solutes. With radiations of high ion density, the primary products formed are the hydrogen and hydrogen peroxide molecules whereas the free radicals, H and OH, predominate with radiations of low ion density. In reactors the dissociation of water is attributed mainly to the effects of fast neutrons. Dissolved hydrogen represses the decomposition of water, whereas hydrogen peroxide, dissolved oxygen and impurities promote it. For water containing moderate amounts of impurities a steady state is reached which represses further dissociation. In effect, the hydrogen produced in the corrosion of metal components may be sufficient to inhibit the decomposition of the water if the system is sealed. Wroughton and DePaul[5] have pointed out that several chemical reactions, not normally expected in hot water, may take place in a reactor system in the presence of a radiation flux. Nitrogen may be introduced into the system if non-deaerated feed water is used or if air is entrapped during filling. The presence of nitrogen dissolved in the water results in one of the following two reactions in the reactor:

$$N_2 + 3H_2(H_2O) = 2NH_3(H_2O)$$

$$N_2 + O_2(H_2O) = 2HNO_3(H_2O)$$

Whether ammonia or nitric acid is formed depends upon whether oxygen or hydrogen is present in excess. During actual operation of the reactor the water becomes highly radioactive because of the nuclear reactions O^{16} (n, p)N^{16} and O^{17}(n, p)N^{17}. The N^{16} has a half-life of 7.3 seconds with 7 Mev gamma rays, and the N^{17} is a delayed neutron emitter with a half-life of 4.1 seconds and 1 Mev neutrons. Both are intense beta emitters. In water-moderated thermal heterogeneous reactors no appreciable decomposition of the water occurs provided the impurities are kept at a low level. In an aqueous homogeneous reactor, however, rapid dissociation will take place because of the high ionization produced by the fission products, and may correspond to a production of as much as 16,600 liters of hydrogen per Mwh if the back reaction is completely inhibited.

Mechanisms of Corrosion

Three types of metallic corrosion are generally encountered in practice which need to be considered in relation to the behavior of irradiated metals in corrosive environments:[6]

(1) **Direct Chemical Reactions.** These take place when metals are placed in non-electrolytes in which the reaction products are soluble. An example of this type of reaction is the corrosion of iron in an alcoholic solution of iodine or bromine. Irradiation may affect the rate and distribution of the attack by altering the structure of the metal surface, by decomposing the solution or by raising the temperature of the system.

(2) **Direct Solution.** The attack of solids by liquid metals occurs by direct dissolution and is governed by diffusion and convection processes in the liquid metal. Irradiation may influence the rates of mass transfer by altering the structure of the metal surface or by giving rise to differential heating of the system.

(3) **Electrochemical Corrosion.** This type accounts for the majority of metallic corrosion processes, including corrosion in aqueous, fused salt and gaseous environments. Electrochemical attack takes place when local anodic and cathodic sites are present on a metal surface in an electrolyte, or if the metal is covered with an ionic reaction product in which ions and electrons migrate. The surface may be dissolved uniformly, or pitting may occur at certain points. The presence of stress or disturbed metal can accelerate corrosion and promote cracking. Erosion by suspended solids in a moving solution or gas may destroy protective films and increase the corrosion rate. Contact with dissimilar metals may lead to galvanic attack. The causes of corrosion currents may be ascribed to inhomogeneities in the metal, in the surface films or in the electrolyte. Irradiation can give rise to effects which may either increase or decrease the rates of corrosion, depending on the particular mechanisms and combination of factors that govern the corrosion reaction.

Radiation Effects on Corrosion

Influence of Light and of X-rays. As early as 1839, Becquerel[7] investigated the influence of light on the behavior of metals immersed in aqueous solutions and obtained results indicating that the electrode potential was sensitive to the degree of illumination. Practically no further examination of this phenomenon was made until 1919, when Bengough and Hudson[8] reported on the corrosion of copper in distilled water. In all cases the specimen side most directly exposed to light tarnished most rapidly. Later, Bannister and Rigby[9] made an extensive study of the influence of light on the electrode potential and corrosion rates of metals. Their results showed a definite influence of light in the case of lead, zinc, aluminum and iron in the presence of oxygen; the aerated and illuminated electrode became markedly cathodic. The maximum effect was obtained with light in the violet and near ultra-violet regions. With other metals, the direction of change in potential was governed by the nature of the electrode reactions. Bowden[10] made a careful study of the acceleration of the electrodeposition of hydrogen and oxygen by light of short wave-length using a mercury cathode and platinum anode in $N/5$ sulfuric acid solutions. On illuminating the electrodes with ultra-violet light there was an immediate drop in over-potential, showing an increased rate of electrode reactions. The shorter the wave-length the greater was the effect, the threshold being 4000 Å.

The effect of X-radiation on the corrosion of copper in potassium cyanide solutions was found by Pestrecov[11] to be appreciable. After long-term irradiation, however, the metal appeared to become passive.

The action of alpha particles has also been noted.[12] The exposure of silver to solutions containing polonium results in the formation of silver oxide on the surface of the specimen due to the effects of alpha particles in solution.

Corrosion of Nuclear Reactor Materials in Aqueous Solutions

(1) *Corrosion of Fissionable Metals.* Several alloys of uranium appear to eexhibit reasonable corrosion resistance in the absence of irradiation.[13] However, the effect of irradiation is quite catastrophic, since the corrosion resistance is greatly lowered when tests are carried out during or after irradiation exposures. Table I includes examples of pre- and post-irradiation corrosion resistance of uranium alloys.

Other promising alloys which failed in the presence of nuclear irradiation include the fully homogenized epsilon U_3Si compound and alloys of uranium containing 9% molybdenum. The effect was greater in martensitic zir-

TABLE 1. EFFECT OF IRRADIATION ON THE CORROSION RESISTANCE OF URANIUM ALLOYS IN WATER.

Alloy Composition	% Atom Burnup	Corrosion Resistance
$U - 3\%$ Nb	None	No failure after 2000 hrs. at 260°C. Weight loss 4.3 mgm/cm²/day
(gamma quenched)	0.1	Disintegrated after 1 hr at 260°C
$U - 5\%$ Zr $- 1.5\%$ Nb	None	No failure after 360 days at 265°C. Weight loss 2.7 mgm/cm²/day
(gamma quenched)	0.04	Cracking after 63 days at 260°C. Weight loss 23 mgm/cm²/day

conium, niobium and zirconium-niobium alloys of uranium and homogenized U_3Si compound than in the gamma uranium-molybdenum alloys.

(2) *Corrosion of Non-Fissionable Metals.* The earliest published reference to corrosion problems in nuclear reactors is the statement in the Smythe report to the effect that corrosion by aqueous solutions was of great concern in the development of the Hanford piles. Allen[14] covers the subject briefly in one of the first surveys of radiation effects. After examining the radiation chemistry of organic materials, he points out that some interesting reactions might be expected in the corrosion of metals by organic materials, such as lubricating oils, under nuclear irradiation. Radiation produces free radicals in organic liquids and it might be expected that low-melting metals, such as lead, tin, bismuth, arsenic, cadmium, zinc, and aluminum which react with free radicals to form organo-metallic compounds, might corrode when irradiated under oil or organic liquids.

Hittman and Kuhl[15] have reported the results of preliminary experiments carried out at Brookhaven on the effects of high level gamma radiation, from 300 curie and 1800 curie Co^{60} sources, on the corrosion of aluminum in tap and distilled water at room temperature and on the reactivity of copper and mild steel in 2N hydrochloric acid. A chance observation on a partly irradiated aluminum tube immersed in tap water indicated that the irradiated section of the tube had corroded visibly less than the unirradiated zone (Figure 4.1). More closely controlled experiments were then carried out in which samples of aluminum were exposed to Co^{60} gamma radiation to a dose of 300,000 r/h for 42 days, in both tap water and distilled water at room temperature. Control samples were placed in distilled and tap water at the same temperature. The irradiated samples gained less weight than the non-irradiated ones, and metallographic examination showed that the surface pits on the irradiated specimens were shallower than those on the control samples. Hittman and Kuhl ascribe the difference in corrosion behavior to the fact that the chief effect of the radiation is to render the solution in the irradiated systems more oxidizing by the formation of hydrogen peroxide and oxidizing free radicals. This effect might have a tendency to promote the formation of a denser, self-healing type of protective film. On the other hand, experiments with copper and iron in 2N hydrochloric acid showed an opposite effect, namely, that radiation increased the rate of corrosion. The corresponding weight losses were as follows:

Weight Loss in 2N Hydrochloric Acid

	Irradiated, 50 × 10⁶R	Non-Irradiated
Copper	0.419 gm	0.039 gm
Iron	5.23 gm	2.84 gm

The corrosion rate of copper in acid solutions is strongly dependent upon the presence of oxidizing agents; the radiation decomposition of these solutions results in the formation of oxidizing agents which would promote higher corrosion rates in the presence of irradiation. The dissolution of iron in acids is under cathodic control. The depolarizing action of the hydrogen peroxide and oxidizing free radicals formed by the radiation accelerates the rate of the reaction. Hittman and Kuhl point out that

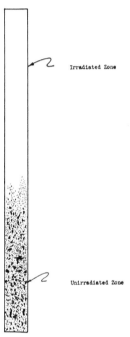

Irradiated Zone

Unirradiated Zone

Figure 4.1. Aluminum gamma radiation exposure tube after one month's use in water pit.

radiation effects on corrosion need not necessarily be detrimental, and a thorough study of any particular system must be made before the effects of radiation can be determined.

There has been work in progress at Oak Ridge on the effect of reactor radiations upon corrosion of several metals and alloys in aqueous homogeneous reactors. The corrosion behavior of zirconium and its alloys, titanium, and stainless steels in uranyl sulfate solutions at high temperatures and pressures has been reported by Jenks.[16] In general, the corrosion rates of the core specimens were observed to be dependent upon power density. Results obtained with Zircaloy-2* are shown in Figures 4.2 and 4.3. In-pile

* Editors' note. An alloy of zirconium.

TABLE 2. EFFECT OF DEUTERON BOMBARDMENT ON CORROSION OF ZIRCALOY 2
IN DEGASSED WATER AT 315°C

Irradiation	Film Thickness, cm
100 μamp-hours/cm^2	3×10^{-4}
200 μamp-hours/cm^2	5.8×10^{-4}
None	$\frac{1}{10}$th of the irradiated rates

autoclave experiments were also carried out. These were conducted with solutions containing depleted uranium and higher corrosion-rates were observed than in comparable out-of-pile studies. Jenks also discussed briefly the effects of electron irradiation upon the corrosion of Zircaloy-2 in a thermal loop. Ionizing radiation had little effect on the rate of corrosion of Zircaloy-2.

Radiation effects on water systems containing air or nitrogen in reactors have been discussed by Wright and Hurst.[17] They found it essential to maintain close control of the purity and acidity of the water in order to avoid water decomposition and excessive corrosion of metals in the water circuit. This control could not be achieved by using buffered systems; the required purity was maintained by passing a fraction of the circulating water through a suitable ion-exchange unit. Solutions of nitrogen and water

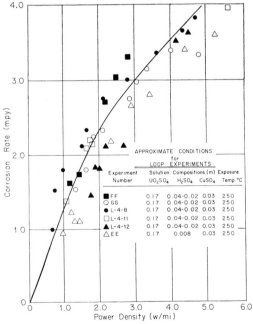

Figure 4.2. Zircaloy-2 core coupon corrosion rates vs power density at coupon position.

Approximate Conditions for Experiments

Symbol	Solution Composition (m)			Exposure Temperature (°C)
	UO_2SO_4	H_2SO_4	$CuSO_4$	
	0.17	0.04	0–0.02	250
	0.17	0.04	0–0.04	280
	0.17	0.00	0.007–0.02	250
	0.17	0.00	0.007–0.02	280
	0.30	0.00	0.04	250
	0.04	0.02	0.05	280
	0.04	0.04	0.04	250
	1.36	0.04	0.00	280
	1.36	0.04	0.00	250
	0.17	0.04–0.02	0.03	250

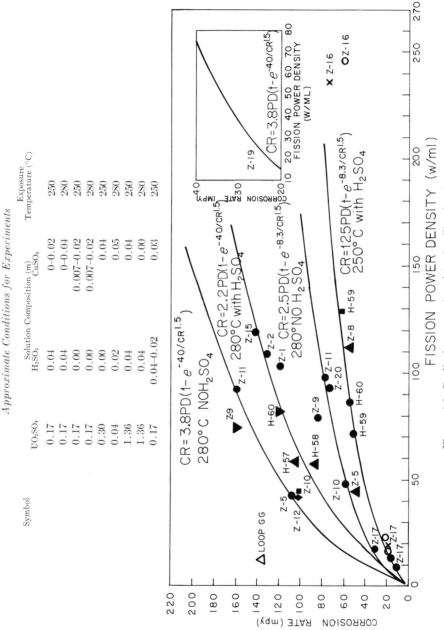

Figure 4.3. Radiation-corrosion data for Zircaloy-2.

and air and water were irradiated at doses up to 10^{18} thermal neutrons/ cm^2. and the only products found in solution after irradiation were nitric acid and hydrogen peroxide. At higher radiation doses, ammonium ion was formed in the nitrogen-water solution, but not in the air-water system. The concentration of nitrate was found to depend on the ratio of gas volume to liquid volume. It was concluded that nitric acid production in water reactors, to which nitrogen has access, may be considerable and could control the size of the ion-exchange unit required.

Primak and Fuchs[18] have presented a detailed study of nitrogen fixation in the CP-3 heavy water reactor at the Argonne National Laboratory and of the accelerated corrosion of metal parts on humid days. Exposure of metals, such as aluminum, copper, lead, nickel and Inconel which are subject to nitric acid attack, to humid air in a reactor resulted in the formation of nitrates on the surface of the specimen. Oxides formed in copious amounts when lead was exposed to radiation in humid oxygen. No reactions were observed when the oxygen, nitrogen or air was dry. Quantitative experiments were carried out with nickel samples in sealed ampules of vitreous silica tubing containing the desired atmospheres. No reaction products were found on specimens irradiated for 30 Mwh in ampules containing dry oxygen, nitrogen or air. However, after irradiation in moist oxygen, a small amount of a black oxide was observed and copious quantities of $Ni(NO_3)_2 \cdot 3H_2O$ were found on the nickel specimens after 30 Mwh irradiation in humid air. A number of irradiation exposures were made for various lengths of time in air that had been saturated with water at $28°C$ and in air containing water vapor at a pressure of 4.03 mm mercury. The results are shown in Figure 4.4. As the humidity is lowered, the amount of soluble nickel salts formed reaches a saturation level at a smaller radiation dosage. Primak and Fuchs summarize the various energy sources that take part in the ionization process as follows: (1) gamma rays from the fissioning fuel rods, from the moderator, the aluminum thimble and can, the silica ampule and the nickel specimen; (2) fast neutron recoils involving scattering of oxygen, nitrogen and hydrogen in the gas; and (3) C^{14} recoils and protons from the $N(n, p)C^{14}$ reaction in the gas. The dose from the gamma rays is estimated to be 411 rep/sec, from fast neutrons 15 rep/sec, and from C^{14} recoils 440 rep/sec, giving a total dose of 865 rep/sec. The results are interpreted in terms of the over-all reaction near saturation: $Ni + 3H_2O + 3O_2 \rightarrow Ni(NO_3)_2 \cdot 3H_2O$.

It is assumed that at some point the rate of removal of fixed nitrogen declines under the conditions of these irradiations and the concentration of nitrogen oxides in the gas phase then increases. The initial products of nitrogen fixation decompose under irradiation and, with the declining removal rate of nitrogen oxides from the gas phase, the concentration of these oxides increases until the decomposition rate becomes equal to the formation rate and saturation ensues. The rate of nitrogen fixation at the reactor power of 275 kw was 10^{12} atoms nitrogen/cm^2/sec., which corresponded to a yield of about unity.

These observations are a striking demonstration of how radioactive corrosion products can be spread around a reactor, where they may be a health hazard or a source of spurious scientific results.

The chemistry of pressurized water reactors has been reviewed by Rockwell and Cohen,[19] who pointed out the necessity for testing the corrosion resistance of component metals in the presence of a significant neutron flux, which "... calls for elaborate testing procedures and may require about a dozen men working for nearly two years to test a few grams of material surrounded by flowing water at 500°F." No significant acceleration of corrosion by radiation was observed for zircaloy in degassed water at 315°C under the test conditions. Pre-irradiation also did not affect corrosion rates.

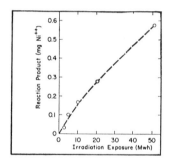

Formation of soluble nickel in CP-3's central thimble in vitreous-silica ampule containing 17.7 cm^3 air saturated at 28° C at total pressure of 1 atmos., and 5.1 cm of 28-mil nickel wire.

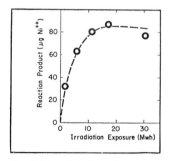

Figure 4.4. Formation of soluble nickel in CP-3's central thimble in vitreous-silica ampule containing 17.7 cm^3 air of humidity 4.03 mm Hg of water at a total pressure of 1 atmos. at 28° C, and 5.1 cm of 28-mil nickel wire.

TABLE 3. CORROSION IN WATER AT 540°F, FLOWING AT 5–10 FT/SEC.

Material	Neutrons/cm^2	Weight increase mgm/dm^2
347 Stainless Steel	None	7
	10^{19}	10
Zr-Sn alloy	None	4
	10^{19}	200
Fuel material clad	None	2
With Zr-Sn alloy	10^{19}	140

The results of other tests, which were carried out in a neutron flux of 10^{13}/cm^2/sec., are shown in Table 3.

Dissolved nitrogen, oxygen and hydrogen in the water may combine under different circumstances to form nitric acid, ammonia or associated ions. The corrosion rate can be influenced therefore by the resulting change in pH and electrical conductivity of the water. Rockwell and Cohen point out that negligible corrosion rates can produce significant amounts of corrosion products from the standpoint of radioactivity; e.g. a rate of 10 mgm/dm^2/month, which occurred at the Idaho Test Facility, represents only 0.001 inch corrosion in 15 years, but is still 30 gm/day total in the system. It has been the practice to use only the purest water readily available and not to rely on any additives for inhibition of corrosion.

Wroughton and DePaul[5, 20, 21] have made a broad survey of the corrosion behavior of structural materials in pressurized water power reactors. The release of corrosion products to the water gives rise to problems of radioactivity and fouling, e.g. the redeposition of insoluble oxides on fuel elements may interfere with heat transfer. A granular mixed-bed ion exchange resin is recommended as a good filter for reducing the "insolubles" (crud) content of the water and the long-lived activity, and also for removing solubles and reducing the short-lived activity. In connection with boiler tube materials, stainless steels are not considered wholly satisfactory because of their susceptibility to stress corrosion cracking; carbon steel and low alloy steels are subject to pitting if oxygen is not carefully controlled; the corrosion resistance of Monel appears to be adequate, but the release of copper and cobalt as impurities into the water makes this an unsatisfactory alloy for use. The increase in the rate of corrosion of metals by water as a consequence of radiation is ascribed to the ionization and dissociation of water and the increased mobility of atoms or radicals in the oxide film. With in-pile irradiation no significant increase in corrosion rate was found at neutron fluxes of about 10^{14} nvt.

There is also the possibility that hydrogen embrittlement of certain structural materials may occur as a result of the ionizing effect of radiation and the consequent generation of hydrogen. Because of such uncertainties, stainless steel cladding generally has been used in the reactor vessel.

Irradiation appears to decompose or make radioactive most inhibitors for stainless, low alloy or carbon steels. The pH of the solution, therefore, is maintained at 9.5 to 11.5 by means of lithium hydroxide additions, since it has sufficient solubility and stability and little radioactivity. With ammonium hydroxide it is necessary to maintain the solution pH at room temperature within the range of 10.5 to 11.5. Hydrogen gas is also a suitable additive for reducing corrosion by suppressing the dissociation of water and for removing oxygen by gamma flux combination. (10 cc of hydrogen is added per kgm of water). The radiation induced reactions of gases dissolved in water become significant when large amounts of air are introduced into the system. If the hydrogen concentration is high, the pH of the water increases since ammonia is formed. On the other hand, if the oxygen concentration is high relative to hydrogen, the pH decreases since nitric acid is formed. Experiments have shown also that radiation tends to accelerate the deposition of corrosion products.

Robertson[22] has described the experiences gained from the NRX reactor regarding corrosion problems and the evolution of deuterium from heavy water. It was found that if the purity of the water was maintained at a sufficiently high level, as represented by a resistivity of about 10^{-6} ohm^{-1} cm^{-1}, radiation decomposition was negligible. However, at high temperatures (250°C) mass transfer of corrosion products occurred which produced selective deposition in some regions. In the reactor, the decomposition of corrosion products was dependent upon the radiation intensity. The deposition could be so great that flow channels would be obstructed, even when stainless steel was used.

The corrosion problems related to the use of water in nuclear reactors is reviewed in the "Symposium on High-Purity Water Corrosion".[23]

Effect of Irradiation Upon Gas-Solid Reactions

The oxidation behavior of irradiated metals may be described with reference to the effects of radiation upon ionic and inorganic solids. The mechanisms underlying the oxidation of metals involve the migration of ions and electrons through the crystal lattice of the surface oxide film, and the direction of any change caused by radiation depends upon the physical effects that occur in the oxide film. Nelson, Sproull and Caswell[24] found that ionic conductivity in KCl dropped by an order of magnitude after exposure to Co^{60} gamma radiation and to short reactor irradiation, whereas it increased by about the same factor after prolonged reactor exposure. They explain this effect by postulating that the ionizing radiations pro-

duce hole-electron pairs which are trapped at lattice vacancies, thus render-
ing them electrically neutral. The number of charged positive-ion vacancies
is decreased and hence the conductivity is lowered. Fast neutrons, however, increase the conductivity by increasing the concentration of both
vacancies and interstitials. Cabrera[25] measured the oxidation rates of aluminum in the presence and absence of ultraviolet light, and found a marked
increase in oxidation rate under ultra-violet irradiation. The results agreed
well with the values predicted from the Mott-Cabrera theory of oxidation.

The influence of irradiation in decreasing the creep rate of cadmium in
air has been ascribed by Makin[26] to the oxidation of the metal by O or O_3
ions produced by the bombardment.

The catalytic activity of metals and metal oxides appears to be enhanced
by irradiation. Farnsworth and Woodcock[27] bombarded a single crystal of
nickel with argon ions and observed an increased activity for the hydrogenation of ethylene. Since argon ions have little penetrating power, the
increased catalytic activity of nickel may have been a surface effect produced by radiation-induced defects in the nickel lattice. However, in the
case of ZnO exposed to γ rays from Co^{60}, Taylor and Wethington[28] report
a decrease in activity for the hydrogenation of ethylene.

The oxidation of irradiated graphite has been studied in some detail.
The increase in the oxidation rate of graphite under nuclear irradiation
was reported by Hurst and Wright[29] at the Geneva Conference. Woodley[30]
exposed graphite specimens to various oxidizing ambients in an in-pile
water-cooled facility at Hanford to determine the effect of pile radiation
and gas composition. Oxidizing environments included carbon dioxide,
oxygen, 70% CO_2–30% He, 85% CO_2–15% N_2, liquid water and water
vapor. The results showed that at room temperature and with a flux of
3×10^{20} nvt

"(1) The low temperature (15° to 30°C) exposure of graphite to CO_2
results in the formation of CO. A portion of the resultant CO eventually
decomposes to form CO_2 and a solid polymer of one or more of the carbon
suboxides.

"(2) The dilution of CO_2 with either N_2 or He decreases its rate of reduction by graphite as a consequence of the decrease in its partial pressure.

"(3) The reaction between graphite and O_2 appears to be about 3 times
as rapid as the reaction of graphite with CO_2. A calculation indicates that
about one molecule of O_2 reacts per 100 ev absorbed in the O_2.

"(4) The radiation induced reaction of graphite with water results in
the formation of CO_2 and H_2. The decomposition of water into hydrogen
and oxygen proceeds rapidly to a steady state. The oxygen subsequently
reacts with graphite to form CO_2.

"(5) The irradiation of graphite under an atmosphere of water vapor carried by nitrogen yields CO_2 and H_2 ."

Kosiba and Dienes[31] studied the graphite-oxygen reaction with irradiated and unirradiated samples over the temperature range of 250°–450°C. The samples were irradiated prior to the oxidation by exposing them to a flux of 4×10^{20} nvt fast neutrons. The oxidation rate of the irradiated samples was 6× greater than the unirradiated samples. The reaction rate of an irradiated specimen in the presence of gamma rays (200,000 r/hr) at 300°C was higher by an additional factor of about 3, which was ascribed to the ionization of oxygen molecules. The ratio of the reaction rates of irradiated and unirradiated graphite decreases with increasing reaction temperature from a ratio of 5–6 at 300°–350°C to about 2.3 at 450°C. The activation energy for the oxidation of unirradiated graphite was 48.8 kcal/mole as compared to 36.1 kcal/mole for the irradiated graphite.

Proton Irradiation Effects Upon Surface Reactions

The effects of exposure to 260-Mev protons of a total flux of 10^{16} protons per cm^2 upon surface reactions were studied by Simnad, Smoluchowski and Spilners. The effects of proton irradiation upon the electrode potentials of tungsten,[32] the rates of solution of ferric oxide in hydrochloric acid[33] and the kinetics of reduction of nickel oxide by hydrogen[34] were investigated.

The electrode potentials of tungsten were measured in aqueous salt solutions. The results are shown in Table 4.

It can be seen that the effect of proton irradiation upon the electrode potential is large and appears to be much greater than the effect of severe cold work. The effects are ascribed to the secondary nucleons produced in inelastic collisions rather than by elastic collisions of the incident protons.

TABLE 4. ELECTRODE POTENTIALS OF PROTON IRRADIATED TUNGSTEN

Treatment	Proton Irradiation	Electrode Potential[a] millivolts (anodic)
Annealed	none	0
Cold drawn	none	22
Annealed and irradiated	1.9×10^{15}/cm² at 130 Mev	72(?)
" " "	1.8×10^{15}/cm² at 260 Mev	39
" " "	6.8×10^{15}/cm² at 260 Mev	47
" " "	2.2×10^{16}/cm² at 260 Mev	84
Irradiated and annealed[b]	2.2×10^{16}/cm² at 260 Mev	0

[a] The electrode potentials are reported versus the annealed tungsten.

[b] The annealed specimens were heated for 2 hours at 900°C in argon.

In all cases the potentials of the irradiated specimens are anodic (less noble) to the annealed specimens, which means that irradiation makes the tungsten more reactive chemically.

The influence of the crystal structure of metal oxides upon their behavior in aqueous solutions is known to be appreciable. Proton irradiation may be expected to alter the chemical properties of ferric oxide if a sufficient concentration of lattice imperfections is produced by the irradiation. The rates of solution of ferric oxide specimens in N hydrochloric acid consequently were measured and it was observed that proton irradiation significantly increases the solution rate of ferric oxide in hydrochloric acid. (Fig. 4.5). This effect may be related to the production of lattice defects, such as vacancies, displaced atoms and dislocations. In view of the fact that the resistance of most metals to chemical attack is governed largely by the properties of thin surface oxide films, these results are pertinent to the problem of chemical attack on metals subjected to nuclear irradiation. Even if the metal itself suffers little radiation damage, the films formed on its surface may be disrupted sufficiently to lead to an increased attack in corrosive environments.

The reduction of metal oxides by hydrogen is influenced by the presence of imperfections in the oxide lattice. Nickel oxide was chosen for a preliminary study since this oxide is formed as a stable single phase, NiO, when nickel is heated in oxygen. The rates of hydrogen reduction of irradiated and non-irradiated specimens were measured continuously by attaching the samples to a sensitive spring and observing the rate of contraction of the spring as reduction proceeded. Some of the results obtained are shown in Table 5 and Figure 4.6. The proton irradiation markedly shortens

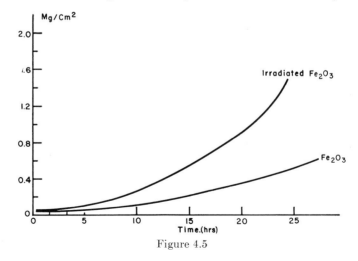

Figure 4.5

TABLE 5. EFFECT OF PROTON IRRADIATION UPON THE INDUCTION PERIOD
IN THE HYDROGEN REDUCTION OF NiO

Oxide Thickness microns	Reduction Temperature °C	Induction-Period Control, minutes	Irradiated, minutes
15	250	1200	275
15	275	100	30
60	275	110	30
15	300	20	14
60	300	20	11
15	350	10	4
60	350	9	8
15	400	5	5
60	400	4	4

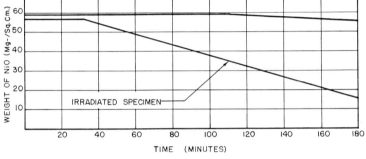

Figure 4.6. Reduction of NiO at 275° C

the induction period at the lower temperatures and also greatly increases the rate of reduction. The temperature at which the reduction is carried out also has an influence upon the effect of the irradiation, i.e no effect is observed when the reduction is carried out at temperatures above 400°C. The hydrogen reduction of nickel oxide is governed by a nucleation and growth mechanism and the kinetics of the process depends upon the number of nucleation sites that are available for reduction to start and proceed. Evidently, proton irradiation increases the number of reduction sites. At temperatures above 400°C the irradiation damage is annealed out rapidly and the hydrogen reduction rates are the same for irradiated and non-irradiated specimens.

Addendum

The effects of irradiation on some corrosion-resistant fuel alloys have been reported by Kittel, Greenberg, Paine and Draley*. The alloys studied were uranium-base alloys, U-3 weight per cent Nb, U-5 weight per cent

* *Nuclear Science and Engineering,* **2,** 431 (1957).

Zr, 1½ weight per cent Nb, and U-3.8 weight per cent Si (U₃Si). Irradiation induced length changes in specimens of the alloys were measured and the effects of irradiation on aqueous corrosion resistance of the alloys were examined. The uranium-niobium alloy was found to be unsuitable from the standpoint of dimensional and surface stability, and its corrosion resistance was destroyed by irradiation. The uranium-zirconium-niobium alloy was fairly stable dimensionally under irradiation, but its corrosion resistance was destroyed by between 0.046 and 0.074 atomic per cent burnup. The uranium-silicon alloy was dimensionally stable under irradiation in the cast condition, and showed no increase in corrosion rate at 290°C after 0.090 atomic per cent burnup, although it cracked after several days corrosion testing.

References

1. Dienes, J. G., in "Nuclear Fuels," Van Nostrand, New York, 1956.
   Brooks, Harvey, *Ann. Rev. Nuclear Sci.*, **6**, 215 (1956).
   Cottrell, A. H., *Metallurgical Reviews*, **1** (4), 479 (1956).
   Sutton, C. R. and Leeser, D. O., *Chem. Eng. Progress Symp.*, **50** (12), 208 (1954).
   Sisman, O. and Wilson, J. C., *Nucleonics*, **14** (9), 59 (1956).
   Simnad, M. T., *Int. J. Appl. Radiation and Isotopes*, **1**, 145 (1956).
   "Nuclear Metallurgy," Vol. 3, published by Amer. Inst. Mining Met. Engrs., New York, 1956.
2. Allen, A. O., "Int. Conf. Peaceful Uses of Atomic Energy," Vol. 7, p. 513, 1955.
   Dainton, F. S., *Ann. Rev. Nuclear Sci.*, **5**, 213 (1955).
   Hochanadel, C. J., and Lind, S. C., *Ann. Rev. Phys. Chem.*, **7**, 83 (1956).
3. Saller, H. A., *Nucleonics*, **14** (9), 86 (1956).
4. Dugdale, R. A., "Bristol Conf. on Defects in Crystalline Solids," Physical Society, London, 1955.
5. Wroughton, D. M. and DePaul, D. J., *Nuclear Metallurgy*, **3**, 55 (1956).
6. Evans, U. R., "Metallic Corrosion, Passivity and Protection," Longmans, Green and Co., New York 1948; Edwin Arnold Ltd., London, 1948.
7. Becquerel, E., *Compt. Rend.*, **9**, 561 (1839).
8. Bengough, G. D. and Hudson, O. F., *J. Inst. Metals*, **21**, 97 (1919).
9. Bannister, C. O. and Rigby, R., *J. Inst. Metals*, **58**, 227 (1936).
10. Bowden, F. P., *Trans. Faraday Soc.*, **27**, 505 (1931).
11. Pestrecov, A., *Collection Czech. Chem. Comm.*, **2**, 198 (1930).
12. Erbacher, O., *Z. physikal. Chem.*, **182**, 243 (1938).
13. Paine, S. H. and Kittel, J. H., "Int. Conf. Peaceful Uses of Atomic Energy," paper No. 745.
14. Allen, A. O., MDDC-962 (1947) (U. S. Atomic Energy Commission).
15. Hittman, F. and Kuhl, O. A., BNL-2257 (1955) (U. S. Atomic Energy Comm.).
16. Jenks, G. H., ORNL-2222 (1956) (U. S. Atomic Energy Commission).
17. Wright, J., "Int. Conf. Peaceful Uses of Atomic Energy," papers No. 445 and 900.
18. Primak, W. and Fuchs, L. H., *Nucleonics*, **13** (3), 38 (1955).
19. Rockwell, T. C. and Cohen, P., "Int. Conf. Peaceful Uses of Atomic Energy," paper No. 536.

20. Wroughton, D. M., Seamon, J. M. and Brown, P. E., "Symposium on High-Purity Water Corrosion," American Soc. for Testing Materials, 1956.
21. Wroughton, D. M., Seamon, J. M., and Beeghly, H. F., *Chem. Eng. Progr. Symp. Ser.*, **52**, 87 (1956).
22. Robertson, R. F. S., "Int. Conf. Peaceful Uses of Atomic Energy," Vol. **7**, p. 556, 1956.
23. "Symposium on High-Purity Water Corrosion," Amer. Soc. Testing Materials, 1956.
24. Nelson, C. M., Sproull, R. L., and Caswell, R. S., *Phys. Rev.* **90**, 364 (1953).
25. Cabrera, N., *Phil. Mag.* **40**, 175 (1949).
26. Makin, M. J., *J. Nuclear Energy* **1**, 181 (1955).
27. Farnsworth, H. E. and Woodcock, R. F., "Symposium on Catalysis," Amer. Chem. Soc., Div. of Petroleum Chem., Dallas 1956, p. 39.
28. Taylor, H. A. and Wethington, W., ibid.
29. Hurst, R. and Wright, J., "Int. Conf. Peaceful Uses of Atomic Energy," paper No. 900.
30. Woodley, R. W., HW-40142 (1955) (U. S. Atomic Energy Commission).
31. Kosiba, W. L. and Dienes, G. J., in "Advances in Catalysis," Academic Press, 1957.
32. Simnad, M. T. and Smoluchowski, R., *Phys. Review*, **99**, (6), 1891 (1955).
33. Simnad, M. T. and Smoluchowski, R., *J. Chem. Phys.*, **23** (10), 1961 (1955).
34. Simnad, M. T., Smoluchowski, R., and Spilners, A., to be published.

Chapter 5

RADIATION EFFECTS IN DIELECTRIC SOLIDS

R. Smoluchowski

Carnegie Institute of Technology
Pittsburgh, Pa.

In contrast to the study of irradiation effects in metals, there has been relatively little systematic work done on non-metals at least as far as the response to nuclear radiations is concerned. There is, of course, an enormous body of information available about effects of light and of x-rays on various dielectric materials, but these lie outside the scope of this review. Semiconductors and organic materials will not be considered since they have been discussed elsewhere in this book.*

Scientific interest in nuclear irradiation effects in non-metals is twofold: first, on the experimental side, the effects are large and easily measurable; secondly, on the theoretical side, there are large gaps in the quantitative, and frequently in the qualitative, understanding of the observed phenomena. The scientific interest lies primarily in the study of relatively well known substances such as alkali halides, diamond, graphite, quartz, etc. The practical interest, from the point of view of reactor technology and operation of various devices in high fluxes of nuclear radiation, is centered on such materials as uranium oxide, beryllium oxide, mica, quartz and others. Many observations of these materials have been accumulated[1] but little theoretical analysis has been attempted.

Mechanisms of Energy Losses

An incident charged particle,[2] upon entering a solid, loses most of its energy through electronic excitation and ionization and only a small fraction of its energy goes into elastic collisions (about 0.1 per cent). As the particle slows down, the electronic excitation becomes more difficult and the elastic collisions become more important. Finally, after the energy of the incident particle is reduced to an energy level, as determined from the relation

$$E_t = \frac{M_1}{m} \epsilon_t$$

* See chapters 6 and 10.

in which M_1 is the mass of the incident particle, m is electronic mass, and ϵ_t is a threshold energy for electronic excitation, all further energy losses are through elastic collisions and displacements. The value of ϵ_t is comparable in magnitude to the width of the energy gap between the valence and the conduction band and is often known. The loss of energy of the moving particle per unit length of path, either through electronic excitation or through elastic collisions and displacements, essentially is inversely proportional to the energy. This is in contrast to inelastic collisions,[3] in which the incident particle is absorbed by the target nucleus and the resulting excited nucleus emits secondary nucleons which produce various irradiation effects. In this type of mechanism, which becomes significant for energies of incident particles higher than about 90 Mev, the effects produced per unit length of path increase with energy. While incident neutrons do not by themselves produce electronic excitation and ionization, all secondary particles, i.e., atoms displaced by incident radiation of any kind, produce electronic effects. Thus all radiations, e.g. neutrons, protons, deutrons, alpha particles, electrons, gamma rays, x-rays, etc., produce in dielectric materials defects which result primarily from electronic excitation.

Defects in Dielectrics

In the class of inorganic dielectric materials, the only stable primary defects produced by irradiation are vacancies, interstitials and perhaps dislocations. Defects in alkali halides are the only types which have been studied in some detail.[4] Since, the crystal structure of alkali halides consists of equal numbers of positive and negative ions, there must be either an equal number of positive and negative vacancies per unit volume or an equal number of vacancies and corresponding interstitials per unit volume. These are the so-called Schottky and Frenkel defects respectively. The negative and positive ion vacancies have charges associated with them and, thus, they can attract free electrons or holes producing F and V_1 centers respectively. These in turn may form various kinds of aggregates each usually having a characteristic optical absorption band. In general, negative ion vacancies are less mobile than positive ion vacancies. The latter, in effect, are the only carriers of ionic current, if the temperature is not too high.

The significant evidence for the existence of dislocations in alkali halides has been obtained from observation of etch pits as well as by the use of "decoration" techniques.[6] No conclusive evidence for the formation of dislocations in alkali halides by irradiation seems to be available as yet.

Mechanism of Defect Formation

As mentioned above, defects in dielectric materials can be produced both by elastic collisions and by electronic excitation. Elastic collisions can produce displaced atoms, that is, vacancy-interstitial pairs, if the energy acquired by the struck atoms is greater than some minimum value E_d. Formulas for calculating the total number of atoms thus displaced have been proposed[2] and, for metals, the comparison with experiment is in agreement within a factor of 2 to 5. In dielectric materials, however, the number of defects produced by collisions is usually very small compared to the defects produced by electronic excitation.

There are two major possible mechanisms of formation of defects in alkali halides by electronic excitation. One is the mechanism proposed by Seitz and Markham[2] which considers the presence of jogs in dislocations already existing in the crystal. Atoms near such jogs are weakly bound and electronic excitation may be sufficient to displace them into a position which is a continuation of the incomplete plane of atoms of an edge dislocation. The vacancy which thereby is created may then diffuse away from the dislocation. A jog accepts alternately positive and negative ions and, thus, Schottky defects are produced, i.e., equal number of positive and negative ion vacancies. Conversely dislocation jogs can act as sinks for interstitials and vacancies.

Another mechanism of defect formation by electronic excitation has been proposed by Varley.[7] In this mechanism, the incident radiation is assumed to produce multiple ionization of a halogen ion, which becomes positively charged and finds itself surrounded by eight positive neighboring ions, a configuration of high electrostatic energy. This energy can be lowered if the ion leaves its normal lattice position and becomes an interstitial. In this manner, halogen vacancies and halogen interstitials would be formed. The validity of this mechanism depends, among other things, upon the lifetime of the multiple ionized halogen ion.

Production of vacancies always leads to a decrease in crystalline density, whether or not stable interstitials are produced at the same time. On the other hand, production of vacancies alone leaves the lattice constant, as measured by x-rays, essentially unchanged while the formation of interstitials leads to an increase in the lattice constant.

Effects in Alkali Halides

Examples of the types of changes produced in dielectric materials can be illustrated from the results of recent studies of irradiation effects in alkali halides, quartz and diamond.

Lithium fluoride is a favored material for experimental research, since under neutron irradiation the lithium nuclei split and the fast fragments (alpha particle and He_3) by themselves produce irradiation effects. Figure 5.1 shows the change of lattice constant[8] as a function of total flux of neutrons. It is clear that, in this instance, the lattice expansion is caused by Frenkel defects, produced by atomic displacements. There are about 1200 defect pairs produced per one splitting lithium atom as compared to a theoretical value of 1900. With progressive irradiation more and more defects are produced which coalesce to form clusters. This gradually results in the elimination of point defects and accounts for the return of the lattice constant to its normal value, as can be noted in Figure 1. The formation of clusters at high total irradiation fluxes has been confirmed by x-ray studies.[9]

Since, as mentioned before, ionic conductivity in alkali halides results from the presence of positive ion vacancies, it might be supposed that defects introduced by irradiation would lower the electrical resistivity of alkali halides. Actually, as illustrated in Figure 5.2, when a proton irradiated NaCl crystal is slowly heated, its resistivity rapidly increases initially, but subsequently is restored to its normal value as the defects begin to anneal out at higher temperatures.[10] The initial increase of resistance may be interpreted in terms of a progressive clustering of point defects and a consequent progressive decrease in the number of single positive ion vacancies, i.e., of current carriers. For the same post-irradiation thermal treatment, the changes in stored energy or the heat emitted is shown in Figure 5.3. It can be seen that a peak in the evolved energy occurs at about 200°C, which coincides with the temperature for the sharp drop in the resistivity curves. Thus it appears that the decomposition of defect clusters releases positive ion vacancies which decrease the resistivity. Figure 5.4 shows a typical absorption spectrum of irradiated NaCl in which most of the bands

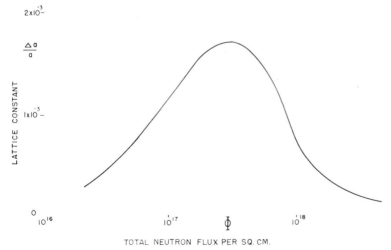

Figure 5.1. Relative change of lattice constants of LiF as function of total neutron flux per cm sq. (reference 8).

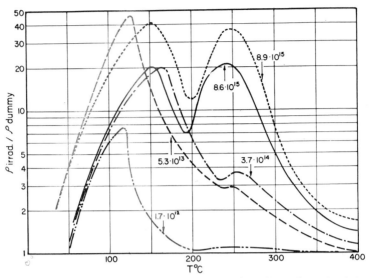

Figure 5.2. Ratio of resistivity of proton irradiated NaCl to the resistaivity of a normal crystal as function of temperature increasing at a rate of 2°C per min. (reference 10).

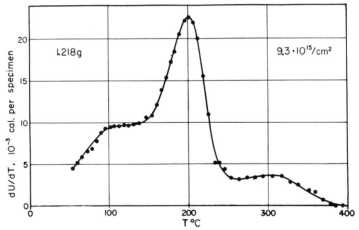

Figure 5.3. Heat emitted by a proton irradiated NaCl crystal heated in the same manner as the crystals in Fig. 2. (reference 10).

can be correlated with particular defect clusters. The broad peak at 4650Å is due to a high concentration of F-centers, i.e., negative ion vacancies which have captured an electron. Figure 5.5 shows the variation of various color bands with temperature and the corresponding annealing out of the change in density produced by proton irradiation.[11] It is interesting to

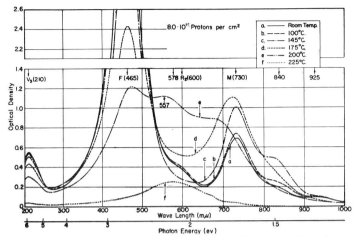

Figure 5.4. Optical density of proton irradiated NaCl as function of wavelength at various stages of annealing (reference 10).

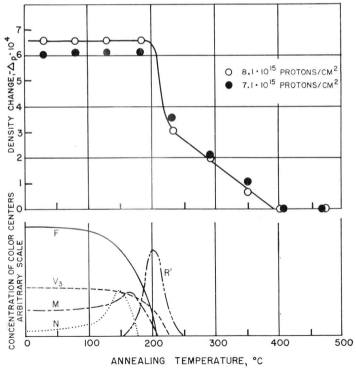

Figure 5.5. Annealing out of absorption bands and of density change in proton irradiated NaCl as function of increasing temperature as in Fig. 2 (reference 11).

note that, while below 200°C there is no indication of annealing of defects, significant changes in the relative intensity of various absorption bands are apparent. This confirms the conclusion that during the first stages of annealing only clustering occurs with no disappearance of defects, either by recombination or at dislocation jogs. It is also of interest to note that the rapid drop in resistivity and in density change and the rapid increase of heat emission all coincide with the annealing out of R′ centers, which are known to consist of large clusters.

From a knowledge of the total stored energy, the intensity of the absorption bands and the change in density it is possible to calculate the number of defects produced per incident proton. This number varies between 2,000 and 4,000. The actual value depends upon the total proton flux, since at higher fluxes some radiation annealing occurs and the apparent effectiveness of each incident proton is lowered.

The intensity of the F band as function of the energy of the incident proton is shown in Figure 5.6, which is a plot of the number of F centers produced per proton vs. the energy of the protons. The exactly hyperbolic relationship experimentally obtained is in accord with theory of defect formation by electronic excitation. In Figure 6, the change of resistivity of tungsten also is plotted, indicating an opposite type of dependence on the incident proton energy which is in accord with the inelastic collision mechanism discussed previously and denotes an absence of any influence of elec-

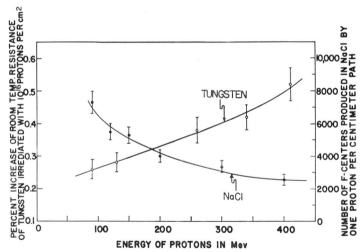

Figure 5.6. Number of F-centers produced in NaCl by one proton per cm path and the increase of resistivity of tungsten irradiated with 10^{16} protons per cm sq. as function of energy.

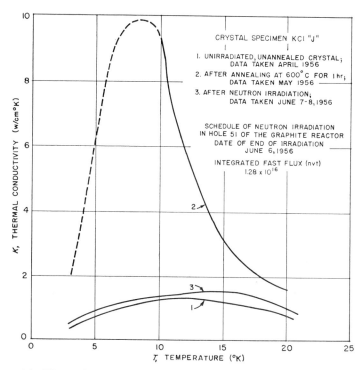

Figure 5.7. Thermal conductivity of KCl as function of temperature in unirradiated and in neutron irradiated conditions (reference 12).

tronic excitation. The two curves illustrate how the effects of proton irradiation on two different materials may have an entirely different energy dependence depending upon the predominating mechanism.

Thermal conduction of alkali halides also can be strongly affected by irradiation. This is to be expected, since at low temperatures phonons are strongly scattered by lattice defects. Figure 5.7 shows the marked influence of neutron irradiation[12] on reducing the thermal conductivity of an annealed KCl crystal. The usual explanation for the appearance of a maximum in the thermal conductivity vs. temperature curve is based upon the change with temperature of the relative importance of the influence of the specific heat and of mean free path on thermal conductivity. A rather strange effect obtained on gamma irradiation of KCl is illustrated in Figure 5.8. In this case irradiation results in an increase in thermal conductivity, presumably because of radiation-induced annealing of strains which may have existed in the crystal.

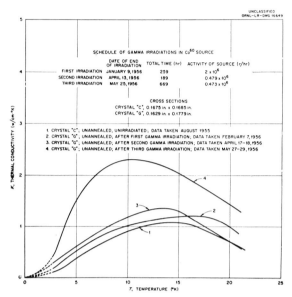

Figure 5.8. Thermal conductivity of KCl as function of temperature in unirradiated and in gamma irradiated conditions (reference 12).

Effects in Quartz

Mitchell and Paige[13] have made a rather complete study of the effects of irradiation on the optical properties of vitreous and crystalline quartz in an attempt to identify the corresponding lattice defects. Their analysis will be discussed briefly. Figure 5.9 shows the absorption bands, A and C, in neutron irradiated crystalline quartz. It is known, from other research, that in quartz the A band increases in intensity with increasing concentration of aluminum as an impurity, and that the intensity of the C band increases linearly with neutron irradiation, the latter being due to atomic displacements. This is not true of the A band. In quartz irradiated only with x-rays, both the A and C bands rapidly saturate, indicating that x-rays produce free electrons and holes which are trapped in already existing lattice defects. Figure 5.9 also reveals the E band and the absorption limit at 8.1 ev in neutron irradiated crystalline quartz. This absorption limit corresponds to vitreous quartz and differs from the 8.5 ev value for crystalline quartz.

Additional important information has been obtained from both optical and thermal bleaching. Optical bleaching simply removes electrons or holes from lattice defects, whereas thermal bleaching removes the defects themselves. Optical bleaching of gamma irradiated quartz is a uniform function of the wavelength, while that of neutron irradiated quartz ex-

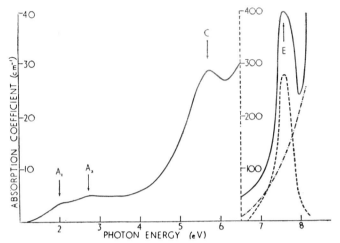

Figure 5.9. Absorption spectrum of neutron-irradiated crystalline quartz showing bands A, C, E and the absorption limit (reference 13).

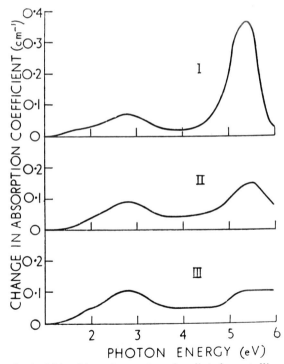

Figure 5.10. Optical bleaching of a neutron irradiated crystalline quartz: I—80 min.; II—next 160 min.; III—next 320 min. (reference 13).

hibits initially a sharp maximum at 5.4 ev, which disappears after progressive annealing. This behavior is illustrated in Figure 5.10. Similarly, thermal bleaching of an x-ray irradiated quartz crystal exhibits no preferential peak at 5.4 ev but a very strong peak in a neutron irradiated crystal. Essentially the same behavior is observed in irradiation of fused quartz, except that the absorption limit remains unchanged at 8.1 ev.

Since both the C and E bands are produced by neutrons and not by x-rays, they are related to radiation generated lattice defects. It is known also that C bands can be bleached optically. Therefore, a C-center has to be a trapped hole or a trapped electron. From O'Brien and Pryce's analysis[14] of magnetic resonance studies of defects in quartz, it follows that an A center must capture one electron in order to bleach. Since the A center bleaches when C-light falls on a C-colored crystal, it may be concluded that a C-center is a center containing a trapped electron. Thus the C-center consists of either an O^{-2} vacancy or an Si^{+4} interstitial. It follows, too, that the E-center involves a trapped hole. One knows also that the E-center does not involve a Si-vacancy because the E band is not produced by x-rays in crystals in which there is evidence of the existence of Si-vacancies. Thus, the E-center must be a hole trapped at an interstitial O^{-2} ion

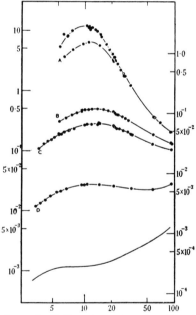

Figure 5.11. Thermal conductivity of neutron irradiated crystalline quartz as function of temperature: A—.05 × 10^{18}; B—1.8 × 10^{18}; C—4.3 × 10^{18}; D—34.2 × 10^{18} neutrons per cm sq. Bottom curve: vitreous quartz (reference 15).

and the C-center must be an electron trapped at an O^{-2} vacancy. Preferential bleaching at 5.4 ev is interpreted as a recombination of C and E defects which are close to each other.

Similar to KCl there is a marked change of thermal conductivity[15] in neutron irradiated quartz. Figure 5.11 shows the progressive decrease in the thermal conductivity of quartz upon irradiation. The top curve is typical of the normal perfect crystalline state and the decrease in conductivity with increasing dose of irradiation is readily evident. The conductivity of a highly irradiated sample is only slightly better than that of vitreous quartz (lowest curve).

Effects in Diamond

In diamond, each carbon atom has covalent bonds with each of its four neighbors. Thus, when vacancies and interstitials are produced upon neutron irradiation, there are four electrons in the vacancies and the interstitials consist of neutral carbon atoms. The interstitial carbon atoms have a strong affinity for each other and presumably form larger complexes starting with C_2 molecules oriented along the [110] direction. Each of these defects has its own electronic configuration with a characteristic resulting spin. Studies of magnetic spin resonance, i.e., microwave absorption, are in good agreement with this model.[14]

The interstitial defects naturally expand the diamond lattice and the density of the crystal is decreased by as much as 4 per cent upon irradiation

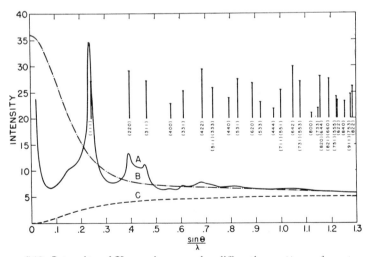

Figure 5.12. Intensity of X-rays in a powder diffraction pattern of neutron irradiated diamond (curve A); scattering of a carbon atom (curve B); incoherent scattering (curve C) (reference 16).

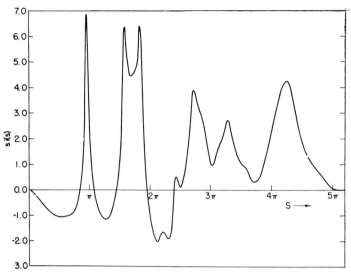

Figure 5.13. Same as curve A in Fig. 12 but corrected for atomic scattering and for incoherent scattering (reference 16).

A-OBSERVED EXCESS AND DEFICIT IN THE
RADIAL DENSITY OF IRRADIATED DIAMOND
B-EMPTY AND FILLED SHELLS IN DIAMOND
C-COMPUTED EXCESS AND DEFICIT IN THE
RADIAL DENSITY OF IRRADIATED DIAMOND

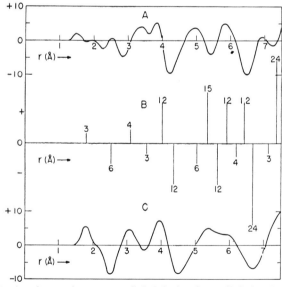

Figure 5.14. A—observed excess and deficit in the radial density of irradiated diamond; B—same for normal diamond; C—same as A computed from the theoretical model (reference 16).

156

with 10^{20} neutrons per cm sq. An interesting analysis of the x-ray diffraction pattern[16] of heavily irradiated diamond has been made recently by Keating. Figure 5.12 shows the powder diffraction pattern (Line A) of irradiated diamond which, compared to the very sharp lines of normal diamond pattern, clearly indicates an almost amorphous state. Line B is the scattering per carbon atom and line C is the incoherent scattering. Figure 5.13 is the same pattern as in Figure 5.12, but corrected for the two scatterings B and C.

In a diamond lattice each carbon atom is surrounded by a shell of four nearest neighbors and four equally distant empty interstitial positions. Thus, if defect pairs are produced by neutron irradiation, no change in the number of nearest neighbors should take place. Similarly, in a perfect lattice the possible atomic positions in the second nearest shell are always empty and irradiation would always increase the occupation of nearest neighbors in this shell. The third shell is normally full and irradiation would always lower its degree of occupation. A similar analysis may be made for other shells and their occupancy may be expressed in terms of f (the fraction of occupied interstitial sites) and g (the fraction of occupied

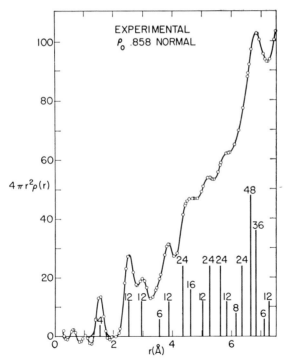

Figure 5.15. Radial distribution curve for irradiated diamond and for a normal crystal (with reduced density). (reference 16).

normal sites). By comparing the calculated theoretical distribution curve with experimental data, Keating obtained values of $f = .18$ and $g = .65$, as a best fit. Thus, an irradiation of 6×10^{20} neutrons per cm sq displaces about 30 per cent of the atoms in diamond. The agreement of theory with experiment is illustrated in Figure 5.14 in which the deviations from uniform density are plotted for the various shells of ideal diamond (curve B), for observed irradiated diamond (curve A), and for calculated irradiated diamond (curve C). A comparison of the radial distribution curve for irradiated diamond, assuming a density of that of normal diamond, with the ideal lattice is shown in Figure 5.15.

Conclusion

It is evident from this brief survey that in non-metals variety of irradiation phenomena is observed which often is greater than in metals. In some instances, a reasonably reliable identification of the defects, of their configuration and of their annealing behavior is possible. Also many changes of properties can be analyzed. This is, however, only the beginning and a great deal of additional work remains to be done.

References

1. Proceedings Int. Conf. Peaceful Uses of Atomic Energy, Geneva, 1955, vol. 7.
2. F. Seitz and J. S. Koehler, *Solid State Physics*, **2**, 307 (1956).
3. R. Smoluchowski, *Phys. Rev.*, **94**, 1409 (1954); Chapter XIII in "Molecular Engineering" Technology Press, Cambridge, Mass.
4. F. Seitz, *Rev. Mod. Phys.*, **26**, 7 (1954).
5. J. J. Gilman and W. G. Johnson, *J. Appl. Phys.*, **27**, 1018 (1956).
6. S. Amelinckx, *Phil. Mag.*, **1**, 269 (1956).
7. J. H. O. Varley, *Nature*, **174**, 886 (1954).
8. G. Mayer, P. Perio, J. Gigon and M. Tournarie, *Proc. Geneva Conf.*, **7**, 647 (1955).
9. A. Guinier, private communication.
10. K. Kobayashi, *Phys. Rev.*, **102**, 348 (1956).
11. K. Kobayashi, *Phys. Rev.*, **107**, 41 (1957).
12. A. Foner Cohen and L. C. Templeton, Oak Ridge Nat. Lab., "Solid State Division Progress Report," ORNL-2188 (1956).
13. E. W. J. Mitchell and E. G. S. Paige, *Phil. Mag.* **1** (ser. 8), 1085 (1956).
14. M. C. M. O'Brien and M. H. L. Pryce, Rep. Bristol Conf. on Defects in Solids (1954).
15. R. Berman, F. E. Simon, P. G. Klemens and T. M. Fry, *Nature*, **166**, 277 (1950).
16. D. Keating, to be published.

Chapter 6

IRRADIATION EFFECTS IN SEMI-CONDUCTORS*

H. Y. Fan and K. Lark-Horovitz

Purdue University, Lafayette, Indiana

Introduction

Semiconductors are a class of material, the electronic properties of which are most sensitive to imperfections of the crystal lattice. This is evidenced by the controlling effect of small amounts of chemical impurities which are one type of lattice imperfections. Irradiation by high-energy particles can, therefore, produce radical changes in the properties of a semiconductor by creating defects in the crystal lattice. These defects may introduce new energy levels.[10] Thus the electrical conductivity of a semiconductor may change by orders of magnitude as a result of irradiation, whereas in metals the changes are measured in percent. Many other properties are likewise sensitive to irradiation, making irradiation effects in semiconductors of interest. From the practical point of view, semiconductor devices may find applications where they are exposed to irradiation. In fact, semiconductor devices have been investigated as radiation detectors[72, 101, 110, 114] and as batteries converting radiation energy to electrical energy.[75, 116] Therefore the effects of irradiation on semiconductors are also of practical importance.

The first experiments on the irradiation of semiconductors were carried out in 1943 using 10 Mev deuterons from the Purdue Cyclotron and thin germanium films deposited on aluminum. These experiments showed that the films were disordered to such an extent that additional bombardment did not have any effect. Later by investigating the films more carefully it was found that all evaporated films are p-type† and it is only possible to obtain readily an interpretation of radiation effects by using single crystal materials.[16]

A systematic investigation was started in the fall of 1947 when germanium and silicon bulk samples were first bombarded[68] in the Purdue

* Supported by a Signal Corps and an A.E.C. contract.
† Proc. National Electronic Conference 8, 506, 1953.

Cyclotron with 10 Mev deuterons and with alphas from polonium. These experiments were continued in collaboration with the Oak Ridge group using fast neutrons from the ORNL[29–38] reactor, and observations were made of the resistance changes of bulk germanium samples during irradiation; and were followed by observations during irradiation on germanium diodes*.[108]

At present the solid state group at Purdue University is engaged in investigations of the changes of bulk properties of semiconductors after irradiation with deuterons, electrons and alpha particles.[44, 44a] The Oak Ridge solid state division investigates a great variety of semiconductors exposed to fast neutrons.[4] Electron irradiation of germanium and silicon is studied at the Bell Telephone Laboratories.[22-24] P-N junctions are studied under electron irradiation at the R.C.A. research laboratories.[69] A number of laboratories are also engaged in the investigation of radiation damage in semiconducting devices. (Symposium on nuclear radiation effects on semiconductor devices. New York, Feb. 27–28, 1957).

Types of Irradiation

We shall consider charged particles, electrons (of a fraction of a Mev to 6 Mev) and deuterons and α-particles of several Mev energy, and fast neutrons in a reactor. These particles have considerable range in ordinary materials and enable the study of effects produced in the bulk material rather than purely surface effects.

The thermal neutrons in a reactor may in some cases produce considerable effects by causing transmutations of the constituent atoms of the material. The result is equivalent to introducing impurities into the material. Thus Ga, As, and Se atoms are produced in germanium;[10] gallium is produced in the largest amount and tends to make the semiconductor p-type in conduction. In the case of indium antimonide irradiated in a reactor[95] the effect of transmutations is so large as to be comparable with the effect of fast neutrons, on account of the large capture cross section of In for slow neutrons. The effect of transmutations is permanent in the sense that it cannot be removed by high temperature annealing. We shall not discuss this effect further but shall consider only the effect of lattice defects produced by the high energy particles. Recently, irradiation of germanium with Co gamma radiation as suggested some time ago by Lark-Horovitz has also been investigated.[29, 30] The defects are actually produced by Compton and photoelectrons.

---

* Exposures of Ge diodes by the Nepa group had shown that prolonged exposure in the reactor destroys the rectification characteristics.

Structure Changes

Disordering of a crystal lattice under extensive irradiation may lead to observable structural changes*. Close packed metals even after extensive irradiations show no changes in lattice parameter or line broadening. Black phosphorus samples irradiated in the Brookhaven reactor for about one month at $\sim$50°C show an expansion $(\Delta c/c) \times 100 = 0.03\% \pm .02\%$.[28] It is possible that atoms trapped in the open spaces of the black phosphorus lattice produce the effect observed. In addition a large number of extra lines are seen which are not observed in unirradiated material. The irradiated material is stronger and harder and less hygroscopic.

Both in silicon[18, 20] and in germanium[27] the x-ray diffuse scattering is changed by irradiation. A very striking effect of this type is observed[98] in single crystals of InSb irradiated by neutrons to $1.09 \times 10^{20} = nvt$.

White tin on neutron irradiation transforms to grey tin similar to samples "seeded" with grey tin.[45-47] The sample is irradiated at $\sim$80°K and the transformation measured by dilatometry at the temperature of transformation reaction of about -50.3°C. During the irradiation itself no grey tin is formed as shown by x-ray diffraction at 80°K. Neutron irradiation thus can be used to produce uniform nucleation. Electron irradiation[81] $(3.5 \times 10^{18}$ electrons/cm^2 near 78°K) and quenching does not produce transformation in specimens held in the transformation range for a week. Apparently the single point defects produced are insufficient to nucleate the transformation.

Irradiation of vitreous selenium with α-particles produces hexagonal Se[82] and the same effect can also be produced by deuteron irradiation. (Liebschutz, Purdue, unpublished.)

Types of Defect

Fast charged particles lose most of their energy by producing electron excitations, which lead to transient changes in the properties of a semiconductor, and which decay with a very short relaxation time. We are concerned only with the effect of lattice defects resulting from the displacement of atoms. In the case of insulators, electron excitation may be associated with sufficient energy to lead to the displacement of atoms. For semiconductors, however, atoms are displaced only by elastic collisions of the nuclei either directly with the bombarding particles or with other atoms which had acquired large energy in being displaced. Displaced

* This is the type of radiation damage which was discovered in the early days of radioactivity in the so-called "metamict" crystals. For a recent review see Faessler A. Untersuchungen zum Problem des metamikten Zustandes. Z. Krist, 104, 81–113 (1942)

atoms, lodged in interstitial positions and the vacant lattice sites left behind, are the lattice defects produced by the irradiation.

More complicated defects may be produced.[1] The displaced atoms with such energy as they can acquire in these irradiations have small mean free paths and the secondary displacements are produced in a small neighborhood. Therefore, clusters of interstitials and especially vacancies may be produced which have different effects than isolated vacancies and interstitials. When the irradiation is not carried out at sufficiently low temperatures, clusters may also appear as a result of thermal migration if such clusters are energetically more stable. The estimated average number of total displacements per primary displacement, $\bar{N}_d$, for various types of irradiations is given in Table 1. For deuteron and α-particle irradiations, several secondary displacements are expected on the average, whereas for the electron irradiations of low energy the number is less than one. The observed effects of the heavy particles are in fact more complicated than the effect of electrons in many respects, which may well be caused by the production of more complicated defects.

Clusters are not the only possible complications in this type of defects. Because of the small mean free path of the displaced atoms, the energy received by a primary displaced atom from a bombarding particle is dissipated in a small region. Aside from the energy associated with the total interstitial-vacancy pairs produced, energy is dissipated in producing

TABLE 1. EXPERIMENTALLY DETERMINED REMOVAL RATE OF CONDUCTION ELECTRONS AND ESTIMATED PRODUCTION RATES OF DISPLACEMENTS

n and N are carrier and displacement concentrations, respectively. n_t and N_t are respectively number of carriers and number of displacements in the sample per unit area of the irradiated surface. ϕ is the irradiation flux per unit area. $\bar{N}_d$ is the total number of displacements per primary displacement.

Material	Particle and energy in Mev	T ($^\circ$K)	$E_c - \zeta$ (ev)	Carrier removal rate		Thickness, micron	Displacement production rate		$\bar{N}_d$
				$-dn/d\phi$ (cm^{-1})	$dn_t/d\phi$		$dN/d\phi$ (cm^{-1})	$dN_t/d\phi$	
Ge	(e) 4.5	90	0.02–0.06	4			4.3		1.48
	(d) 9.6	90	0		12.0	100		12.8	3.89
	(a) 19	90	0.05		22.8	33		14.0	4.40
	(a) 4.5	293	0.01		180	thicker than range		87	3.70
Si	(e) 4.5	273	<0	(13.7)			3.2		1.76
	(d) 9.6	200	<0		11.7	175		13.5	4.23
InSb	(e) 4.5	80	<0	11			3.28*		1.33

* Calculated for electrons using the Feshbach formula. [Phys. Rev. 74, 1759 (1948)].

lattice vibrations which corresponds to a large, local increase of temperature or thermal spike. The defect produced by this effect may be regarded as the result of local melting and rapid resolidification. Brinkmann[1] considers the case where secondary displacements lead to vacancy clusters, each surrounded by a region containing interstitials; the atoms around such a multiple vacancy rearrange themselves by virtue of the thermal spike and eliminate the vacancy. The result of this process is called a displacement spike. In any event, we get disordered regions, each containing many atoms. The effect of such defects should be different from that of single interstitials and vacancies. Recently,[99, 109] Gonser and Okkerse reported that x-ray measurement on deuteron-irradiated GaSb and InSb gave indications of the presence of this type of defects.

The effect of irradiation on the electrical properties of germanium, silicon and InSb shows, on the whole, good correlation with the estimated production of displaced atoms. One of the major effects of irradiation is to change the concentration of charge carriers in the semiconductor. Under suitable conditions, as explained in a later section, the change in the number of carriers may be expected to be the same or a small multiple of the number of displaced atoms.

Table 1 shows the observed change in the number of carriers and the calculated number of displaced atoms, produced in the specimen by each bombarding particle. For the irradiation by electrons which have a range much larger than the thickness of the samples, the numbers given are reduced to unit length of path. The number of displacements per primary displacement is calculated according to the expression,

$$N_d = \frac{E_m}{E_m - E_d}\left(0.766 + 0.352 \ln \frac{E_m}{4E_d}\right), \tag{1}$$

based on the works of various workers.[7, 9, 13, 44a] E_m is the maximum energy that can be transferred to an atom by a bombarding particle. E_d is the threshold energy required for displacement. The value used for E_d is 30 ev, as explained in the next section. The calculation is approximate, especially in view of the uncertainty in E_d. Comparison of the observed change in carriers with the calculated number of displacements shows that the two agree within a factor of 4 in all cases. This result suggests that interstitials and vacancies are mainly responsible for the change of carrier concentration.

Threshold Energy for Displacement

The threshold energy, E_d, for defect production may be determined by varying the energy of bombarding electrons. Such work was first reported by Klontz and Lark-Horovitz[10, 59-62] for germanium using electrons from a

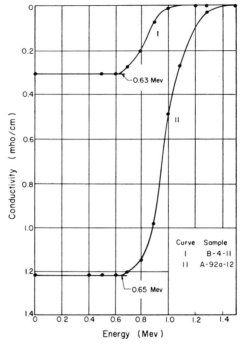

Figure 6.1 Conductivity after irradiations by a constant flux of electrons of successively higher energies, for two n-type germanium samples. Measurements by E. E. Klontz.

Van de Graaff machine. N-type samples were used, the resistivity of which increases with irradiation. Each sample was irradiated with a constant number of electrons of successively higher energies. Fig. 1 shows the variation of conductivity for two samples irradiated at liquid nitrogen temperature. It is seen that little change occurred for electron energies below ∼0.63 Mev. From measurements at liquid nitrogen and dry ice temperatures, the threshold electron energy was placed to be 0.63 ± 0.02 Mev corresponding to a value of E_d = 30 ev ± 1 ev.

Instead of conductivity, Rappaport and Loferski[77] measured carrier lifetime to detect the production of lattice defects. The samples used contained a p-n junction*. Besides producing lattice defects, the bombarding electrons generate an electro-voltaic effect at the p-n junction by exciting hole-electron pairs. The electro-voltaic effect is determined by the lifetime

* Recently Curtis, Cleland and Pigg[40] have observed the effect of reactor and fast Co[60] irradiation on lifetime of injected minority carriers. The lifetime was decreased by neutrons at a rate that is several orders of magnitude greater than the carrier removal rate.

of electrons and holes produced by the excitation. If the carrier lifetime is decreased by the introduction of lattice defects, the measured electro-voltaic effect will change with irradiation. By varying the electron energy, the authors found $E_d = 12.9$ ev for both germanium and silicon. Recently, Brown and Augustyniak[25] found by using extended irradiations that small changes in conductivity are also observed in germanium for electron energies at least as low as 0.4 Mev which corresponds to $E_d \leq 17$ ev. The authors also found an orientation effect, i.e., the conductivity changed more for electrons incident along the (111) direction of the crystal than for irradiations along the (100) or (110) directions. In this respect, it had been pointed out by Kohn[65] that an atom in the germanium lattice can be displaced along certain directions with much smaller energy than for other directions*. However, the indication of the experiments is that the effect on conductivity begins at about the same electron energy for all orientations of the samples.

The later experiments established that defects may be produced with displacement energies smaller than 30 ev. On the other hand, the irradiation effect on conductivity should not drop so sharply near 0.6 Mev electron energy, as shown by Klontz's measurement, if the threshold energy is 13 ev or 17 ev. In view of all the observations, it seems likely that, although special types of displacements requiring low energies can be produced with a small probability†, for electrons of sufficiently high energy the large part of displacements produced correspond to an average threshold energy ∼30 ev.

Resistivity and Hall Effect

Electrical conductivity, σ, and Hall coefficient R are two of the most important properties to study for a semiconductor. From these properties, the concentration of charge carriers, n, and their mobility, μ, can be determined:

$$R = \pm \frac{r}{ecn}$$

$$\sigma = en\mu,$$

where the plus and minus signs apply to p-type and n-type samples, respectively. The coefficient r is of the order of unity and is known as the ratio of Hall mobility to drift mobility. The carrier concentration is very sensitive to lattice imperfections which may hold electrons in their neighborhood, introducing energy levels for localized electrons. Such an energy

---

* We are indebted to Dr. W. Kohn for a detailed account of his calculations.[66]

† This also seems to be confirmed by recent measurements of Klontz and MacKay measuring removal rates at 0.5 Mev.

level may be either a donor or an acceptor level, depending on whether or
not the imperfection center is electrically more neutral when the level is
occupied by an electron. In Fig. 2, D and A are donor and acceptor levels
associated with impurities which determine the type of conduction. d and a
are respectively donor and acceptor levels associated with lattice defects.
A defect center may introduce more than one level, donor as well as acceptor levels.

The probability, f, for an energy level to be occupied by an electron, f,
depends on the energy as compared to the Fermi level, ζ. Levels far below
ζ are fully occupied, while those way above ζ are practically empty. The
transition of f from unity to near zero takes place in an energy range of a
few kT around ζ, as shown on the left of Fig. 2. It is clear from Fig. 2 that
the addition of donor levels, d, below ζ and the addition of acceptor levels,
a, above ζ should have no effect on the carrier concentration. Adding acceptor levels below ζ reduces the concentration of conduction electrons in
n-type and increases the hole concentration in p-type semiconductors.
The opposite effect is produced by adding donor levels above ζ.

The Fermi level is related to the carrier concentration. In n-type samples, ζ is located in the upper half of the energy gap and, the higher, the
larger the concentration of conduction electrons. In p-type samples, ζ is
located in the lower half of the energy gap and, the lower, the larger the
hole concentration.

In discussing the effect of irradiation on the carrier concentration of a
semiconductor, it is essential to specify the Fermi level or the carrier con-

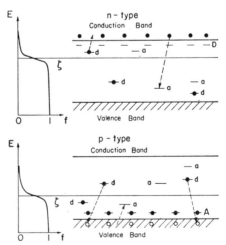

Figure 6.2 Energy level diagrams showing the effect of donor and acceptor levels,
for an n-type and a p-type semiconductor. The diagrams on the left show the probability of electron occupation as a function of energy.

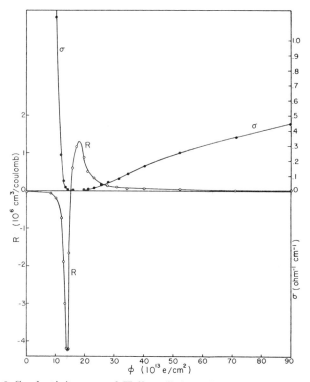

Figure 6.3 Conductivity, σ, and Hall coefficient, R, as function of electron flux for an InSb sample irradiated by 4.5 Mev. electrons at 80°K. Measurements by L. W. Aukerman.

centration in the sample used.[44, 44a] The data in Table 1 are given in each case for the n-type sample of largest carrier concentration or highest Fermi level, so as to show as fully as possible the effect of all irradiation-produced acceptor levels in reducing the conduction electrons; donor levels are ineffective under the condition.

In the three semiconductors Ge, Si, and InSb, irradiation tends to produce a definite Fermi level, ζ_F, i.e. definite electron and hole concentrations. For silicon, ζ_F is near the middle of the energy gap so that irradiation tends to make the material intrinsic, regardless of whether the sample is n- or p-type initially. For Ge and InSb, ζ_F is in the lower half of the energy gap (as measured after electron bombardment). Thus initially n-type samples can be converted to p-type*. Typical curves showing the variation of Hall coefficient and conductivity are given in Fig. 3 for an InSb sample

* However p-type InSb irradiated at around room temperature with neutrons is converted to n-type as shown by the Hall effect at low temperatures.[93-95]

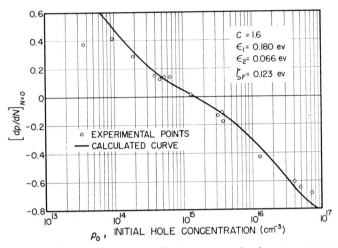

Figure 6.4 The initial rate of change of hole concentration in p-type germanium per calculated displacement, N, as a function of the initial hole concentration at 195°K, for neutron irradiation. The curve is calculated by assuming that the number of defects introduced per incident neutron is 1.6. After J. H. Crawford and J. W. Cleland.[4]

irradiated by 4.5 Mev electrons at 90°K.[91] The sample was initially n-type. The negative Hall coefficient, R, increased in magnitude with irradiation as the electron concentration was reduced. It changed sign and became positive as the sample was converted to p-type and began to approach a steady value toward the end. The conductivity, σ, first decreased with irradiation as electron concentration was reduced, increased again as the hole concentration became large after the conversion of the sample to p-type, and finally began to approach a steady value as did the Hall coefficient. When p-type samples of low initial resistivities were irradiated, the hole concentration was reduced, and ζ and R increased to approach the same steady values as the converted sample.*

In germanium, ζ_F for 4.5 Mev electron irradiation is found to be close to 0.2 ev above the valence band.[44a] Deuteron irradiation at 200°K gives a $\zeta_F \sim 0.1$ ev,[44] and $\zeta_F = 0.123$ ev was estimated for neutron irradiation at 195°K.[34] Fig 4 shows the rate of change of carrier concentration for various p-type samples as a function of the initial hole concentration, p_0. The curve shows that the rate is zero for $p_0 \sim 1.4 \times 10^{15}$ cm^{-3} corresponding to $\zeta_F = 0.123$ ev.

Each of the two types of levels, donor and acceptor, can only reduce the

* Highly conducting CdS bombarded by α particles shows a similar behavior to n-type Ge; the conductivity first decreases, then increases again. In poorly conducting CdS only an increase in conductivity is observed.[92] It would be interesting to investigate more systematically CdS with known impurity content.

number of one type of carriers. Since both holes and electrons can be reduced, depending on the initial Fermi level, acceptor as well as donor levels must be introduced by the irradiation. According to James and Lark-Horovitz,[6] interstitial atoms give donor levels and vacancies give acceptor levels. They postulated that in germanium and silicon the interstitials and the vacancies give two levels each as shown in Fig. 5. There are four levels associated with each interstitial-vacancy pair and two electrons are introduced with the donor levels of the interstitial atom. When the Fermi level in the sample lies above all four levels, each interstitial-vacancy pair takes away two electrons from the crystal, and if ζ lies below all the levels each pair gives up two electrons or takes away two holes from the crystal. In samples which have ζ lying between the second and the third levels, irradiation will have very little effect on the carrier concentration, ζ_F being about halfway between those two levels.

The model can be used to obtain approximate agreement with the experimental observations. The essential point is that each interstitial atom may produce more than one donor level and each vacancy may produce more than one acceptor level. The assumption of two levels for each type of defect should be accepted with some reservation.

Experimentally, the energy levels of the irradiation-produced defects can be determined by observing the rate of change of carrier concentration as a function of the Fermi level in various samples.[44] Another method is to observe the variation of resistivity and Hall coefficient[31-35, 50-52] with temperature in irradiated samples. Before irradiation there is a range of temperature, the well known exhaustion range, where the $\log R$ vs $1/T$ curves are rather flat. The slope of the curves after the irradiation correspond to the energy of the defect level which traps the carriers as the temperature is lowered. Still another method for level determination is to observe the sensitivity and spectral response of photoconductivity as explained in a later section.

Fig. 6 shows the defect levels in germanium that have been deduced so far in different types of irradiation. The electron irradiation has been investigated most extensively.[44a] It may also be expected to give fewer complicated defects as compared to the heavy particle irradiations. More than

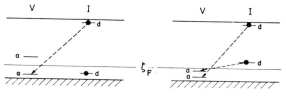

James – Lark-Horovitz Model

Figure 6.5

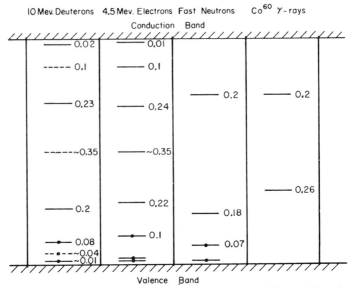

Figure 6.6 Energy levels observed in germanium irradiated by: 9.6 Mev deuterons, (Kleitman), 4.5 Mev. electrons (Klontz, MacKay, Pepper and Stoeckman), fast neutrons, and Co[60] γ-rays (ORNL). The numbers give the level energies (in ev) measured from the edge of the nearest band.

four levels are found, and there is some evidence that the level near the middle of the energy gap is associated with complicated defects rather than individual vacancies and interstitial atoms.

Also in the case of silicon, both electron[52] and deuteron irradiation[70] are most efficient in removing carriers only in samples of very high conductivity. For the case of deuterons, as shown in Fig. 7, the removal rate is about the same for n-type samples with ζ inside the conduction band and p-type samples with ζ inside the valence band, indicating that the number of donor levels introduced is about the same as the number of acceptor levels. For samples with ζ inside the energy gap, the removal rate is very small. The sharp change takes place at values of ζ near the edges of the energy gap. Thus, the defect levels are either near the conduction band or near the valence band. The simplest picture indicated by these results is that each interstitial atom introduces a donor level at $\sim$0.025 ev near the conduction band and each vacancy introduces an acceptor level at $\sim$0.055 ev from the valence band. According to this picture, the number of carriers removed by irradiation from the high conductivity samples should be equal to the number of displacements. On this basis, the agreement between the carrier removal rate and the estimated rate of displacement production, as shown in Table 1, is a very satisfactory result. It should be pointed out that some

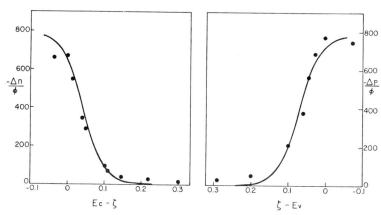

Figure 6.7 Carriers removed per unit range of a 9.6 Mev. deuteron as a function of the Fermi level, ζ, for silicon irradiated at room temperature. n and p are the concentrations of electrons and holes, respectively. ϕ is the deuteron flux received per unit area of the sample surface. E_c is the lowest energy of the conduction band, and E_v is the highest energy of the valence band. The solid curves are calculated by assuming a level at $E_v - 0.025$ ev and a level at $E_v + 0.055$ ev; one of the levels is an acceptor and the other is a donor. (T. A. Longo.)

levels are produced deeper inside the energy gap. In fact, resistivity and Hall coefficient curves of an electron irradiated sample after different fluxes of irradiation have various slopes, as shown in Fig. 8, indicating the presence of levels of various energies. However, such levels must be produced at much smaller rates than the main levels near the band edges. These deep lying levels may be associated with some more complicated defects*.[70a]

Effect on Carrier Mobility

By introducing lattice defects, irradiation increases the scattering and decreases the mobility of carriers. This is the main effect of irradiation on the conductivity of metals. Although large variations of conductivity (by orders of magnitude) in semiconductors are produced mainly through changes of carrier concentration, the effect of mobility change is by no means negligible. In fact, it may be as important as the carrier concentration in producing small changes of conductivity for a short irradiation. For this reason, it is necessary to measure the Hall coefficient for the determination of the removal rate of carriers and considerable error may result if the removal rate is deduced from conductivity by assuming a constant mobility.

The long range Coulomb interaction is most effective for the scattering of carriers, if the lattice imperfection is electrically charged. A considerable

* See also Wertheim.[90]

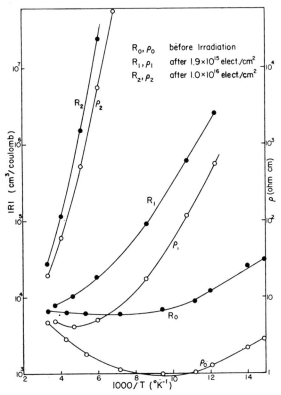

Figure 6.8 Hall coefficient and resistivity as functions of reciprocal temperature for an n-type silicon sample after receiving different irradiations by 4.5 Mev electrons at $0°C$. Measurements by D. E. Hill.

part of the irradiation introduced defects should be charged, since we may expect to have donor levels lying higher than some of the acceptor levels. Even if the defects did not trap carriers, the shift of electrons from donor levels of interstitials to the relatively lower acceptor levels of vacancies will ionize both types of defects. Thus we may expect that the main effect of the defects will be Coulomb scattering. Forster[50-51] studied the change of mobility in deuteron irradiated p-type germanium as a function of temperature and found the behavior to be consistent with the effect of an added Coulomb scattering*. Cleland, Crawford, and Pigg[33, 34] found that for neutron irradiated p-type germanium the decrease of mobility is equivalent to the introduction of nine singly charged centers for each hole carrier added. They found, however, behaviors of mobility in irradiated n- and

* Recently Kleitman obtained a similar result in irradiated germanium which was still n-type.

p-type samples which are not in agreement with the assumption of pure Coulomb scattering.

According to the energy level scheme of Fig. 6, in n-type germanium with a Fermi level lying between the top two levels, each interstitial atom has a charge $+e$ and each vacancy is charged with $-4e$, and each interstitial-vacancy pair removes three electrons. Mobility analyses have been made for such samples under various types of irradiations, electrons, deuterons, and α-particles. Assuming the above model and Coulomb scattering, the rate of displacement production required to account for the rate of change of mobility varies between 1/1.7 and 1/2.9 times the rate of carrier removal. A value of ⅓ is expected according to the model. The reasonable agreement tends to support the assumption that Coulomb scattering is the major effect of the defects.[44a] It serves also as evidence for multi-charged defects In this respect, the result of Cleland, Crawford, and Pigg for neutron-irradiated p-type germanium leads to the same conclusion.

Photoconductivity

The change of conductivity under illumination depends on the excitation of extra carriers by the absorption of light and the decay rate of the excess carriers. Consider first the spectral sensitivity as determined by the excitation. Normally the photoconductivity is appreciable only for photon energies larger than the energy gap so that electrons can be excited from the valence to the conduction band. Such intrinsic excitation creates hole-electron pairs. With the introduction of energy levels inside the energy gap, electrons can be excited from such levels to the conduction band or can be excited from the valence band to such levels. Thus photoconductivity may be observed at longer wavelengths.

Fig. 9a shows the curves of photoconductivity for a germanium sample before and after electron irradiation.[85] Fig. 9b shows similar curves for silicon with deuteron irradiation.[70a] Before irradiation the photoconductive response cuts off near the threshold for intrinsic excitation. The response in the irradiated samples is seen to extend to longer wavelengths. In the case of germanium, the curve extends by about 0.2 ev beyond the cut-off of intrinsic excitation and shows a distinct peak at about 0.35 ev photon energy*. Curves of similar shapes have been observed in n- and p-type irradiated samples. The results indicate the introduction of energy levels at about 0.2 ev from each edge and at the middle of the energy gap. In the case of irradiated silicon, the photoresponse extends by about 0.3 ev beyond the cut-off in the unirradiated sample, indicating the introduction

---

* Similar observations have been made by D. Kleitman and T. Longo in deuteron irradiated germanium.[57]

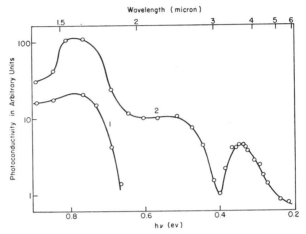

Figure 6.9a Photoconductivity, increase of conductivity for a constant intensity of incident light, as a function of wavelength, for an n-type germanium sample before (1) and after (2) irradiation by 4.5 Mev electrons at 90°K. Measurements by F. Stoeckmann, et al.

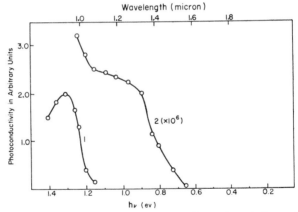

Figure 6.9b Photoconductivity as a function of wavelength for a silicon sample before (1) and after (2) deuteron irradiation. Measurements by T. A. Longo.

of a level either ~0.3 ev below the conduction band or ~0.3 ev above the valence band. As discussed in a previous section, most of the energy levels of the irradiation produced defects in silicon are very close to the top and the bottom of the energy gap. The energy levels responsible for the long wavelength extension of photoresponse seem thus to be associated with a small amount of special defects.[70a]

Consider now the magnitude of photoconductivity. At short wavelengths where photoconductivity is observed also in unirradiated samples, intrinsic excitation plays the important role and a change in the magnitude of photoconductive effect reflects a change in the decay rate of excited carriers. The introduction of lattice defects should increase the hole-electron recombination rate, as indeed is observed in the experiments using the effect of irradiation on carrier lifetime for the determination of threshold energy E_d. On this basis, it would be expected that the photoconductivity corresponding to intrinsic excitation should decrease in magnitude with irradiation. Fig. 9a shows, however, that the photoconductivity is actually stronger in the irradiated germanium. This behavior is caused by the trapping of minority carriers. The concentration of the minority carriers, being normally very small, may be increased appreciably under intrinsic excitation. An excess concentration of the carriers leads to an increase of the number of such carriers trapped in the various energy levels of the defects. Although the free electrons and free holes may recombine with a large rate, a part of the majority carriers which corresponds to the trapped minority carriers decays only with a rate at which the latter are released. The decay rate in the irradiated sample is in fact slow, of the order of seconds at 90°K.

The measurements showed a hole-trapping level at ∼0.1 ev below the conduction band and an electron-trapping level at ∼0.1 ev above the valence band. Similar hole-trapping level in deuteron-irradiated n-type germanium at 90°K is indicated by the work of Kleitman and Longo.

Brown, Fletcher and Wright[24] studied the decay of photoconductivity as a function of temperature for germanium samples bombarded by electrons at 78°K. They found two electron-trapping levels in p-type samples, one of which is at 0.2 ev below the conduction band; these levels were observed in samples bombarded with 2.5 Mev and 3.5 Mev electrons but not with 1.5 Mev electrons. Hole traps in n-type samples were also observed in these experiments.

Effect on Conduction at Low Temperatures

One of the most interesting aspects of semiconductor physics is the phenomenon of impurity band conduction. According to the conventional concept, a semiconductor which derives its charge carriers from donor or acceptor impurities of finite ionization energy should have at low temperatures a resistivity which increases continuously with decreasing temperature. Hung* and other workers at Purdue found that, as the temperature is lowered, the resistivity of germanium samples does increase at first according to the ionization energy of the impurity but, at some temperature, the rate of increase drops drastically and rather abruptly. At the same time, the Hall coefficient, which accompanies the resistivity in the normal rise, reaches a maximum and drops with further decrease of temperature. Hung

* C. S. Hung, *Phys. Rev.* **79**, 727 (1950).

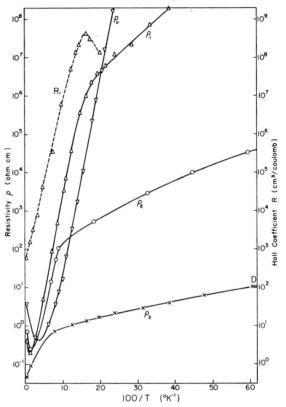

Figure 6.10a Resistivity ρ and Hall coefficient R as functions of reciprocal temperature for four germanium samples which were initially n-type having resistivities of about 30 ohm cm. Subscript 0 refers to the unirradiated sample, subscripts 1, 2, 3 refer to the samples which had been irradiated by 2.1×10^{15}, 1.0×10^{16}, and 5.6×10^{16} deuterons/cm², respectively. The irradiated samples were converted to p-type; the Hall coefficients were positive for the entire temperature range of measurement. Measurements by Kleitman, Fritzsche and Ray.

attributed the anomalous behavior to the conduction by carriers in the impurity states. Such conduction should be strongly dependent on the separation between impurity atoms. Experimentally, the resistivity at which the anomaly takes place is in fact very sensitive to the impurity concentration. The larger the impurity concentration the lower the resistivity and the higher the temperature of the maximum of Hall coefficient. The phenomena have been investigated extensively by Fritzsche and Lark-Horovitz,* and similar behavior has since been observed by other

* H. Fritzsche and K. Lark-Horovitz, *Physica* **20**, 834 (1954), *Phys. Rev.* **99**, 400 (1955). H. Fritzsche, *Phys. Rev.* **99**, 406 (1955).

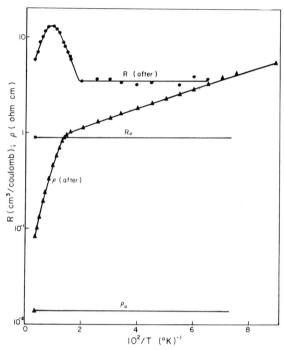

Figure 6.10b Resistivity and Hall coefficient as functions of reciprocal temperature for a silicon sample before and after irradiation by 9.6 Mev deuterons at room
temperature. Measurements by T. A. Longo and G. W. Gobeli.

workers in a number of semiconductors. The theoretical treatment of the
problem is the subject of very active research.

Curve ρ_0 in Fig. 10a shows the resistivity as a function of reciprocal
temperature for a normal germanium sample of low impurity content.
The region of impurity band conduction in such samples corresponds to
very high resistivities, outside of the range of the graph. Curves ρ_1, ρ_2 and
ρ_3 were obtained on three samples which had been irradiated by different
fluxes of 9.5 Mev deuterons. The samples were initially n-type with a small
concentration of donor impurity and were p-type after the irradiation.
Each of these curves shows a bend, having a smaller slope at low temperatures. This behavior is typical of the transition to impurity band conduction in normal samples. The bending takes place at a higher temperature
and a lower resistivity after a heavier irradiation. Curve R_1 shows the
Hall coefficient for the sample which gave curve ρ_1. The Hall effect remains positive and shows a maximum typical of the usual impurity band
conduction. The behavior is similar to the impurity band conduction in
normal p-type samples with acceptor impurities. The results indicate that

the conduction is to be attributed to levels, probably acceptor levels, associated with the defects introduced by the irradiation. It should be pointed out that a flux of 10^{16} deuteron/cm^2 produces an estimated 1.2×19^{19} displacement/cm^3. At such large concentrations, it is not unreasonable to find conduction in the defect levels. Similar phenomena, Fig. 10b, have been observed also in deuteron bombarded silicon. The investigation of this effect may be very helpful for the understanding of the mechanism of compensation of impurity states.

Annealing of the Defects

It has been shown in the early works on deuteron and neutron irradiations of germanium and silicon that the effect of irradiation can be removed by heat treatment.[42a] Heating at 450°C for about 24 hours would practically restore the original conductivity before the irradiation.[42a] Conductivity annealing in electron-irradiated germanium was studied in more detail by Brown et al[22, 23, 48] for the temperature range from room temperature to 340°C. The samples were bombarded by 3 Mev electrons. The change of conductivity with time was observed as the sample was held at successively higher temperatures. An attempt was made to interpret the results by using the following model. The vacancies are assumed to be more mobile than the interstitials. Those which are produced close to the original interstitials recombine directly with the latter, giving a monomolecular process. The vacancies which are not so close to their displaced atoms may in their wandering either come close to these atoms to give monomolecular recombination, or wander away to recombine with other interstitials to give bimolecular recombination. It was found that the results for n-type samples could be fitted by this model with an activation energy of 1.7 ev for the diffusion of vacancies.

Room temperature annealing in electron irradiated germanium has been investigated by Pepper and Klontz[74] using a variety of samples bombarded with different doses of 4.5 Mev and 2.5 Mev electrons.[74] In general, the conductivity and Hall coefficient change with time in the direction of their original values. By comparing with the measurements made during the progress of the irradiation, the fraction of total effect still remaining in the sample may be estimated as a function of annealing time. It was found that, on this basis, the annealing is very slow for samples which remained n-type after irradiation. On the other hand, n-type samples, converted to p-type by irradiation, revert to n-type rather quickly, but after they are reverted to n-type further change in recovering the original resistivity slows down to a negligible rate. Irradiation increases the conductivity of p-type samples of initially low conductivity; in the anealing of such samples, the conductivity and hole concentration may overshoot to become lower than the original values. These observations show that the annealing process is more complex than a simple reversal of the effect of irradiation. They suggest that some of the energy levels of the defects shift, in the annealing, from the lower half to the upper half of the energy gap;[44a] the process would affect p-type but not n-type samples. Such phenomenon may be the result of rearrangement of the interstitital and vacancies into a more stable configuration.

Room temperature annealing in germanium irradiated by polonium α-particles was observed by Brattain and Pearson[21] and later studied by Becker and Lark-Horovitz.[16] Both found that n-type samples converted to p-type show appreciable annealing. Becker and Lark-Horovitz studied also n-type samples before conversion to p-type and samples that are p-type initially. Similar to the case of electron irradiation, unconverted n-type samples show very little annealing when they are not too close to being intrinsic. Also the relatively fast annealing in converted and originally p-type samples is similar to the case of electron bombardment. However, the originally p-type samples anneal only part of the way instead of restoring or even overshooting the original values of resistivity and Hall coefficient. The difference indicates that part of the defects produced by the α-particles do not undergo the rearrangement as postulated in the previous paragraph.

Annealing in germanium has also been observed at lower temperatures. Samples irradiated by 4.5 Mev electrons at liquid nitrogen temperature begin to reduce the change suffered by the conductivity and Hall coefficient upon warming above 170°K. The annealing has to be separated from the phenomena of nonequilibrium electron distribution which complicates the investigation. N-type samples bombarded by deuterons near liquid nitrogen temperature may recover as much as 20 per cent of the carriers removed by the irradiation by warming to room temperature, if the sample had not been converted to p-type. N-type samples that had been converted to p-type by very large fluxes showed, on the other hand, a striking behavior. Instead of annealing back to n-type, they become more p-type, i.e. the hole concentration is increased upon warming, and after warming to room temperature the Hall coefficient showed small variation with cooling, indicating that the increase is maintained down to the bombardment temperature.[44, 51a] The work of Cleland, Crawford, and Pigg[34] shows that germanium samples exposed to fast neutrons seem to exhibit similar annealing behavior. The fact that unconverted n-type samples recover carriers indicates that acceptor levels are removed; the behavior of converted samples implies that even more donor levels are annealed out.

Summarizing, we may say that annealing in irradiated germanium

involves many different processes, that appreciable annealing takes place
at temperatures at least as low as 170°K, and that there are differences in
annealing between samples irradiated with electrons and heavy particles.
Various conjectures may be made regarding the nature of the annealing
processes but reliable conclusions require further experimentation*.

Indium antimonide irradiated at 90°K by 4.5 Mev electrons seems to
show three stages of annealing below room temperature.[91] The first two
stages of annealing are prominent near the irradiation temperature and
around 160°K, respectively, and the third stage begins in the range between
250°K and 300°K. In n-type samples, each stage restores more of the
carriers removed by the irradiation. In p-type samples, however, the
first two stages of annealing remove carriers as did the irradiation, and
only the last stage has the effect of restoring the carriers. In fact, irradiated
p-type samples may convert temporarily to n-type conduction when they
are warmed to near room temperature, whereas irradiation near 90°K con-
verts n-type samples to p-type. The conversion of p-type samples to n-type,
observed by Cleland and Crawford[93-95] with fast neutron irradiation at
about 25°C, may be caused also by such annealing, although it is possible
that the effect of bombardment by heavy particles is inherently different
from that of electron irradiation, as will be discussed in the following
paragraph. It appears from these observations that the acceptor levels
are annealed out preferentially in the first two stages of annealing.

The work of Gonser and Okkerse[99, 100] has been mentioned already in a
previous section. They irradiated GaSb and InSb with 12 Mev deuterons
at liquid nitrogen temperature, leaving a part of each sample unexposed.
They observed the x-ray reflections from the samples and found three
effects: (a) the intensity of the reflection from the irradiated region is
smaller, (b) the lattice parameter of the irradiated part is of the order of a
tenth of a percent larger, and (c) the lines are curved toward the center of
the irradiated region. The authors attribute these effects to the production
of thermal spikes, i.e., regions where the material melted and resolidified
in the structure of the liquid. By observing the shape and the intensity
of the x-ray lines as the samples were warmed up, they deduced that the
spikes of quasi-liquid configuration transform to the normal solid configuration below room temperature. It is not yet certain how important is
the effect of such spikes on the electrical properties as compared to that
of vacancies and interstitials. In the case of electron irradiation the production of spikes might be expected to be much less prominent than in
deuteron irradiation.

Slow Trapping Effects

By carrier trapping we mean a deviation of electron population of
various levels in the energy gap from the thermodyamical equilibrium. An

increase corresponds to a trapping of extra electrons in the localized states, and a decrease corresponds to hole-trapping. The intense electron excitation which occurs during an irradiation produces excess electrons and holes and may give rise to trapping. Although free electrons and holes recombine usually at a fast rate, the trapping may decay very slowly so that the measured properties of a sample may not correspond to the equilibrium condition for a long time after the irradiation. Sometimes the conductivity and Hall coefficient continue to change slowly many hours after the irradiation has been stopped. The effect complicates the investigation; in particular, it has to be separated from the annealing.

The trapping effect is usually pronounced when the semiconductor reaches a high resistivity in the course of irradiation. Fig. 11 shows the resistivity and Hall coefficient of a silicon sample in the progress of irradiation by 4.5 Mev electrons at 0°C. The irradiation was interrupted at

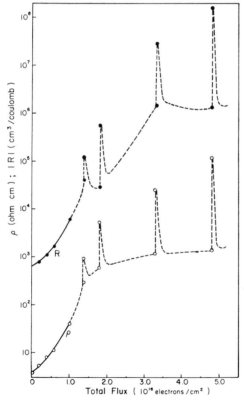

Figure 6.11 Hall coefficient, R, and resistivity, ρ, of an n-type silicon as functions of irradiation by 4.5 Mev electrons at 0°C. The vertical rises show the slow changes with time, which continued for many hours during interruptions of the irradiation. Measurements by D. E. Hill.

several points for long periods of time, during which the resistivity and Hall coefficient kept on increasing. The changes were quite large and might have been attributed to some annealing effect, except for the fact that with the resumption of irradiation the conditions at the beginning of the interruption were restored quickly by a small flux. Such behavior indicates clearly that trapping is taking place during the irradiation.

Similar phenomena have been observed also in irradiations of germanium at low temperatures. Another convincing demonstration of the trapping effect can be obtained from the study of photoconductivity. An n-type sample at 90°K would keep increasing its resistivity for many hours, after an irradiation by 4.5 Mev electrons. If the resistivity is diminished by an intense illumination, it will rise again when the illumination is removed, in the same way as it did after the irradiation. It should be pointed out that the slow effects considered here are different from the trapping discussed in a previous section on photoconductivity. In that case, relatively weak and monochromatic light was used and the observed small increase of conductance decayed in a time of the order of a second.

The slow changes lasting over many hours may be the effect of some surface states rather than the effects of the defects in the bulk material. Some recent observations of photoconductivity in gold-doped germanium, made by Bray et al,* seem to provide an indirect support for this hypothesis. Such material has a high resistivity at liquid nitrogen temperature, and intense illumination may increase the conductance of a sample by several times. In samples with etched surfaces, the high conductance persists for many hours after the light is shut off. However, if a scratch is made on the surface of the sample, then the photoconductivity will decay very fast, thus showing that the slow process is a trapping effect associated with the surface.

Irradiation Effect on Semiconductor Devices

The effect of irradiation on the properties of semiconductors is reflected in the operation characteristics of devices made of these materials. Most devices contain p-n junctions or contact potential barriers, the properties of which will be altered when the carrier concentration of the semiconductor is changed. Thus, a p-n junction barrier can be completely wiped out under prolonged irradiation, when both the originally n- and p-regions approach the carrier concentration corresponding to ζ_F.

Fig. 12 gives the results of Johnson and Lark-Horovitz[108] for an n-type germanium point contact rectifier under neutron irradiation. The forward current, measured with an applied voltage of 3 volts, should be an indica-

* Purdue University Progress Report, P.R.F. 1258, March, 1957.

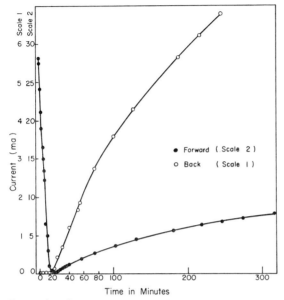

Figure 6.12 Forward and reverse currents of a germanium point contact rectifier as functions of neutron irradiation. After Johnson and K. Lark-Horovitz.

tion of the spreading resistance. The curve is consistent with the change of the conductivity of the bulk material. It drops to a minimum then rises to approach a more steady value; the variation corresponds to the passing of the semiconductor through the intrinsic region to p-type conduction. The current in the back direction is determined by the contact potential barrier. The potential barrier does not hinder the flow of minority carriers, therefore, as electrons are removed and holes are added, the back current rises. The curves show that the rectifier became ohmic after prolonged irradiation. Apparently, there was no more potential barrier when the semiconductor approached the final p-type conduction. When the unit was reassembled with an aluminum point contact, p-type rectification was observed.

Fig. 13 shows the forward and reverse currents of a silicon junction diode as a function of integrated neutron exposure, according to the measurements of Pigg and Robinson.* The currents were measured under an applied voltage of 1 volt so that the forward current should be determined largely by the bulk resistance. Since silicon tends to become intrinsic with irradiation, the minority carrier concentration increases in both the n- and p-regions. Therefore, the reverse current rises with exposure, while

* O.R.N.L. Progress Report ORNL-2188, p. 19, August 30, 1956.

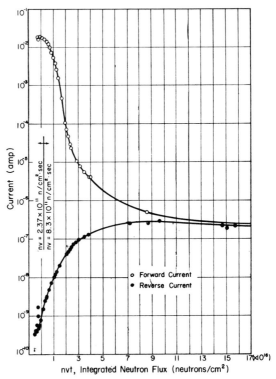

Figure 6.13 Forward and reverse currents at 1 v bias of a silicon junction diode, National Semiconductor Products 1N138A-1, as functions of neutron irradiation. After J. C. Pigg and C. C. Robinson.

the forward current falls with the increase of the bulk resistance. The two currents approach each other as the junction barrier is destroyed.

The characteristics of a potential barrier can be changed before the carrier concentration of the semiconductor has been affected appreciably by the irradiation. The current for a given voltage, in particular the saturation current in the reverse direction, is inversely proportional to the square root of the carrier lifetime. Even a short irradiation may affect the characteristics of a semiconductor device by reducing the carrier lifetime. This effect was utilized by Rappaport and Loferski for the determination of the threshold energy, E_d, as mentioned previously.

Irradiation of semiconducting devices may sometimes improve the electrical characteristics. It has been known for a long time that germanium diodes have a "memory" due to hole injection and hole storage. Lark-Horovitz suggested some years ago that short bursts of irradiation may improve the behavior of the diodes. Recently[106, 109] silicon junction diodes were irradiated with neutrons and a dose of 1×10^{14} to 2×10^{14} neutrons/ cm² reduced hole storage to unmeasurable amounts.

Our discussion has been concerned primarily with the bulk properties of semiconductors. It should be pointed out that any change in surface properties that is produced by the irradiations may be important for the operation of the devices.

General

1. Brinkeman, J. A., On the Nature of Radiation Damage in Metals. *J. Appl. Phys.* **25**, 961 (1954); *Am. J. of Phys.* **24**, 246–67 (1956)

2. Brooks, H., Nuclear Radiation Effects in Solids. *Am. Rev. of Nuclear Science* **6**, 215 (1956)

3. Cottrell, A. H., The Effects of Irradiation on the Physical Properties of Solids. *Brit. J. Appl. Phys.*, Suppl. No. 5, 43–53 (1956)

4. Crawford, J. H. and Cleland, J. W., Radiation Effects in Semiconductors; Progress in Semiconductors. Vol. II, London (1957)

5. Glen, J. W., A Survey of Irradiation Effects in Metals. *Adv. in Physics* **4**, 381 (1955)

6. James, H. M., and Lark-Horovitz, K., Localized Electronic States in Bombarded Semiconductors. *Z. physik. Chem.* **198**, 107–26 (1951); see also AEC Report TID-5011.

7. Kinchin, G. W., and Pease, R. S., The Displacement of Atoms in Solids by Radiation. *Rep. Prog. Phys.* (Inst. of Phys.) **18**, 1–51 (1955)

8. Koch, Lydie., Semiconductors and Nuclear Radiations. *L'Onde Electrique* **35**, 977–80 (Nov. 1955) In French.

9. Koehler, J. S., and Seitz, F., Radiation Disarrangement of Crystals. *Z. Physik* **138**, 238–45 (1954). See also "Defects in Crystalline Solids," Phys. Soc. London (1955), p. 222–31.

10. Lark-Horovitz, K., Nucleon Bombarded Semiconductors in "Semiconducting Materials", Butterworths' Scient. Pub., London (1951) p. 47

11. Seitz, F., and Koehler, J. S., Displacement of Atoms During Irradiation, in "Solid State Physics", Vol. 2, Academic Press, 1956, p. 305–442.

12. Slater, J. C., The Effects of Radiation on Materials. *J. Appl. Phys.* **22**, 237–56 (1951); see also report AEC-500 (1949)

13. Snyder, W. S., and Neufeld, J., Vacancies and Replacements in a Solid Resulting from Heavy Corpuscular Radiation. *BAPS* **1**, 32 (1956)

14. Tucker, C. W., and Senio, P., On the Nature of Thermal Spikes. *J. Appl. Phys.* **27**, 207–9 (1956)

Elements

15. Becker, M., Fan, H. Y., and Lark-Horovitz, K., Infrared Absorption of Nucleon-Bombarded Silicon I. *Phys. Rev.* **85**, 730 (1952)

16. Becker, M. W., and Lark-Horovitz, K., Room-Temperature Polonium Alpha Irradiation of Germanium Single Crystals. *BAPS* **1**, 331 (1956)

16a. Becker, M. W., Room Temperature Polonium—Alpha Irradiation of Thin Germanium Layers. Purdue University Ph. D. Thesis, 1957. Unpublished.

17. Bemski, G., and Augustyniak, W. M., Annealing of Electron Bombardment Damage in Single Silicon Crystals. *BAPS* **1**, 380 (1956)

18. Binnie, W. P., and Liebschutz, A. M., An X-Ray and Electron Diffraction Study

of Radiation Damage in Single Crystals. Atomic Energy Comm. Report AECU-2225 (1952) p. 4–13.

19. Binnie, W. P., and Liebschutz, A. M., An X-Ray and Electron Diffraction Study of Radiation Damage in Single Crystals of Germanium and Silicon. U. S. Report COO-102, 15, (1953)

20. Binnie, W. P., and Liebschutz, A. M., The Elastic Constants of Silicon Before and After Neutron Bombardment from X-Ray Diffuse Scattering. Phys. Rev. 94, 1410 (1954)

21. Brattain, W. H., and Pearson, G. L., Changes in Conductivity of Germanium Produced by Alpha-Particle Bombardment. Phys. Rev. 80, 846 (1950)

22. Brown, W. L., and Fletcher, R. C., Annealing of Bombardment Damage in Germanium: Experimental. Phys. Rev. 91, 237 (1953)

23. Brown, W. L., Fletcher, R. C., and Wright, K. A., Annealing of Bombardment Damage in Germanium: Experimental. Phys. Rev. 92, 591 (1953)

24. Brown, W. L., Fletcher, R. C., and Wright, K. A., Traps Produced by Electron Bombardment of Germanium at Low Temperatures. Phys. Rev. 96, 834 (1954)

25. Brown, W. L., and Augustyniak, W. M., Orientation Dependence and Threshold Energy of Radiation Damage in Germanium. BAPS 1, 156 (1957)

26. Chang, Roger, Etching Behavior of Pile Irradiated Germanium and Silicon Single Crystals. J. Appl. Phys. 28, 385 (1957)

27. Chang, Roger, X-Ray Diffuse Scattering Measurements of Pile-Irradiated Germanium Single Crystals. BAPS 2, 157 (1957)

28. Chipman, D. L., Warren, B. E., and Dienes, G. J., X-Ray Measurements of Radiation Damage in Black Phosphorus. J. Appl. Phys. 24, 1251 (1953). (See also U. S. Report BNL-1479)

29. Cleland, J. W., Crawford, J. H., Jr., and Holmes, D. K., Effects of Gamma Radiation on Germanium. BAPS 1, 135–6 (1956)

30. Cleland, J. W., Crawford, J. H., Jr., and Holmes, D. K., Effects of Gamma Radiation on Germanium. Phys. Rev. 102, 722–24 (May 1, 1956)

31. Cleland, J. W., Crawford, J. H., Jr., Lark-Horovitz, K., Pigg, J. C., and Young, F. W., Jr., The Effect of Fast Neutron Bombardment on the Electrical Properties of Germanium. Phys. Rev. 83, 312 (1951)

32. Cleland, J. W., Crawford, J. H., Jr., Lark-Horovitz, K., Pigg, J. C., and Young, F. W., Jr., Evidence for the Production of Hole Traps in Germanium by Fast Neutron Bombardment. Phys. Rev. 84, 861 (1951)

33. Cleland, J. W., Crawford, J. H., Jr., and Pigg, J. C., Fast-Neutron Bombardment of n-Type Ge. Phys. Rev. 98, 1742–50 (June 15, 1955)

34. Cleland, J. W., Crawford, J. H., Jr., and Pigg, J. C., Fast Neutron Bombardment of p-Type Germanium. Phys. Rev. 99, 1170–81 (Aug. 15, 1955)

35. Cleland, J. W., Crawford, J. H., Jr., Lark-Horovitz, K., and Pigg, J. C., The Effect of Fast Neutron Bombardment on the Conductivity of p-Type Germanium. Phys. Rev. 82, 763 (1951)

36. Crawford, J. H., Jr., Cleland, J. W., Holmes, D. K., and Pigg, J. C., Thermally Unstable Disorder in p-Type Ge Produced by Fast Neutron Bombardment. Phys. Rev. 91, 243 (1953)

37. Crawford, J. H., Jr., Cleland, J. W., Lark-Horovitz, K., Pigg, J. C., and Young, F. W., Jr., Evidence of Hole Traps in Ge Produced by Fast Neutron Bombardment. Phys. Rev. 85, 730 (1952)

38. Crawford, J. H., Jr., and Lark-Horovitz, K., Fast Neutron Bombardment Effects in Germanium. Phys. Rev. 78, 815 (1950)

39. Crawford, J. H., Jr., and Lark-Horovitz, K., Thermal Equilibrium in Neutron Irradiated Semiconductors. *Phys. Rev.* **79**, 889 (1950)

40. Curtis, O. L., Jr., Cleland, J. W., and Pigg, J. C., Effect of Irradiation on the Hole Lifetime of n-Type Ge. *BAPS* **1**, 157 (1957)

41. Cussins, W. D., Effects Produced by the Ionic Bombardment of Germanium. *Proc. Phys. Soc. B.* **68**, 213 (1955)

42. Davis, R. E., Johnson, W. E., Lark-Horovitz, K., and Siegel, S., Neutron-Bombarded Germanium Semiconductors. *Phys. Rev.* **74**, 1255 (1948)

42a. Davis, R. E., Nucleon Bombardment of Semiconductors. Purdue University M. S. Thesis, 1949. Unpublished.

43. Fan, H. Y., Infrared Absorption of Nucleon-Bombarded Silicon II. *Phys. Rev.* **85**, 730 (1952)

44. Fan, H. Y., and Lark-Horovitz, K., Fast Particle Irradiation of Germanium Semiconductors. *Report of the Conference on Defects in Crystalline Solids.* Bristol, 1954 (London: Physical Society) p. 232 (1955)

44a. Fan, H. Y., and Lark-Horovitz, K., Irradiation of Semiconductors, presented at Garmisch International Conference, in print.

45. Fleeman, J., Effect of Neutron Irradiation on the Phase Change in Tin. *Phys. Rev.* **91**, 237 (1953)

46. Fleeman, J., The $\beta \rightarrow \alpha$ Transformation in Tin. *Phys. Rev.* **94**, 1422 (1954)

47. Fleeman, J., and Dienes, G. J., Effect of Reactor Irradiation on the White-to-Grey Tin Transformation. *J. Appl. Phys.* **26**, 652–4 (June, 1955)

48. Fletcher, R. C., and Brown, W. L., Annealing of Bombardment Damage in a Diamond-Type Lattice. *Phys. Rev.* **92**, 585–90 (1953)

49. Fletcher, R. C., Brown, W. L., and Wright, K. A., The Absence of Bombardment Annealing in the Electron Bombardment of Germanium. *Phys. Rev.* **96**, 833 (1954)

50. Forster, J. H., Fan, H. Y., and Lark-Horovitz, K., Conductivity of Deuteron Irradiated Germanium and Silicon. *Phys. Rev.* **86**, 643 (1952)

51. Forster, J. H., Fan, H. Y., and Lark-Horovitz, K., Deuteron Irradiation of Germanium Near Liquid Nitrogen Temperature. *Phys. Rev.* **91**, 229 (1953)

51a. Forster, J. H., Electrical Properties of Nucleon Bombarded Semiconductors, Purdue University, Ph.D. Thesis, 1953. Unpublished.

52. Hill, D. E., Electron Bombardment of Silicon. *BAPS* **1**, 321 (1956)

53. Johnson, W. E., and Lark-Horovitz, K., Neutron Irradiated Semiconductors. *Phys. Rev.* **76**, 442 (1949)

54. Keesom, P. H., Lark-Horovitz, K., and Pearlman, N., The Influence of Neutron Bombardment on the Low Temperature Atomic Heat of Silicon. *Phys. Rev.* **89**, 900 (1952)

55. Keesom, P. H., Lark-Horovitz, K., and Pearlman, N., The Effect of Neutron Bombardment on the Low Temperature Atomic Heat of Silicon. *Science* **116**, 630 (1952)

56. Keesom, P. H., Lark-Horovitz, K., and Pearlman, N., The Influence of Neutron Bombardment on the Low Temperature Atomic Heat of Silicon. *U. S. Report COO-102*, **8** (1953)

57. Kleitman, D., and Longo, T. A., Deuteron Irradiation of Germanium at 90°K. *Phys. Rev.* **100**, 1261 (1955) (A)

57a. Kleitman, D., and Lark-Horovitz, K., N-Type Deuteron Irradiated Germanium—Low Temperature Carrier Removal Rates. *BAPS* **1**, 156 (1957)

58. Klontz, E. E., Production of Lattice Defects in Germanium by Electron Bombardment. *U. S. Report AECU-2267 or AECU-2664.* (1952)

59. Klontz, E. E., Electron Bombardment of Germanium. *U. S. Report COO-102*, 28 (1953)

60. Klontz, E. E., Resistance Changes in Germanium Single Crystals During Electron Bombardment. *U. S. Report COO-104*, 131 (1953)

61. Klontz, E. E., and Lark-Horovitz, K., Electron Bombardment of Ge. *Phys. Rev.* 82, 763 (1951)

62. Klontz, E. E., and Lark-Horovitz, K., Displacements Produced by Electron Bombardment of Germanium. *Phys. Rev.* 86, 643 (1952)

63. Klontz, E. E., Pepper, R. R., and Lark-Horovitz, K., Electrical Properties of Electron Bombarded Ge. *Phys. Rev.* 98, 1535 (1955) (A)

64. Klontz, E. E., and Lark-Horovitz, K., Electron Bombardment of Semiconductors. Atomic Energy Comm. Report AECU-2225 (1952) p. 56–65.

65. Kohn, W., Bombardment Damage of Ge Crystals by Fast Electrons. *Phys. Rev.* 94, 1409 (1954) (A)

66. Kohn, W., Bombardment Damage of Germanium Crystals by Fast Electrons. Report, Sept. 1953. Unpublished.

67. Lark-Horovitz, K., Becker, M., Davis, R. E., and Fan, H. Y., Nucleon Bombarded Silicon. *Phys. Rev.* 78, 334 (1950) (A)

68. Lark-Horovitz, K., Bleuler, E., Davis, R. E., and Tendam, D., Deuteron Bombarded Semiconductors. *Phys. Rev.* 73, 1256 (1948)

69. Loferski, J. J., and Rappaport, P., Electron Voltaic Study of Electron Bombardment Damage and Its Thresholds in Ge and Si. *Phys. Rev.* 98, 1861 (1955)

70. Longo, T. A., and Kleitman, D., Neutron Irradiated Silicon. *Phys. Rev.* 100, 1260 (1955) (A)

70a. Longo, T. A., and Lark-Horovitz, K., Purdue Progress Report, PRF 1046, April 1956; Symposium on Nuclear Irradiation of Semiconductor Devices and Materials, New York City, Feb. 27, 1957; Irradiation of Silicon with 9.6 Mev Deuterons, *BAPS* 1, 157 (1957) (A).

71. MacKay, J. W., and Klontz, E. E., Effects of Multiple Scattering of Electrons on the Production of Defects in Fast Electron Bombardment of Germanium. *BAPS* 1, 156 (1957)

72. McKay, K. G., Electron Hole Production in Germanium by Alpha Particles. *Phys. Rev.* 84, 829–32 (1951)

73. Moyer, W. A., Smith, W. A., Jr., and Cunningham, O. L., Irradiation of Germanium by Fast Monoenergetic Neutrons. *U.S. A.E.C.-KAPL 1455* (May, 1956), p. 33.

74. Pepper, R., Klontz, E. E., Lark-Horovitz, K., and MacKay, J., Hall and Resistivity Measurements During Electron Bombardment of Germanium and Indium-Antimony. *Phys. Rev.* 94, 1410 (1954) (A)

75. Rappaport, P., The Electron-Voltaic Effect in p-n Junctions Induced by Beta-Particle Bombardment. *Phys. Rev.* 93, 246 (1954)

76. Rappaport, P., Minority Carrier Lifetime in Semiconductors as a Sensitive Indicator of Radiation Damage. *Phys. Rev.* 94, 1409 (1954) (A)

77. Rappaport, P., and Loferski, J. J., Threshold for Electron Bombardment-Induced Lattice Displacements in Si and Ge. *Bull. Am. Phys. Soc.* 30, 34 (1955)

78. Schulz-DuBois, E., Nisenoff, M., Fan, H. Y., and Lark-Horovitz, K., Spin Resonance in Neutron Irradiated Silicon. *Phys. Rev.* 98, 1561 (1955) (A)

79. Shulman, R. G., Hole Trapping in Germanium Bombarded by High Energy Electrons. *Phys. Rev.* 102, 1451–5 (1956)

80. Shulman, R. G., Brown, W. L., and Fletcher, R. C., Hole Trapping Due to Lattice Defects in Germanium. *Phys. Rev.* **96**, 833 (1954) (A)

81. Sosin, A., Effect of Electron Irradiation and Quenching on the White-to-Gray Tin Transformation. *BAPS* **1**, 129 (1956). See also Atomic Energy Comm. Report NAA-SR-1550 (1956).

82. Stech, B., Structuraenderungen Kristallen durch Beschuss mit α-Teilchen. *Z. Naturforsch.* **7a**, 175–185 (1952)

83. Stevens, D. K., Magnetic Susceptibility of Annealed and Fast Neutron Bombarded Germanium. *U. S. Report ORNL-1599*, 37 p. (1954)

84. Stevens, D. K., Cleland, J. W., and Crawford, J. H., Jr., Magnetic Susceptibility of Fast Neutron Bombarded Ge. *Phys. Rev.* **94**, 1409 (1954) (A)

85. Stoeckman, F., Klontz, E. E., Fan, H. Y., and Lark-Horovitz, K., Photoconductivity of Electron-Bombarded Ge. *Phys. Rev.* **98**, 1535 (1955) (A)

86. Taylor, W. E., Comparison of Thermally Induced Lattice Defects in Germanium and Silicon with Defects Produced by Nucleon Bombardment. *Phys. Rev.* **86**, 642 (1952) (A)

87. Truell, Rohn, Teutonico, L. J., and Levy, Paul W., Detection of Directional Neutron Damage in Silicon by Means of Ultrasonic Double Refraction Measurements. *Phys. Rev.* **105**, 1723 (1957)

88. Waite, T. R., Theory of Diffusion Limited Reactions; Annealing of Radiation Damage in Germanium. *BAPS* **1**, 156 (1957)

89. Weissman, S., and Chang, R., X-Ray Diffraction Studies of Radiation Damage of Germanium Single Crystals. *Phys. Rev.* **99**, 657 (1955) (A)

90. Wertheim, G. K., Energy Levels in Electron-Bombarded Silicon. *Phys. Rev.* **105**, 1730 (1957)

Compounds

91. Aukerman, L. W., and Lark-Horovitz, K., Electron Bombardment of Indium Antimonide. *BAPS* **1**, 332 (1956)

92. Broser, I., and Warminsky, R., Modifications Produced by α-Particle Irradiations in CdS Crystals. *Z. Naturforsch.* **6a**, 85–102 (1951) (in German)

93. Cleland, J. W., and Crawford, J. H., Jr., Radiation Effects in Indium Antimonide. *Phys. Rev.* **93**, 894 (1954)

94. Cleland, J. W., and Crawford, J. H., Jr., Radiation Effects in Indium Antimonide. *Phys. Rev.* **94**, 1410 (1954)

95. Cleland, J. W., and Crawford, J. H., Jr., Neutron Irradiation of Indium Antimonide. *Phys. Rev.* **95**, 1177 (1954)

96. Cleland, J. W., and Crawford, J. H., Jr., Fast-Neutron Bombardment of GaSb. *Phys. Rev.* **100**, 1614–18 (Dec. 19, 1955)

97. Cleland, J. W., and Crawford, J. H., Jr., Radiation Effects in Gallium Antimonide. *Phys. Rev.* **99**, 637 (1955)

98. Crawford, J. H., and Wittels, M. C., Peaceful Uses of Atomic Energy. VII p. 660, Fig. 9 (1956). A review of investigation of radiation effects in covalent and ionic crystals.

99. Gonser, U., Structure Spikes in Deuteron-Irradiated III–V Compounds. *BAPS* **1**, 157 (1957)

100. Gonser, U., and Okkerse, B., Radiation Damage Experiments in III–V Compounds, *Phys. Rev.* **105**, 757–9 (1957)

101. Gremmelmaier, R., and Welker, H., The Effect of Neutrons on an Indium Phosphide p-n Junction. *Z. Naturforsch.* **11a**, 420 (1956)

102. Odencrantz, F. K., Alpha-Particle Bombardment of PbS Semiconductors. *Phys. Rev.* **88,** 166 (1952) (A)

103. Pigg, J. C., Cleland, J. W., Crawford, J. H., Jr., and Lark-Horovitz, K. Pile Irradiation of Semiconducting Cu_2O. *Phys. Rev.* **82,** 763 (1951) (A)

104. Pickard, D. F., The Effect of Gamma Radiation Upon Lead Sulfide Coated Glass Fire Detection Cells (Fireye). Quarterly Report for Period Feb. 10–May 10, 1952. *U.S.A.E.C.–CF-52-5-211*, May 28, 1952 (Decl. Nov. 28, 1955), 23 p.

Devices

105. Braunstein, R., Radiative Recombination in Semiconductors as an Indicator of Radiation Damage. *BAPS* **1,** 157 (1957)

106. Florida, C. D., Holt, F. R., and Stephen, J. H., Irradiation of Transistors. *Nature (London)* **173,** 397 (1954)

107. Fonger, W. H., Loferski, J. J., and Rappaport, P., Electron Bombardment Induced Noise in p-n Junctions. *BAPS* **1,** 135 (1956)

108. Johnson, W. E., and Lark-Horovitz, K., Neutron Irradiated Semiconductors. *Phys. Rev.* **76,** 442–43 (1949)

109. Gorton, R., Effects of Irradiation upon Diodes of the Silicon Junction Type. *Nature* **179,** 864 (April 27, 1957)

110. Mayer, J., and Gossick, B. R., Use of Au-Ge Broad Area Barrier as Alpha Particle Spectrometer. Purdue Signal Corps Progress Report, **7,** p. 9 (Mar. 1956)

111. Moyer, J. W., Electron Irradiation of Silicon p-n Junctions. *Atomic Energy Comm. Report KAPL-1146* (1954)

112. Miller, W., Bewig, K., and Salzberg, B., Note on the Reduction of Carrier Lifetime in p-n Junction Diodes by Electron Bombardment. *J. Appl. Phys.* **27,** 1524 (Dec. 1956)

113. Oak Ridge National Laboratory *Quarterly Progress Report—Physics Division.* Atomic Energy Comm. Report ORNL-865 (1951) p. 87—Semiconductor bombardment research; p. 98—Bonded wire resistance strain gages; p. 77—Phase transition on neutron bombardment; p. 106—Effect of pile irradiation on performance of electrical leads.

114. Orman, C., Fan, H. Y., Goldsmith, G. J., and Lark-Horovitz, K., Germanium p-n Barriers as Counters. *Phys. Rev.* **78,** 646 (1950)

115. Pasynkov, V. V., The Action of Radiation from Radioactive Substances on a (Se) Photocell. *Zhur. Tekh. Fiz.* **25,** 1376–85 (1955) (in Russian)

116. Pfister, H., Elektronenbestrahlung von p-n Sperrschichten in GaAs. *Z. Naturforschung.* Band 12a. Heft 3. (Mar. 1957) p. 217

117. Wright Air Development Center, Materials Lab., Wright Patterson AFB, Ohio. Young, Robert C. Gamma Irradiation of Crystal Diodes. WCRT-TN-54-255. Dec. 1954.

118. Wright Air Development Center, Electronic Components Lab. Wright-Patterson AFB, Ohio. Panos, R. J. Gamma Irradiation of Germanium Transitors. WADC-TN-55-639. Dec. 1955.

119. Wright Air Development Center, Electronic Components Lab., Wright-Patterson AFB, Ohio. Panos, R. J. Gamma Irradiation of Germanium and Silicon Transistors. WADC-TN-56-115. March 5, 1956.

Chapter 7

EFFECTS OF RADIATION ON THE CORE COMPONENTS OF NUCLEAR REACTORS

C. E. WEBER

General Electric Company
*Knolls Atomic Power Laboratory**
Schenectady, New York

This paper will consider the behavior of engineering components in a reactor core under radiation. The nuclear reactor core components will be considered from a metallurgical design point of view where during design of new or improved components compromises must be made among many factors which may limit their performance. Obviously other disciplines besides metallurgy, such as solid state physics, nuclear physics, and mechanical engineering play a major and interwoven role. In a heterogeneous reactor, in which the fuel is distributed in a fairly definite geometrical pattern or lattice within the mass of the moderator, core components of common interest are:

1. Fuel elements.
2. Poison control elements.
3. Structural members.
4. Coolant
5. Moderators

This paper will deal primarily with poison control elements, fuel elements, and the structural components,† and will be discussed without reference to a particular reactor design. It is pertinent to point out that most fundamental investigations on radiation effects related to development of these components are aimed at studying the material itself rather than the engineering component under design, the latter must be built and perform

* The Knolls Atomic Power Laboratory is operated for the United States Atomic Energy Commission by the General Electric Company under Contract No. W-31-109 Eng-52.
† Ed. note: See paper by Hennig for discussion of moderators.

satisfactorily as a reactor component. For example, a fissionable material must only be able to withstand certain types of damage; namely, that due to the dynamic and static effects of the fission products.[1] If a relatively thin fuel specimen were tested under conditions of no externally imposed stresses with negligible thermal stresses present, its stability (to fracture, for example) would depend on the intrinsic ability of the lattice to contain the fission products. However, if this material is incorporated into an engineering component, namely a fuel element, the latter must withstand internally imposed thermal stresses, externally imposed vibration and pressure stresses, in addition to other stresses which may arise from differential expansion of the cladding and the core materials. A stable fuel material may turn out to be highly unstable when used in a fuel element. However, even though many of the observed radiation effects with nuclear components are perhaps exotic as viewed from a conventional engineering point of view, it is believed that sufficient tools and information are available to begin to rationalize these observations and to make them more useful for practical engineering design. Therefore, this paper will not attempt to completely review the radiation stability of nuclear components, but will stress certain concepts and interesting observations which should be of value to personnel working in this field.

Types of Core Components

Due to their wide difference in behavior, core components can be grouped into two broad classes—fissionable and non-fissionable. Unfortunately, from a design point of view, B^{10} which is of considerable interest for applications as a neutron absorber material in either burnable poison control elements or non-burnout control rods, is fissionable. On absorbing a neutron, B^{10} splits into He^4 and Li^7 and, to a first approximation, the effect of these elements on parent metal alloys or compounds is identical to the effect of fission products from uranium. The similarity between boron and uranium will be demonstrated in subsequent sections.

Performance of Nuclear Components

Before analyzing factors affecting stability of nuclear components and effects of radiation on their properties, examples of types of damage observed with test components will be presented to provide a framework for such discussions. However, it should be pointed out that the more interesting or dramatic cases have been chosen and that these examples are not fully representative.

The first example is taken from work by Anderson and co-workers[2] and concerns a Zircaloy clad core alloy of zirconium containing 0.21 wt per cent B. The B^{10} concentration in the core alloy was 1.75 atom per cent.

Figure 7.1

This sample was irradiated to about 90 atom per cent burnup* (fission) of the B^{10}, which is equal to 1.6 atom per cent burnup of the core alloy atoms. On irradiation the core alloy was markedly embrittled by the fission products, the core alloy swelled due to the increase in volume produced by the fission products, and longitudinal cracks developed in the cladding which extended radially into the core alloy. A typical crack is shown in Figure 7.1, with a transverse cross section shown in Figure 7.2. A transverse cross section shown in Figure 7.3, illustrates the extensive splitting of a zirconium clad, 10 atom per cent uranium-zirconium alloy irradiated to 1.2 atom per cent burnup. Radial type splits are again shown (figure 7.4) in unclad zirconium base alloys containing 20 atom per cent uranium and irradiated to 3 per cent burnup of the total core atoms. On the other hand, samples have gone to even higher burnup, where samples of the same material irradiated to 4.5 atom per cent burnup did not split.[3] In the case of the zirconium clad sample, the element was irradiated to an alloy atom

* With fissionable materials, the unit of exposure which may result in damage is the per cent of the core alloy atoms fissioned. Burnup has been defined as the number of fissionable atoms fissioned divided by the sum of the original number of fissionable and non-fissionable atoms present in the core alloy times 100. For example, in a uranium-zirconium alloy, the damage introduced into the core alloy is a direct function of the number of impurity atoms introduced through fission of the uranium. The impurity atom concentration in the resultant alloy is approximately twice the burnup figure. The massive burnup of fuel on a reactor level is expressed in terms of megawatt-days of exposure in the reactor per ton of fuel (MWD/T). Exposure data reported as "nvt" cannot be related to a fraction of atoms fissioned without knowledge of the neutron spectrum and appropriate cross section for fission which was used in conducting the particular test reported as an "nvt" dosage.

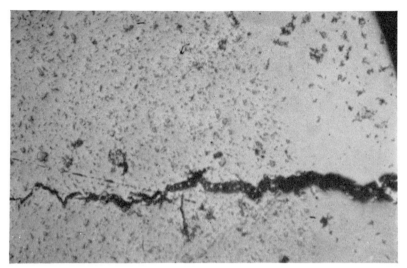

Figure 7.2. Transverse cross section of irradiated 0.21 Wt. % B^{10}-Zr Alloy showing typical crack extending towards the alloy center.

burnup of 1.2 per cent, which resulted in swelling, embrittlement of the core alloy, and gross longitudinal splitting of the element with the cracks extending to the center of the specimen.

As pointed out by Weber and Hirsch,[4] dispersion of the fissionable phase throughout a ductile matrix may reduce fission product damage. The behavior of such a system is shown in Figure 7.5 as reported by Anderson.[5] The titanium matrix contains 1.2 wt per cent B^{10} or 5.2 atom per cent, irradiated to about 40 atom per cent burnup of the B^{10}. Whereas these samples were smooth originally, it can be seen that wherever a boron particle was near the surface, local bumping occurred due to swelling of the boron. As predicted by Weber and Hirsch,[4] the material was reasonably

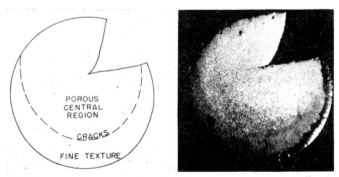

Figure 7.3 Transverse cross section of a zirconium clad, $10^{a}/_{o}$ U-Zr alloy irradiated to $1.2^{a}/_{o}$ burnup.

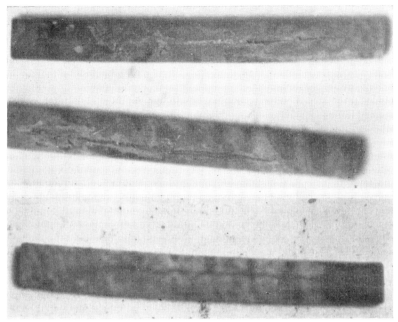

Figure 7.4 Longitudinal cracks in unclad 20 atom % uranium-zirconium alloys irradiated to 3% Total core atom burnup
Maximum Fuel Temperature—605°C
Volume Increase of Samples −24%

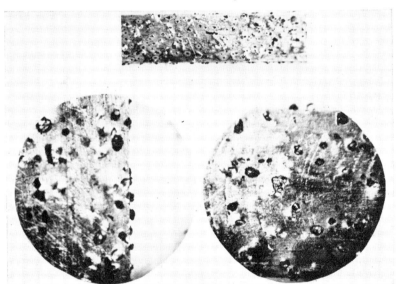

Figure 7.5a (above) Irradiated section of blend sample—typical of all samples.
Figure 7.5b (lower) Dispersion of a fissionable phase in a ductile matrix.

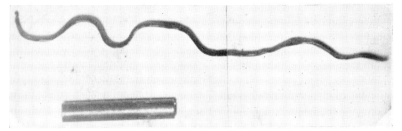

Figure 7.6 Irradiated Uranium Pseudo Single Crystal

ductile after irradiation, as shown by simple beam loaded bend tests. In contrast, a similar composition made up as an alloy showed extreme embrittlement.

No set of examples would be complete without an example of the anisotropic growth of uranium under irradiation as shown in Figure 7.6, from work carried out by Cadwell and co-workers.[6] The anisotropic growth (without a change in density) of α-uranium with the crystalline grains highly oriented in a preferred direction is well-known, with fine-grained randomly oriented uranium being the most dimensional stable, as reported by Paine and Kittel.[7] Since uranium is relatively soft at higher temperatures, restraint of the anisotropic growth through use of a higher strength cladding should be possible, as has been the case.

Two non-fissionable control rod materials of general interest are hafnium and europium oxide dispersed in a stainless steel matrix. Components fabricated from these materials should be much more resistant to radiation damage than boron-containing materials.[5] No data are available on the effect of radiation on the mechanical properties of hafnium. By analogy, radiation damage should be similar to that observed in zirconium and in general similar to non-fissionable metals as a class.

With respect to rare earth oxide dispersions in steel, Anderson and co-workers[8] have shown that irradiation of stainless steel containing Gd_2O_3 increases the yield strength without much change in ductility as indicated by load-deflection measurements.

Engineering Design

To examine and analyze the behavior of core components for a selected reactor design, the various phenomena and the demands being made on these components must be cataloged and related to known or predicted properties of the materials. The complexity of the situation that may exist in these components has been pointed out by Howe,[9] in which he described the anatomy of a fuel element as shown in Figure 7.7. While this particular analysis covers a fuel element, the general approach is applicable to other fissionable and non-fissionable core components. This analysis was further extended by Weber,[1] with emphasis on the large number of interdependent variables. The key points to note are that in a fissionable material the fission event displaces lattice atoms in the core of the component, after which the fission product atoms come to rest in the core matrix material. While the role of impurity atoms in materials suitable for reactor applications can be neglected, fission product atoms are effective to a much greater magnitude. The great number produced and the size and nature of the fission atoms are such as to render them normally insoluble in the base fuel matrix. Effects of residual strain can be noted, and these predominate even after all other types of defects have been annealed out. Fission product diffusion at operating temperatures will cause agglomeration of the fission gases and bring about excessive swelling; this will be discussed in a later section.

Since heat is generated internally in core components either through fission heating or gamma heating, a temperature gradient will exist, creating thermal stresses. Additional stress, or more correctly strain, in the core and cladding materials is the result of gradual accumulation of the fission product atoms in the core material and the resultant core volume increase. In addition, should the gas atoms diffuse and agglomerate, a much larger and potentially catastrophic swelling would occur. Over and beyond these internally imposed stresses are all of the stresses which may be imposed by the reactor designer in cooling the element. For example, a num-

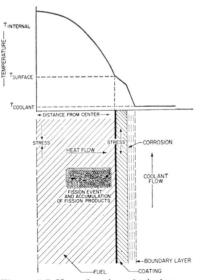

Figure 7.7 Heat flow in a fuel element

ber of elements may be assembled into a subassembly and differential thermal expansion may impose a mechanical stress on the individual elements, varying in magnitude from element to element. Slight vibration excited by the coolant flow may occur, or the pressure of the coolant may stress the elements. Finally, under a given design condition resistance to mechanical shock may become an additional design parameter.

The fissionable elements represent the worst cases while the non-fissionable structural materials and poison control materials undergo much less damage. In the case of coolants such as liquid metals, no damage occurs from neutron and gamma ray absorption. Gamma rays cause little or essentially no damage to metallic materials, while neutrons displace lattice atoms and cause effects analogous to work hardening or precipitation hardening. In general, neutron damage may cause an increase in hardness and yield strength, lower ductility, and a shift of brittle-ductile transition temperatures to higher temperatures. Fortunately, from a reactor design point of view, most power reactors are operated at temperatures where most of the damage in non-fissionable metals anneals out at the operating temperature. Perhaps one of the most important consequences of radiation damage may be the shift of ductile-brittle transition temperature with continued neutron bombardment. For example, Bruch[10] and Makin[11] have shown that the ductile-brittle transition temperature of molybdenum is increased above room temperature upon exposure to fast neutrons. Carbon steel is also embrittled in a similar manner exhibiting a significant reduction in notch-impact strength and severe loss in ductility. By comparison, stainless steels show only minor loss in ductility and a noticeable increase in yield strength.

Referring again to resistance of materials to both internally and externally imposed stresses and the resultant strains, the effect of irradiation on the mechanical properties is a very important variable. The mechanical properties of the more conventional structural materials are relatively well-known. For the fissionable materials, both boron and uranium-containing alloys, which are more drastically affected by irradiation, less data have been reported; therefore, the status of the mechanical properties of these materials after irradiation will be reviewed. Excellent data on the postirradiation mechanical properties of uranium have been reported by Hueschen,[12] and additional data have been summarized by Pugh[13] which includes the data reported by Konobeevsky.[14] The post-irradiation and stress-strain curve of irradiated uranium taken from Hueschen[12] is shown in Figure 7.8. Uranium is extremely brittle and post-irradiation annealing recovery is negligible. Anderson and Dunning[15] have carried out post-irradiation measurements on the ductility of boron alloys and dispersions of boron in ductile metal systems. These data are reported since they are

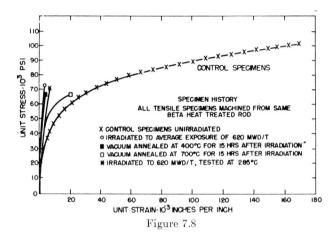

Figure 7.8

of direct interest to the design engineer as control rod materials, analogous to uranium systems, and demonstrate the mechanical advantages of dispersion systems. Due to complexities in post-irradiation measurements, tensile tests were not run, but simple bend tests were carried out to provide information on relative ductility before and after irradiation. Figures 7.9A and 7.9B show the load deflection curves for titanium-boron[10] and zirconium-boron[10] alloys showing marked embrittlement. In contrast, data on the pre- and post-irradiation bend ductility of a 1 wt per cent boron[10]-titanium dispersion alloy are shown in Figure 7.10. This element consisted of a dispersion of boron[10] particles in a titanium matrix. The

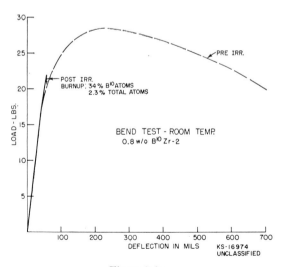

Figure 7.9a

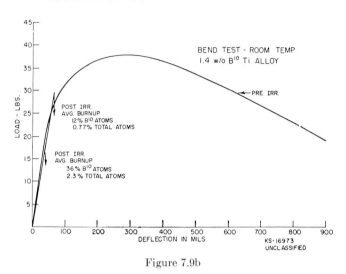

Figure 7.9b

extreme embrittlement of the alloys and the ductility of the dispersed systems is in agreement with the predictions of Weber and Hirsch.[4] Similar improvements in post-irradiation ductility have been observed in UO_2 dispersion fuel elements with steel as the ductile matrix. The data of Konobeevsky and co-workers[14] on the microhardness and impact strength of irradiated uranium are presented in Table 1.

Data on the thermal conductivity of fuel alloys, in particular, and also of structural and poison alloys are important for the calculation of tem-

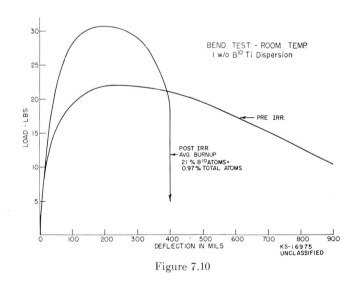

Figure 7.10

TABLE 1. EFFECT OF IRRADIATION ON THE MECHANICAL PROPERTIES OF URANIUM

Metal Condition	Micro Hardness kg/mm²		Ultimate Tensile Strength kg/mm²		Impact Strength kg/cm²	
	Before	After	Before	After	Before	After
Cast (with increased carbon content)	327	416	55	21	2.1	0.6
Cast	333	413	45.2	13.4	2.92	0.76
Heat Treated	368	440	55.3	28.4	2.2	0.71
Hot Rolled	351	417	41.1	27	3.7	0.94

Note: Zero elongation after irradiation for all samples.

peratures and thermal stresses. Little data are available on the post-irradiation thermal conductivity, and even on the post-irradiation electrical conductivity of irradiated alloys. Some effects of radiation upon the resistivity of a uranium alloy are shown in Table 2.[14] If natural uranium was used for the irradiation, the burnup of this material would have been at least 0.01 per cent of all the uranium core alloy atoms. The maximum change in specific electrical resistivity is about 28 per cent and it might be expected that the change in thermal resistivity should be proportional to the change in electrical resistivity. Billington[16] reports that Woods and Jones found a 10 to 15 per cent decrease in thermal conductivity of uranium irradiated in a reactor; the exact burnup is not stated. Johnston[17] measured the change in electrical resistivity of a 0.21 wt per cent B[10]-zirconium alloy and found an average increase in resistivity of about 18

TABLE 2. PROPERTIES AND MICROSTRUCTURE OF A URANIUM ALLOY BEFORE AND AFTER IRRADIATION

No.	Heat Treatment	Specific Gravity		Specific Electrical Resistivity (ohm mm m⁻¹)		Thermal Coefficient of Electrical Resistivity × 10³		Microstructure	
		Before	After	Before	After	Before	After	Before	After
1	Quenching (homogeneous state)	17.26	17.23	0.686	0.682	0.01	0.01	homogeneous	homogeneous
2	Quenching, annealing at 500° for 100 hrs (heterogeneous state)	17.35	17.20	0.531	0.682	1.5	0.01	heterogeneous	homogeneous
3	The same as in 2 (Foil)	—	—	0.523	0.603	1.14	0.39	—	—

per cent. The burnup was 60 per cent of the boron[10], which corresponds to 1 atom per cent burnup of the total core atoms. Higher boron[10] samples (0.78 wt % B[10]) were irradiated to an average burnup of about 2.6 atom per cent, with an observed resistivity increase of approximately 50 per cent. Changes of this magnitude in fuel and poison materials can be important to the designer and more data are definitely required.

The mechanical properties of irradiated uranium, indicate that marked embrittlement and loss of ductility occur as a result of irradiation. The question may be asked, "Are the observed post-irradiation properties the same as the properties during irradiation?" Recent work indicates that this is not the case for uranium and may not be the case for other fissionable materials. Cottrell and co-workers[18] have recently reported results of creep tests on uranium wires (loaded as a spring under a dead weight) which revealed a marked irradiation effect. During irradiation, the uranium deformed under very small loads (1000 to 2000 psi); however the deformation stopped when the irradiation field was removed. In the absence of radiation, at the same temperature, no deformation occurred. This marked acceleration under irradiation was attributed to internal stresses arising from the anisotropic nature of the uranium metal. They surmised that each individual grain deforms anisotropically, thus setting up a state of internal stress. No macroscopic deformation occurs in randomly oriented material, but superposition of a small directional external load then results in creep elongation.

Isotropic material, which does not exhibit the anisotropic growth observed in uranium has not been studied, but even in an isotropic material a constantly increasing strain is imposed in each grain due to accumulation of fission products. Such material may exhibit similar increased creep behavior as uranium depending on the relative effectiveness of the two mechanisms.

The results of Cottrell's work throw serious doubt as to the wise applicability of post-irradiation measurements with respect to their providing a design basis for the behavior of fissionable components during irradiation. New data are required to provide such a basis.

Engineering Performance as Related to Materials Behavior upon Irradiation

To interpret the engineering behavior of nuclear reactor components, one must consider the intrinsic effects of radiation on the core materials, per se. In particular, the fundamental knowledge gained in this field must be related to engineering practice. It is convenient to consider damage to core materials in terms of dynamic and static effects. Dynamic effects result from the heating or displacement of atoms which occur when fast neutrons or fast fission products pass through a lattice. Static effects arise from the introduction of foreign atoms into the lattice either by fission products coming into thermal equilibrium or tranmutation by neutron capture introducing dissimilar metallurgical species. The latter effect is generally small but can lead to measurable effects on extended exposure of non-fissionable materials.

*Dynamic Effects**

Bombardment of metals by fast neutrons and fast fission products will displace the lattice atoms by so-called "bumping collisions". Most of the displaced atoms and vacancies diffuse and recombine at the normal operating temperatures of power reactors. This is true for either neutron bombardment or fission product bombardment. This displacement event can be considered analogous to heating the material locally for a short period of time. The affected region has been termed a "thermal spike". In a more refined analysis, Brinkman[19] has broken this region into a "thermal spike" and a "displacement spike". The volume of material affected is small and the decay of heat to the surrounding atoms is very rapid. The distribution of "temperature" as a function of time is shown in Figure 7.11. Choosing a temperature of 1000°C, a zone about 40 Å in radius is heated to at least this temperature for 10^{-10} sec. which is long compared to the rate of vibration of the lattice atoms.

In general, the dynamic effects of fast particle bombardment are slight. The increase in diffusion is negligible. Creep rates of non-fissionable metals are essentially unchanged by bombardment. The exception to this generalization is the recrystallization of uranium alloys reported by Konobeevsky[14] and confirmed and extended by Bleiberg, Jones, and Lustman.[20] It was observed that upon irradiation of two phase alloys at a low sample temperature, the amount of the metastable high temperature phase present increased while the low temperature phase, thermodynamically stable at the average sample temperature, decreased. This apparent reversal of thermodynamics was explained as being due to the displacement spike causing a local heating of the material to a temperature at which the high temperature phase was stable, with recrystallization occurring on cooling. Since the "molten zone" cools from the outside, nucleation would occur on the cooler outer walls, and with only one phase present the materials should recrystallize without transformation. This has been observed by Tucker[21] in low chromium alloys of uranium for the retained beta phase and the transformed alpha phase, the former being metastable at the irradiation temperature. This behavior of both single phase and hetero-

* Ed. note: For a more detailed discussion see paper by G. J. Dienes.

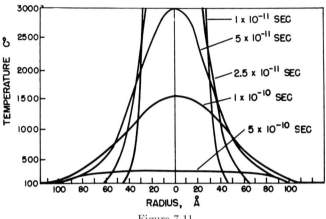

Figure 7.11

geneous alloys lends support to the hypothesis that the dynamic effect of the recoiling fission products is analogous to local heating. Such phenomena should be considered in engineering design since the properties of fuel systems such as density, thermal conductivity, and coefficient of expansion can be significantly different for two different crystalline phases of a metal system.

Other phenomena which appear to be singularly related to bombardment are accelerated creep in uranium, mentioned previously and the anisotropic linear growth of uranium.

Static Effects

The accumulation of the fission products from both boron and uranium account for the major extent of radiation damage in core materials. The reason for this is apparent upon consideration of the metallurgical nature of the fission products and their alloying effects, as their concentration increases during reactor operation. A simple grouping of the fission products of uranium by type and size is shown in Table 3.

(a) *Embrittlement.* The first major static effect is the general embrittlement of the metallic alloys by the fission products created "in situ". These atoms are very effective hardening agents, causing marked embrittlement

TABLE 3. COMPOSITION AND RELATIVE SIZE OF FISSION PRODUCTS

Type of Element	Metallic	Rare Earths	Alkali and Alkaline Earths	Rare Gases
Per Cent Total	∼36	∼31	∼17	∼12
Size Relative to Uranium	Equal	Large	Very Large	Very Large

at very low concentrations (<0.1%) and at high concentrations producing overall strain hardening regardless of any creep relaxation of the type observed by Cottrell.[18] Annealing studies have confirmed predictions of the permanent nature of the damage and indicate that the "dynamic" damage is small compared to the "static" effects. It should be noted that these generalizations are not necessarily valid for fissionable compounds such as B_4C or UO_2.

(b) *Swelling.* A second major effect to consider in design is the swelling of the core alloy which results primarily from the increase in number of atoms present in the core as a result of fission and secondarily from the "average" larger size of each fission product relative to the parent atom, as first pointed out by Howe and Weber.[22]

This swelling has been expressed as R, the unit increase in volume per unit amount of the total core alloy atoms fissioned (commonly the per cent increase in volume for one per cent of the alloy atoms fissioned). A volume increase of about 3 fold was predicted on the basis that the atomic volumes of the element in the pure state are additive in the composite alloy. This has been confirmed experimentally by Paine and Kittel,[7] and for zirconium-rich systems by experimenters at the Knolls Atomic Power Laboratory.[23] Data on uranium-zirconium alloys are shown in Figure 7.12. and similar data for zirconium and titanium-rich alloys containing boron in Figure 7.13. While considerable experimental scatter exist in the data; this growth appears to be linear with concentration. From a component point of view, with increasing concentration of fission products, the core

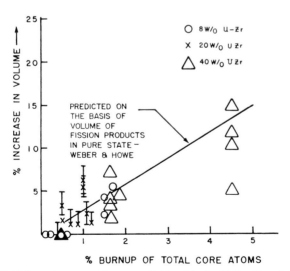

Figure 7.12 Volume increase—burnup relationship for U-Zr alloys below 600° C

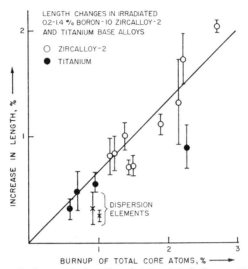

Figure 7.13 Length changes in irradiated 0.2 —1.4ʷ/ₒ Boron-10 Zircalloy—2 and titanium base alloys.

swelling can result in excessive strain of cladding materials, possibly interfere with coolant flow, cause mechanical deformation of the core structures,
or produce other effects depending on the component design, unless such
swelling has been taken into consideration in the design of the component.

Fission Product Diffusion and Gas Agglomeration. Swelling due to the
accumulation of fission products in a lattice should be essentially independent of sample temperature over a range in which the impurity atoms are
"immobile" and agglomeration of clumps of fission products through diffusion does not occur. In the writer's opinion, this appears to be the case
for isotropic materials such as zirconium-base alloys.

At higher temperatures the increase in volume should be very temperature sensitive due to extensive diffusion of the impurity atoms and agglomeration of clumps of such atoms throughout the fissionable material.
The fission product atoms may concentrate at impurities or grain boundaries with the non-gaseous atoms weakening the material and the gaseous
atoms causing accelerated swelling from internal gas pockets in the core
material. LeClaire and Rowe[24] first established experimentally that the
normally insoluble fission gases diffuse in a normal manner when produced
in situ in a metal lattice with activation energies of the order of those for
self-diffusion. As the gas atoms agglomerate, small internal gas bubbles
will form, and if the material can yield plastically creep will occur at a rate
dependent on the strength of the material and the rate of change of internal pressure. As reported by Pugh,[13] Lomer and Foreman found the expan-

sion of uranium at high temperatures to be consistent with the creep strength of uranium. At lower temperatures, below about 400°C, the expansion is significantly less.

Similar results have been observed for other systems and a crude rule of thumb is that the temperature at which agglomeration of rare gas atoms becomes rapid is about 50 per cent of the absolute melting point of the system. From a design point of view, operation in this high temperature zone can be catastrophic since expansion rates of 30–50 per cent increase in volume per unit per cent alloy atom burnup have been observed. Work on zirconium base alloys performed at KAPL,[3] has shown the same behavior plus an even greater rate of expansion when the material was thermally cycled above 600°C, which is the region where the relative amounts of the phases present is temperature dependent.

A series of tests have been carried out on zirconium base alloys, containing 18–22 wt per cent uranium, in which the samples were irradiated to a burnup ranging from about 0.5 to 2.0 atom per cent. Some samples were held at constant temperature, while others were cycled in and out of the neutron flux, causing a cyclic temperature change in the samples. Below approximately 600°C, the material behaved normally, i.e., the amount of swelling was consistent with the increase predicted due to accumulation of fission products in the lattice. At temperatures close to the transformation temperature, a five to tenfold increase in swelling was observed due to the normal gas agglomeration and formation of micro-porosity in the metal. Cycling of specimens in and out of the range of phase transformation produced even greater swelling rates. A five to tenfold increase over the high temperature non-cycled rate was observed, with the formation of macro-porosity and in some cases split type failure as previously shown in Figure 2. A cross section of the porous central region is shown in Figure 7.14. The relative swelling for three cases (irradiated in the MTR) is shown

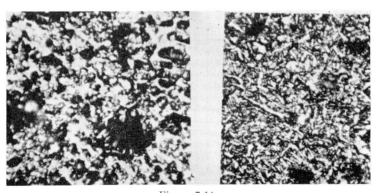

Figure 7.14

graphically in Figure 7.15. The lower curve represents normal swelling; the middle curve, swelling due to gas agglomeration at a high temperature; and the upper curve indicates accelerated agglomeration due to thermal cycling. This acceleration effect is similar to the observations of Reynolds et al,[25] who reported that the rate of release of fission gas activity from uranium was accelerated by cycling across the α-β and the β-γ phase transformations. One possible explanation for the effect is that the fission gas atoms tend to follow grain boundaries. Johnston[26] has studied swelling of uranium-zirconium alloys by post irradiation annealing and has confirmed that gas agglomeration starts at about 600°C, the magnitude being a function of time and concentration as expected from both diffusion and creep phenomena. In this case, post-irradiation testing appears to be an acceptable "stand-in" for in-pile testing.

Other classes of materials of potential interest, either as "fissile" phases in dispersion type elements or as core materials in container type elements, are the high melting intermetallic and ceramic compounds, such as UAl_4, UO_2, or B_4C. Uranium dioxide, for example, has a much higher melting point than most metallic fuel materials. Thus, for the same operating temperature, e.g. 400°C, the fission products which are formed should be much less mobile in UO_2 than in uranium alloys. In addition, the static effects of impurity atoms may be much different in UO_2 as compared to uranium.

Figure 7.16 shows a cross section of powdered UO_2 before irradiation, while Figure 7.17 shows similar material after irradiation to a high burnup of the uranium. In general, it appears that considerable sintering takes place which may be due to formation of mixed fission product oxides. In

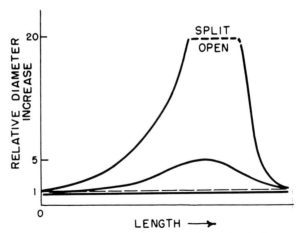

Figure 7.15 Effects of irradiation on dimensional changes

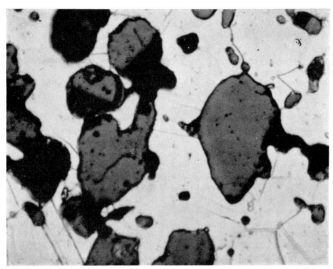

Figure 7.16 Transverse—1000×

the fission process of uranium in a lattice of uranium oxide, the fission product atoms should be at least partially oxidized since oxygen should diffuse readily at the operating temperatures of power reactors. As the concentration of impurity atoms increases, oxidation may tend to promote sintering material together. An interesting hypothesis is that the mixtures of oxides may be more compatible from the molecular point of view, being

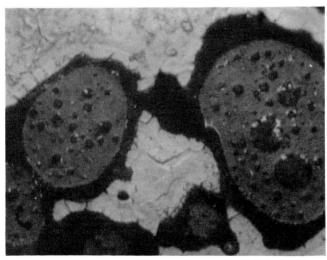

Figure 7.17 Powdered UO_2 irradiated to a high burnup

analogous in a general broad sense to minerals, than would the mixtures of metal atoms in a metal lattice.

Designing for Minimum Damage in Nuclear Components

The first cardinal rule is not to use fissionable materials as structural materials and to use non-boron-containing control materials. In considering non-fuel bearing structural materials, attention also should be given to possible shifts in the "brittle-ductile" transition temperature, which may induce brittleness at normal reactor operating temperatures. With fissile materials, three general techniques have been described by Weber:[1] Dilution, dispersion, and the use of container type elements. In the latter (in contrast to the dilution type element) the fissile material is placed in a container which itself is not damaged by the fission process in the fuel. The fuel is not bonded to the container wall and internal voids are provided in the container for the fission gases to escape from the fuel to prevent any excessive pressure on the container wall. For example, B_4C powder contained in a small gas-tight cylinder could be used as a poison control element. By choosing a container of proper diameter and wall thickness, and allowing a large enough internal void, all of the helium formed could be retained as a free gas without excessive stress in the container walls. Since all of the fission gases may not be released, this type of element provides a convenient safety factor. Irradiation tests on boron carbide have shown that only about 2 to 5 per cent of the helium formed at approximately 30 per cent burnup of the boron was released during irradiation at about 260°C. In addition, only 15 to 20 per cent of the helium was released in subsequent post-irradiation annealing at temperatures as high as 815°C.[27]

Another factor to consider is the effect of a metallurgical bond between the fissile core and the cladding upon performance. Cracks initiating in the core may not necessarily propagate across an unbonded zone between the core and the cladding in contrast to a metallurgically bonded element. The Chalk River (NRX) Reactor fuel elements have been observed to work well without a bond present, while delivering very significant amounts of heat. Use of the higher melting materials to minimize gas diffusion may be important. Planned internal porosity in fuel elements may leave room for sufficient internal expansion, which perhaps may minimize the development of stresses in the cladding; this may be of particular significance if high yield strength cladding metals are used.

Author's note: Much of the work on this subject has not yet been published as original papers, but only in reviews or as declassified abstracts from classified work. Reference is given to the people responsible for the work where possible, but proper credit must await formal publication of work carried out over the past years.

References

1. Weber, C. E., "Fuel Element Design", J. of Metals **8**, No. 5 (May 1956).
2. Anderson, W. K., Neisz, W. A., et al, Unpublished Data, Knolls Atomic Power Laboratory.
3. Willis, A. H., "The Irradiation Stability of Low Weight Per Cent Uranium-Zirconium Alloys", Submitted for publication in *Trans. AIME*.
4. Weber, C. E. and Hirsh, H. H., "Dispersion Type Fuel Elements", International Conference on the Peaceful Uses of Atomic Energy, Geneva, Switzerland, *Conference Paper No. P/561* (August 1955). Also, *Progress in Nuclear Energy*, Vol. 1, Series V (1956).
5. Anderson, W. K., "Rare Earths Show Promise as Reactor Control Materials", *Nucleonics* **15**, No. 1 (January 1957).
6. Cadwell, J. J., Unpublished Data, Hanford Atomic Products Operations, General Electric Company.
7. Paine, S. H. and Kittel, J. H., "Irradiation Effects in Uranium and Its Alloys", International Conference on the Peaceful Uses of Atomic Energy, Geneva, Switzerland, *Conference Paper No. P/745* (August 1955).
8. Anderson, W. K., Unpublished Data, Knolls Atomic Power Laboratory.
9. Howe, J. P., "The Metallurgy of Reactor Fuels", International Conference on the Peaceful Uses of Atomic Energy, Geneva, Switzerland, *Conference Paper No. P/825* (August 1955).
10. Bruch, C. A., McHugh, W. E., and Hockenbury, R. W., "Embrittlement of Molybdenum by Neutron Irradiations", *Trans. AIME* **203**, 281 (1955).
11. Makin, E. J., Gillies, E., "The Effect of Neutron Irradiation on the Mechanical Properties of Metals. Part 2-Molybdenum and Tungsten." Atomic Energy Research Establishment, Harwell, U. K. *AERE, M/R 2062* (September 1956).
12. Hueschen, R. E., Kemper R. S., and Kelley, W. S., "The Effect of Irradiation on the Tensile Properties of Uranium", 2nd Nuclear Engineering and Science Conference, *Paper No. 57-NESC-13* (March 1957).
13. Pugh, S. F., "Radiation Damage in Fissile Materials", *Progress in Nuclear Energy*, Vol. 1, Series V (1956).
14. Konobeevsky, S. T., Pravdyuk, N. F., and Kutaitsev, V. I., "Effect of Irradiation on Structure and Properties of Fissionable Materials", International Conference on the Peaceful Uses of Atomic Energy, Geneva, Switzerland, *Conference Paper No. P/681* (August 1955).
15. Anderson, W. K. and Dunning, D. N., "Absorber Materials for Reactor Control", 2nd Nuclear Engineering and Science Conference, *Paper No. 57-NESC-66*, (March 1957).
16. Billington, D. S., "Radiation Damage in Non-Fissile Materials", International Conference on the Peaceful Uses of Atomic Energy, Geneva, Switzerland, *Conference Paper No. P/744* (August 1955).
17. Johnston, W. V., Unpublished Data, Knolls Atomic Power Laboratory.
18. Cottrell, A. H., and Roberts, A. C., "Creep of Alpha Uranium During Irradiation with Neutrons", *AERE M/R 969* (Harwell) (1956).
19. Brinkman, J. A., *J. Appl. Phys.* **25**, 961–970 (1954); also, unclassified AEC Reports, NAA-SR-198 (1952), NAA-SR-262 (1953), and NAA-SR-1459 (1955).

20. Bleiberg, M. L., Jones, L. J., and Lustman, B., "Phase Changes in Pile-Irradiated Uranium-Base Alloys", *WAPD-T-300* (1956).
21. Tucker, C. W., and Senio, P., *J. Appl. Phys.*, **27**, 207–209 (1956).
22. Howe, J. P. and Weber, C. E., "Limitations on the Performance of Nuclear Fuels", *TID-2012*, Vol. 4, No. 1 (March 1954).
23. Willis, A. H., "Dimensional Changes in Fissionable Metallic Materials During Irradiation", To be submitted for publication in Trans. AIME.
24. LeClaire, A. D. and Rowe, A. H., *Revue de Metallurgie*, **52**, No. 2, 94 (1955).
25. Reynolds, M. B., Low, J. R., and Sullivan, L. O., "Study of Irradiation Stability of Austenitic Type 347 Stainless Steel", *Trans. AIME* (April 1955). Also, *J. Metals*, **7**, No. 4, 555–559 (1955).
26. Johnston, W. V., Unpublished Data, Knolls Atomic Power Laboratory.
27. Valovage, W. D., "Effect of Irradiation on Hot Pressed Boron Carbide", Knolls Atomic Power Laboratory Report, *KAPL-1403*.

Chapter 8

EFFECTS OF RADIATION ON SHIELDING, MODERATORS, AND AUXILIARY COMPONENTS OF NUCLEAR REACTORS*

Gerhart R. Hennig

Argonne National Laboratory
Lemont, Illinois

Introduction

This review deals with a large number of different subjects and can, therefore, not receive as much of an exhaustive coverage as would be desirable. It has been attempted to list references where more detailed information can be found. Because of the personal interest of the author, sections dealing with radiation effects on moderators and particularly on graphite may have been emphasized unduly. Most of the material in other sections of the review has been collected and abstracted from the literature rather than from personal experiments of the author or close associates.

The review will deal, in this order, with shielding, associated reactor materials, liquid moderators, and solid moderators.

Shielding

In Table 1 is shown a considerably modified version of a table published by Sisman and Wilson.[1] It lists a series of substances which may conceivably be used for reactor components. The arrows indicate the radiation level in a typical reactor at which a substance will show noticeable changes and the level which will render the substance useless. It must be realized that these arrows are to some considerable extent arbitrary and depend among other things upon the use to which a substance is put: glass, for instance, becomes useless as a window much sooner than as a container. The position of the arrowheads indicates whether the damage is due mainly to ionizing radiation or to neutron recoil. The dosage units used for neutron irradiation are integral flux (*nvt*) of epithermal neutrons. Later in the

* Based on work performed under the auspices of the U. S. Atomic Energy Commission.

report a dosage unit of Mwd (megawatt day of power produced per adjacent ton of uranium in graphite-moderated reactors) which has become customary for radiation effects on moderators, is sometimes used. One Mwd corresponds to approximately $nvt = 10^{17}$. Dosage is also sometimes measured by the more indirectly related units of thermal nvt; in graphite-moderated reactors, in certain select positions and near room temperature, one Mwd is[2] equivalent to an integral $nvt = 6.5 \times 10^{17}$, which is predominately thermal.

For irradiations in reactors, the simultaneous dosage of ionizing radiation associated with an epithermal neutron flux $nvt = 10^9$ is usually of the order of one rad unit. Although this equivalence has been implied in Table I, it is of course also somewhat arbitrary and depends upon the irradiation location, the type of reactor, and the material under investigation. More data and details for some of the substances listed in Table 1 are quoted in reference 1.

Reactor shielding consists usually of metallic, ceramic, neutron absorbing, and hydrogenous materials, used separately or in combination. From Table 1 it appears that damage to metallic shielding is insignificant; although metals become generally more brittle, harder and less ductile, these changes will hardly ever limit the life of a metallic reactor shield.

Shields frequently incorporate concrete[3] and are therefore ceramic in

Table I

RADIATION STABILITY OF VARIOUS SUBSTANCES

a: Transparent Medium; b: Structural Material; c: As Lubricant
d: Electrical Insulators

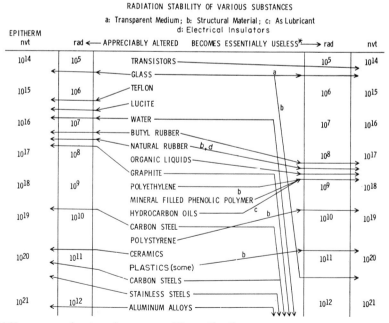

* Very approximate values vary with application.

nature; the concrete is sometimes loaded with barytes or iron[4] oxides to attenuate the gamma flux more efficiently.[5, 6, 7] Table 1 shows that in general ceramics resist radiation damage very well. It is, however, sometimes necessary to cool a ceramic shield because, as will be discussed in connection with ceramic moderators, these substances are sensitive to thermal shock.

A third type of materials sometimes used in shielding are those containing boron or cadmium whose large capture cross section for neutrons reduces the flux of this radiation. These materials, it should be noted, are also used in control rods, where they are bound to suffer considerably heavier exposures and usually also higher temperatures than in shielding.

A fourth type often used in reactor shielding is hydrogenous material. Because of its low mass, hydrogen slows and reflects energetic neutrons very effectively. Solid hydrogenous materials are, however, generally not particularly stable to ionizing radiation; therefore this component of shielding, sometimes in the form of pressed wood,[7] or elastomers,[8] must be studied carefully for radiation damage effects, particularly above $nvt = 10^{17}$.

For special applications, one sometimes uses transparent shields, such as lead, cerium glass or heavy liquids such as acetylene tetrabromide or zinc chloride solutions contained between glass plates; these, however may lose their transparency after relatively short exposures.[9] Shields of this type or shields utilizing liquids in general may give rise to corrosion problems,[10] which will be discussed subsequently in connection with liquid moderators.

Auxiliary Reactor Components

Among the most important auxiliary reactor components are electrical leads and in particular thermocouples; it is indeed fortunate that these are usually metallic and do not appear to suffer excessive radiation damage. Thermocouples will remain useful indefinitely, most tests have not detected any consistent changes in their accuracy as a result of exposure.

Of the commonly used thermocouples, chromel-alumel may sometimes show small radiation effects. Tests[11, 12] in the MTR (Materials Testing Reactor) and at the Oak Ridge National Laboratory have not detected any calibration changes exceeding 0.2°C for this type of thermocouple after very heavy reactor exposures, but measurements[13] in the British BEPO reactor have revealed transient changes as well as gradual changes as large as one degree in calibration. It is not clear whether these divergent results are due to differences in material or possibly due to insulation failure to be discussed later. Bombardments of chromel alumel couples with cyclotron accelerated protons did not produce measurable changes in their calibration.[14]

The insulation used in thermocouples is much more likely to cause trouble than the couple itself. Many insulators; become more conducting by orders of magnitude during reactor exposure.[15] Some of the materials in Table 1 are used as electrical insulators; in this application Teflon breaks down after a flux of about 5×10^{18}, various types of rubber become useless as indicated in the figure, while polyethylene, in spite of extensive hardening and embrittlement remains useful when exposed even beyond $nvt = 10^{19}$.

Thermocouples insulated with asbestos have given satisfactory service in low impedance circuits after dosages exceeding an nvt of 10^{21}.[16]

It is nearly inevitable that reactors, particularly power reactors, will require the use of oils or greases to lubricate moving parts in locations where the gamma and neutron fluxes are high. Many common lubricants are particularly unsuited for use in a radiation field. According to Table 1, lubricants will fail at fluxes of about 10^{18} or lower. The failure of oils is usually due to progressive polymerization leading to hardening, greases apparently go through a softening stage due to depolymerization of the gelling agent but eventually harden, too, because they also contain oils. Considerable effort is being expended to synthesize more stable lubricants.[17] It appears that such efforts can extend the life of lubricants by some factors between unity and ten, but that extension by orders of magnitude beyond $nvt = 10^{18}$ has not yet been attained.

Moderators

Radiation effects on organic liquid moderators, water, beryllium, beryllia, and graphite will be described. Radiation effects are only part of many factors which have to be considered in the choice of a moderator. The five moderators listed suffer increasingly large property changes from exposure to radiation in the order: water, beryllium, beryllia, graphite, and organics. However, the slowing-down power for fast neutrons (per unit volume), and therefore the moderating ability, increase in the order: graphite, beryllia, beryllium, organics, and water. Neutron economy due to smaller parasitic absorption (per unit volume) in the moderator increases in the order: water, organics, beryllium, beryllia, graphite. Other factors such as cost, temperature stability, structural strength, ease of replacement, etc., have to be taken into consideration when relative economic advantages of these moderators are evaluated. Some of these factors, particularly in their relation to radiation effects, will be discussed in connection with each moderator.

Organic liquids have been considered as combination moderators and heat transfer media because some of them, particularly those which resist radiation decomposition, have considerably lower vapor pressures than water and do not cause as much corrosion as water. Furthermore, they do not become intolerably radioactive, whereas water acquires troublesome, penetrating, although short-lived activity of N^{16}. A detailed description of organic moderator coolants has been published by Bolt and Carrol.[18] Although not yet actually used in a reactor, these substances appear fairly promising.[19, 20, 21] Particularly stable are polyphenyls; for reasons of economy, viscosity, etc., di- and triphenyl are generally considered. When irradiated in a reactor these lose some hydrogen and polymerize slowly to higher polyphenyls. It is possible to retard this polymerization by radical inhibitors, for instance, sulfur, which, however, introduces problems of radioactivity. The polyphenyls are usable up to temperatures of about 450°C, above this temperature polymerization is rapid. After an exposure of about $nvt = 10^{19}$ of fast neutrons, the polyphenyls have become useless due to excessive polymerization and even coking. In an operating reactor, the moderator life could, of course, be indefinitely extended if polymers were constantly removed by distillation, or by other suitable methods. Even though direct corrosion does not appear to pose a problem in such a reactor, the deposition of polymer or of cokelike scale on the fuel may cause overheating and failure of the fuel cladding, unless the radiation products are removed.

Water, particularly heavy water, has been used nearly as extensively as graphite as a moderator. Part of the value of water as a moderator, particularly for power reactors, derives from its physical properties and the fact that engineering experience with steam power plants predates the atomic age by a century. Another part of the value of water as a moderator is due to the stability of water toward radiation. Radiation effects on water have been investigated very extensively,[22, 23, 24] the results abstracted here were reported principally by Hart, Allen, Hochanadel, and their coworkers.

The primary effect of radiation on water is probably excitation and ionization of the molecules. However, no conclusive evidence has been obtained for the presence of such ions produced by radiation in liquid water. It appears that the primary effect is followed extremely rapidly by dissociation into the free radicals, hydrogen atom and hydroxyl.

$$H_2O \rightarrow H + OH \tag{1}$$

The further fate of these free radicals depends on the type of radiation used. Gamma rays, x-rays, or low energy electrons have low ionizing efficiency and therefore produce radicals relatively far apart, so that most of the radicals diffuse away before they recombine. On the other hand, accelerated particles like protons, neutrons, or fission recoils are highly ionizing and produce a "track" of radicals so close together that many of these recombine before they can diffuse out of the track. Recombination will produce water and hydrogen and hydrogen peroxide.

$$3H + 3OH \rightarrow H_2O_2 + H_2 + H_2O \qquad (2)$$

Those radicals which diffuse out of the track where they were produced, can undergo a variety of reactions. If the water is extremely pure, free of dissolved gases, and has not yet accumulated much H_2 and H_2O_2 from radiation, then these diffusing radicals will eventually recombine and produce more H_2 and H_2O_2. If, furthermore, the temperature of the water is high, the hydrogen peroxide will decompose and thus the end products of radiolysis of pure water will be hydrogen and oxygen. However, one finds much less of these decomposition products in irradiated pure water than equations 1 and 2 would lead one to anticipate, the reason being that as soon as small concentrations of decomposition products accumulate, reaction 1 is reversed. This reversal is due predominantly to the radicals which escape recombination in the track. These escaping radicals are able to undergo a large variety of reactions; and in fact the radiation chemistry of water has been largely clarified by adding small amounts of substances like iron, formic acid, etc., and determining the reactions of these addenda with the escaped free radicals. In initially pure water they remove the decomposition products by a chain reaction

$$H + H_2O_2 = H_2O + OH$$
$$OH + H_2 = H_2O + H \qquad (3)$$

in which a hydrogen atom reacts with peroxide to form a hydroxyl radical, which in turn reacts with hydrogen gas to reform hydrogen atoms and so on. This chain will continue unless the radicals are destroyed by chain breaking impurities. One of these is oxygen, at least at temperatures below about 100°C.

$$2O_2 + 2H \rightarrow 2HO_2 \rightarrow H_2O_2 + O_2 \quad \text{low temp.} \qquad (4a)$$
$$\downarrow$$
$$HO_2 \rightarrow H + O_2 \quad \text{higher temp.} \qquad (4b)$$

It is in fact possible to predict rather precisely the production or removal of peroxide during irradiation from kinetic expressions based upon these mechanisms and the various rate constants determined for them. The predictions embodied in such equations are, however, invalidated if appreciable amounts of impurities other than hydrogen and oxygen are present in the water. In impure water, considerably more hydrogen and peroxide or oxygen are usually produced. This excessive radiolysis can usually be traced to the removal of the chain carrying radicals by the impurities, which thereby suppress the recombination reaction (equation 3).

A special case of an impurity which increases radiolysis is boric acid.[25] In a reactor, solutions of this substance produce dense tracks of radicals from which the radicals are not very likely to escape. Thus, considerable

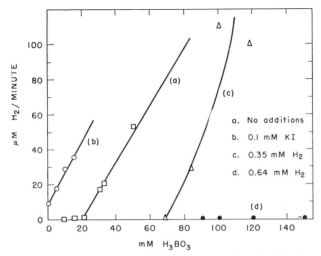

Figure 8.1. Radiation Decomposition of Boric Acid Solution

radiolysis occurs (Fig. 1a). This radiolysis is further increased (Fig. 1b) by addition of other impurities like iodide ion which scavenge those radicals which had managed to escape from the track. On the other hand, the radiolysis of boric acid solutions can be suppressed (Fig. 1c) by addition of hydrogen, as implied in equation 3. Increasing the ratio of gamma to neutron flux also reduces radiolysis by increasing the concentration of free radicals required for reaction 3.

In utilizing water as a moderator, corrosion problems are encountered, particularly at elevated temperatures.[26, 27] Corrosion of the container is very likely to increase the radiolysis of water because the corrosion products, particularly if soluble in water, may suppress the recombination reaction 3 by scavenging the free radicals. This chain of events can to some extent be suppressed by repurifying the water constantly, and this is in fact done in most reactors.

It is not known definitely whether the corrosion process itself is accelerated due to radiation, other than by the production of oxygen or peroxide, and hydrogen. Corrosion being influenced sometimes by a diffusion controlled process, the question arises whether diffusion is ever accelerated by radiation. Most measurements on metals have failed to show such an effect, principally because at the temperatures where diffusion can be measured, the effects of radiation anneal extremely rapidly. It is in fact generally agreed that at lower temperatures, diffusion in metals should be accelerated considerably by radiation, but even so it is too slow to be measurable. If the corrosion rate is controlled by the diffusion of ions through oxide films, it may well occur at sufficiently low temperatures that radiation effects still make themselves felt. However, this is pure speculation on the part of the author; to his knowledge, no effects of radiation on the corrosion rate itself has ever conclusively been proved.

Next some actual operating experiences with water-moderated reactors. The first of these, the Argonne CP-3, suffered initially quite appreciable radiolysis of the heavy water moderator. The mechanisms outlined here had not been established at that time. Therefore, when the Canadian heavy water NRX reactor was built, provisions were made for rather appreciable water decomposition.[27] Fortunately the water was quite pure (1–3 ppm of impurity). As a consequence, the decomposition rate was quite low (2 liter/hr) and furthermore decreased by a factor of eight when the water was continually repurified by ion exchange resins. At the present time approximately 1 ppm of the water decomposes per day. It is now known that the low decomposition rate was due not only to the purity of the water but also to the fact that air was carefully kept out of the water which was always kept saturated with helium.

The presence of air introduces several complications. Aside from the chain breaking action of oxygen (equation 4), there occurs an oxidation of nitrogen which produces nitric acid. The observation was made [28, 29] that this nitric acid production occurs only in the gas phase, and not at all in water saturated with air but completely filling a closed container. Therefore if water has to be irradiated in the presence of air it is advantageous to reduce the air space as much as possible. It was this nitric acid formation which had been responsible for the original appreciable gas formation in the Argonne National Laboratory's CP-3 reactor.

It should be thought that on the basis of this accumulated experience, water decomposition could be completely predicted in new reactors. This is, however, not true. When the Borax or boiling reactor experiments were carried out, at Argonne, the water decomposition was observed to be far in excess of expectation. The reason for the excessive radiolysis has been reported recently by Hart and Gordon.[30] Apparently, turbulent stirring, boiling, or bubbling accompanied by rapid removal of hydrogen before the hydroxyl radicals can react, is responsible for the excessive radiolysis of water in boiling water reactors.

Solid Moderators. Beryllium, beryllia, and graphite are, in contrast to the liquid moderators, not suitable as heat transfer media. Therefore, they must be cooled by a separate heat transfer medium, like air, helium, CO_2, liquid metals or others. For power reactors in particular it is important to operate these moderators at high temperatures, and all three, but particularly graphite and beryllia, are very well suited for high temperature applications.

Beryllium metal has been used as part of the moderator and reflector in the MTR, the Oak Ridge LITR, and a few other reactors. Beryllium, however, is a relatively active metal which is very difficult and expensive to fabricate. On the other hand, beryllium, like other metals, suffers no large scale radiation damage at room temperature, although it is rendered even more brittle by irradiation.[31, 32, 16]

Beryllia seems to have very attractive properties particularly for applications where the moderator runs at very high temperatures. It is of course one of the most heat resistant ceramics, and furthermore its thermal conductivity is unusually high. However its ceramic properties constitute also a disadvantage since it is brittle and has a very low ductility. When using beryllia one must therefore always avoid excessively rapid temperature changes or differentials. A few tests have been carried out[33] in which a thin, 1″ i.d. beryllia tube was heated on the inside and cooled externally. A heat flow of 100 watts/cm² near 1500°C caused failure of the material. This danger of thermal cracking is somewhat smaller in beryllia than in most other ceramics because of its high thermal conductivity. Therefore an evaluation of beryllia as a moderator requires the knowledge of how radiation damage will alter the thermal conductivity of beryllia.

Beryllia has two other undesirable properties, which must be considered. One is its surprising toxicity; the other, its extraordinary reaction with water at high temperatures. Table II shows that in the presence of water vapor, an equilibrium pressure of a volatile substance containing BeO and probably also one water molecule, is established.[34, 35] The volatility has been recalculated in the fourth column of Table 2 to give the loss of BeO in μg/liter of moist air passed over the sample. The loss per unit time increases of course with the flow rate of air, until the loss becomes controlled by the rate of diffusion from the surface. This limiting loss, i.e., the largest

TABLE 2. VOLATILITY OF BeO

Temp. (°C)	Equil. Pressure of ($Be \cdot H_2O$) ($10^6 \times$ atm)		μgrams BeO lost/liter moist air	Maximum loss g/cm²/hr
	Steam (1 atm)	Moist air		
1000	4	0.16	0.16	0.0027
1200	33	1.3	1.3	0.021
1400	185	7.3	7.4	0.11
1600	710	28	28	0.39
1800	2100	84	85	1.13
2000	4650	184	186	2.34

Tolerance 0.002

TABLE 3. RADIATION DAMAGE TO BeO

Exposure (Mwd)	Expansion (per cent)		Elastic modulus per cent increase		Thermal resistance ratio after/before		Compressive strength
	A	B	A	B	A	B	B
0							169,000 to 175,000
54	0.04 ± 0.03	0.03 ± 0.05	−1.45	−0.20	1.19	1.37	
109	0.02 ± 0.01	0.04 ± 0.02	−0.36	−0.10	1.54	1.46	
219	0.01 ± 0.01	0.03 ± 0.02	−0.53	+0.11	1.51	1.62	184,000 to 200,000

Samples A: density = 2.7
Samples B: density = 2.9

possible rate of loss at a given temperature, can then be calculated from the Knudsen equation (column 5 of Table 2). The losses are prohibitive at high temperatures; even at lower temperatures they introduce a health hazard, since they exceed the safe tolerance listed in Table 2. It is therefore imperative to dry very carefully any gases that come in contact with a BeO moderator at high temperatures.

Radiation damage in beryllia has been described by Simpson and Gilbreath.[36] The beryllia studied consisted of polycrystalline compacts of beryllia powder, hot pressed between 1000 and 2000°C to a density of either 2.7 or 2.9, which is close to the crystal density of 3.025.

The changes which occurred during bombardment have been listed in Tables 3 and 4. The bombardments were relatively light. Volume changes, if any, were barely beyond experimental error. The modulus apparently decreased initially but seemed to reverse this trend during further bombardment. The thermal conductivity is, as mentioned already, of principal interest; it was found to decrease somewhat, but appeared to level off at an acceptable value.

The thermal conductivity of Table 3 was measured at 100°C. If measured at higher temperatures (Table 4) the decrease due to radiation was even less, because thermal scattering predominates at higher temperatures; this temperature dependence is, of course, not an annealing effect. Anneal-

TABLE 4. RADIATION DAMAGE TO BeO, MEASURED AT ELEVATED TEMPERATURES

	Thermal conductivity (watts/cm °C)		
	Blank	Irrad.	Ratio
200	0.82	0.61	1.35
300	0.65	0.51	1.28
350	0.59	0.47	1.26

ing effects of the radiation induced damage do not occur until the annealing temperature exceeds 620°C; at 960°C the damage produced by a few hundred Mwd of exposure is annealed out completely.

The mechanism of radiation damage in ceramics, beryllia in particular, is not too well understood. In some ceramics, some astonishing recrystallization effects have been observed as summarized by Crawford and Wittels.[37] For beryllium oxide the hypothesis had been advanced that the changes in the physical properties might be due to dissociation of the molecule and occlusion of the liberated molecular oxygen in the lattice. This hypothesis was tested by measuring the gas evolution at high temperatures, and by measuring the magnetic susceptibility. At 1000°C more gas is evolved by irradiated than unirradiated beryllia. This gas is not free oxygen but mostly carbon monoxide, carbon dioxide, and water; these may be reaction products of the oxygen set free by irradiation with impurities introduced from the graphite mold in which the samples had originally been prepared. The diamagnetic susceptibility of BeO is decreased somewhat by irradiation, by an amount which corresponds to oxidation to gaseous oxygen of 500 parts per million of the oxide. This change had been produced by a bombardment of 200 Mwd. If one discounts the effects of ionizing radiation and calculates how many elastic displacements should have been caused by this bombardment, one estimates of the order of thirty thousand per million molecules. It would appear therefore, that very few of the once dissociated beryllia molecules remain dissociated. It must be remembered also that the decrease in diamagnetism is not a definite proof of oxygen production; the change might also be caused by F-centers or similar lattice imperfections.

Beryllia might conceivably serve both as a moderator and a fuel container. Beryllia-uranium oxide compacts were prepared by hot pressing the oxides together. Some measurements were made on the material after exposure to neutrons, although these samples had become intolerably radioactive.

Beryllia which contained 10 per cent by weight of UO_2, showed considerable radiation damage due to the fission recoils. This was true even though these samples were heated appreciably by the fission energy and thus were actually bombarded at elevated temperatures. The expansion rather quickly approached about one per cent, but saturated at about this value. Again considerable annealing was observed at 900°C. The compressive strength decreased somewhat but ceased to change with further exposure. The elastic modulus decreased and saturated at about 30 per cent of the unirradiated value. The thermal conductivity decreased by factors of more than 6, and furthermore did not actually saturate, but continued to decrease although at a much slower than the initial rate. This decrease in thermal conductivity may be sufficiently large to prevent the use of impregnated BeO as a fuel for many reactor applications.

We turn next to a discussion of graphite as a moderator. The mechanical properties of graphite are satisfactory for many reactor applications; it is strong enough to serve as a structural material; furthermore, graphite is one of the few substances which become stronger at high temperatures.

The nuclear properties of graphite are satisfactory but not excellent for a moderator. The absorption cross section of carbon for slow neutrons is about 3.3 mb (millibarns). Fortunately only a very small fraction of this cross section produces the radioactive isotope C^{14}, the remainder produces stable C^{13}. Therefore, very pure carbon will not become appreciably radioactive which is at times a considerable advantage in a moderator.

The moderating efficiency of the graphites which have thus far been used in the construction of existing reactors, can in principle be considerably improved. Moderator graphite has always been artificial graphite which is quite porous. Its density is usually only 70 per cent of the theoretical value of 2.27 g/cc. Therefore its moderating efficiency could be considerably improved if it could be made more dense, and yet remain cheap as well as pure.

The discussion of radiation effects on graphite will be preceded by a description of the most probable mechanism by which radiation affects the physical properties of graphite.[38] The physical property changes which occur may be enumerated in the order of decreasing engineering importance: mechanical properties first, thermal and chemical next, and electrical last.

Graphite is sufficiently metallic so that ionizing radiation produces no property changes. There are abundant nearly-free electrons available to compensate immediately for any ionization produced. The radiation damage in a reactor is therefore entirely due to the energetic neutrons, a few high energy electrons (of energy larger than $\frac{1}{2}$ Mev), and the occasional proton or other particles which may be formed by secondary processes (such as $N^{14}(n, p)C^{14}$).

Figure 2 is a schematic representation of the damaging process as it is believed to occur in graphite. A high energy neutron will produce primary displaced atoms at locations relatively far apart, since the mean free path of neutrons is about 4 cm. Thus the primary displacements (A, Figure 2) are spaced about 4 cm apart along the path (E) of the neutron. The vacancies produced in this primary process are very likely the single vacancies. The energetic, primary displaced atom loses energy principally by excitation and ionization, with only an occasional elastic collision which produces secondary displacements, until its energy is less than a critical value, assumed to be about 10 kev in graphite. It then loses most or all of its energy by elastic collisions, part of which produce secondary displaced carbon atoms (B, Figure 2) progressively closer together along the path of the primary. Near the end of its range the primary displaced atom may displace atoms so close together that they remain as C_2 molecular complexes or at least recombine to form such molecules immediately. The displaced secondary atom will have enough recoil energy on the average to displace one more atom, the tertiary (C, Figure 2). As shown in Figure 2, it appears that the displaced atoms are formed predominantly in clusters, consisting mostly of tertiary atoms near the beginning of the range, and secondary atoms near the end of the range (D).

In order to eject an atom from its lattice position, a collision must transfer to that atom more than the displacement energy, estimated to be 25 ev in graphite, a value which has, incidentally, been confirmed by electron bombardment experiments.[39] Those collisions which transfer less than the displacement energy will excite lattice vibrational modes; this heating of the lattices becomes progressively more important near the end of the range of the primary.

In many collisions, the displaced atom has little or no excess recoil energy available to move far from the vacancy. These atoms will remain as close vacancy-interstitial pairs and may anneal out in a different way from those atoms which recoiled with sufficient energy to be displaced a relatively large distance. The close pairs are most likely to persist along the early portion of the path of the primary displaced atom, because lattice heating near the end of the range may either anneal out these close pairs or cause diffusion and separation of close pairs.

The rate of displacement of atoms can be estimated from the theory of

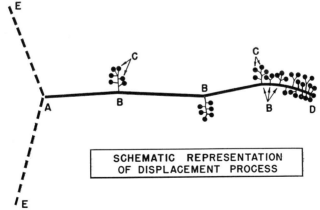

Figure 8.2. Schematic Representation of Neutron Collision with Graphite Lattice Atoms.

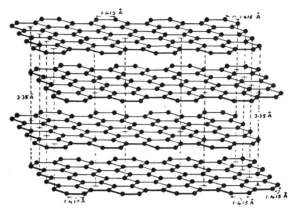

Figure 8.3. Structure of Graphite.

disordering of solids[40, 41] if the energy distribution of the damaging particles is known. This leads to an estimate of 0.35 to 0.7 displacements per 10^4 atoms for each Mwd of reactor irradiation in the locations where most of the irradiations have been performed.

The persistence of the configuration resulting from the damaging event and any further rearrangements or recombinations which may occur when the temperature is raised, depend considerably upon the unique structure of graphite shown in Figure 3. Carbon atoms are very tightly bonded in two-dimensional layers, but these layers are stacked quite loosely with large separations and resultant loose binding between layers. If atoms are displaced by bombardment they will inevitably end up in this interlayer space; this is going to cause a considerable amount of strain and distortion of the layers. It will also cause a net increase in this interlayer spacing and a very much smaller decrease in the opposite direction, and therefore also a volume increase of the whole crystal.

Anticipating some of the results of electrical measurements it can be stated that many of these interstitial atoms and possibly also the vacancies are able to capture electrons from the graphite layers, and become negatively charged. Because of this charge, there will be a tendency for the interstitials, which were originally formed in clusters, to drift apart. It can, therefore, be anticipated that annealing will not cause a direct reversal of radiation damage, but that the centers formed will first separate further, and will only at higher temperatures aggregate or recombine. It may also be anticipated that the interstitial atoms will be mobile at much lower temperatures than the vacancies. We are now ready to discuss the observed changes in mechanical properties, in particular the dimensional changes which the damage mechanism has already predicted to some ex-

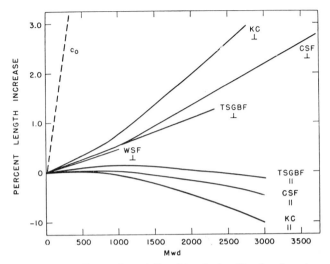

Figure 8.4. Expansion of Graphite during Bombardment

tent. Many of the data describing mechanical and thermal property changes have been reported by Woods, Bupp and Fletcher.[2]

Figure 4 shows that the interlayer spacing as measured by x-rays (curve marked C_0), increases at a very high rate which remains nearly constant up to very heavy bombardments. The anticipated bulk volume increase is also usually observed in polycrystalline graphite, but it is much smaller than the crystallite expansion measured by x-rays. Part of the difference is of course due to polycrystallinity; only some of the crystallites are aligned properly to cause a length change. However, the alignment is usually good, as shown by the fact that polycrystalline graphite under normal condition actually contracts in a perpendicular direction (the designation perpendicular and parallel in Figure 4 designates directions perpendicular and parallel to the extrusion axis which is perpendicular to the c-axis of the majority of the crystallites). It is believed that the discrepancy from the anticipated length change is due to the void spaces in polycrystalline graphite. The crystallites expand as expected but they expand into the voids,[42] and only after very heavy bombardment does this expansion into voids give way to increasing total expansion. The accelerated contraction of parallel-cut samples cannot be explained on this model, but is possibly connected with some stress relief of the expansion in the other directions.

The dimensional changes of graphite are complex. They are very important and have to be known in designing a reactor. Since they differ from graphite to graphite, they must be redetermined for each application. There exist, however, some empirical correlations which allow prediction

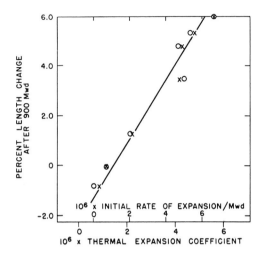

$$\frac{\Delta \ell}{\ell} \cdot 1.8 \; \dot{x} \; 10^{-6} \left[10^6 \, \alpha - 1.5 \right] \left[\text{Mwd} \right]$$

Figure 8.5. Empirical Estimation of Graphite Expansion

of the expansion with bombardment. The simplest such correlation is shown in Figure 5. The rate of expansion, $\Delta l/l$, during the first 900 Mwd is a linear function of the thermal expansion coefficient, α, and is in fact given by the equation

$$\Delta l/l = 1.8 \times 10^{-6} [10^6 \alpha - 1.5] \times [Mwd].$$

It is fortunate that such a correlation exists. The relation has not been tested for ungraphitized carbons, although a similar relation undoubtedly exists for them. Furthermore, the expansion after further, much heavier bombardments can be estimated from this initial expansion as pointed out by Woods, et al.[2]

The length changes can be reversed by heat treating the graphite as shown in Figure 6. Actually it was shown by precision interferometric measurements on irradiated samples that the initial effect of heat treatment is a further length increase followed at higher temperatures by a decrease and eventual recovery to the dimensions of unirradiated graphite. This is easily understood in terms of the model: after an initial strain relief which may cause some further expansion, the displaced atoms become mobile and gradually reintegrate into the normal lattice.

It is immediately obvious that the damage should be diminished if the irradiations were carried out at elevated temperature. This is dramatically shown in Figure 7. Actually the effect of raising the temperature during bombardment is considerably more beneficial than annealing at the same

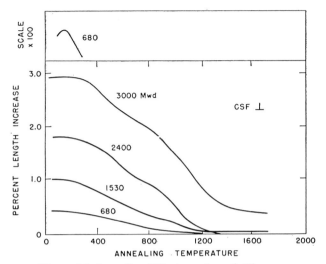

Figure 8.6. Annealing Effects on Length Changes

temperature after bombardment. This important effect is called radiation annealing (also referred to as nuclear annealing, pile annealing). Radiation annealing designates excessive annealing due to radiation over and above ordinary thermal annealing. Radiation annealing is more dramatically

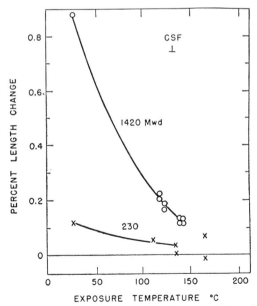

Figure 8.7. Expansion Changes during Bombardment at Several Temperatures

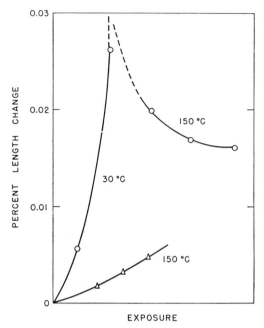

Figure 8.8. Effects of Radiation Annealing on Length Changes

demonstrated if it is allowed to start only after some damage has already accumulated.

As shown in Figure 8 the radiation units are arbitrary. A sample irradiated at 30°C increases in length at a much more rapid rate than a sample irradiated at 150°C. If the cooler sample is now heated to 150°C, it will actually increase in length due to the strain relief discussed earlier. Further irradiation at 150°C will now cause a rapid decrease in length and this decrease is due to radiation annealing.

To summarize the dimensional changes, there are four separate aspects of radiation damage in graphite. These are the property changes at a given temperature, the effects of different temperatures of irradiation, thermal annealing, and radiation annealing due to changes in temperature during bombardment. These same four aspects apply to all property changes observed.

A second set of very important mechanical property changes is shown in Figure 9. It is apparent that the strength increases very rapidly during weak bombardment and does not appear to decrease excessively even after very heavy bombardment. The elastic modulus also increases rapidly. It is very likely that these changes are caused by the interstitial atoms dis-

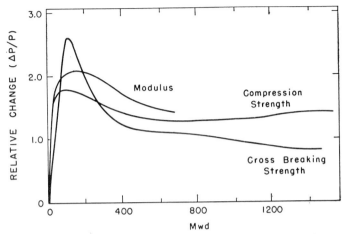

Figure 8.9. Effect of Bombardment on Mechanical Properties.

torting the layer planes; this distortion together with the expansion of the crystallites causes the whole structure to become more rigid.

Of considerable engineering importance are the changes in the thermal properties of graphite after irradiation. These are primarily due to the interstitials which will scatter thermal waves very effectively and therefore decrease the thermal conductivity. Furthermore, the interstitial atoms are unbonded and therefore store a considerable amount of energy in the lattice.

The accumulation of stored energy during bombardment is represented in Figure 10. In the same figure, the increase in the thermal resistance is also shown. It is quite apparent that these two properties change much more initially than later as a result of bombardment. This excessive damage early in the bombardment is usually attributed to the production of simple damage centers. When these simple centers begin to accumulate, they are progressively more likely to interact with newly formed centers to form complex aggregates, such as C_2, C_3, etc. These do not store as much energy because they contain fewer unsaturated bonds.

The phenomenon of radiation annealing is again apparent in the data of Figure 10. Annealing at 125° (for about one hour) after irradiation at 25° leaves much more residual damage than is present after irradiation at 125°.

Release of stored energy by annealing can be studied in several ways. It can be estimated either by combustion of the graphite in a calorimeter or by differential thermal analysis techniques. A typical but not necessarily unique apparatus for such an analysis (see Figure 11) is a device in which

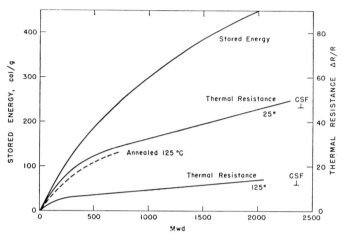

Figure 8.10. Thermal Properties of Bombarded Graphite.

a sample can be heated at a controlled rate and in which its temperature, the temperature of a blank, and the temperature of the enclosure, usually a copper block, can be measured simultaneously. Usually the temperature of the two samples will lag slightly behind the temperature of the copper block; if, however stored energy is released in the sample, its temperature will advance beyond the temperatures of the blank sample. In this way and by suitable calibrations one can determine what fraction of the total stored energy is released at each temperature.

The data from differential thermal analysis is shown in Fig. 12. It is quite apparent that a large fraction of the stored energy can be released at 200°. It is also apparent that this fraction decreases after heavy bombardments. This can be explained by attributing the peak at 200° to simple interstitials. After heavy bombardment more complex interstitials are present which anneal out only at higher temperatures.

It is important to note that the stored energy exceeds the specific heat

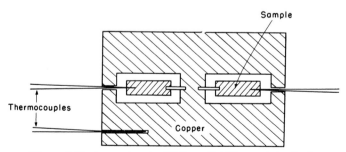

Figure 8.11. Apparatus for Differential Thermal Analysis.

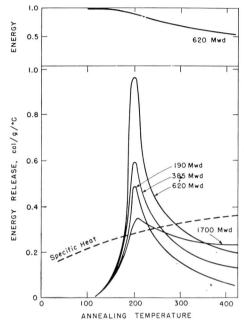

Figure 8.12. Release of Stored Energy

of graphite over an appreciable range of temperatures. This means that more heat is released than is needed to heat the graphite further, so that a catastrophic energy release may occur in a reactor containing heavily irradiated graphite unless the heat is carried away to other cooler parts of the structure. Radiation annealing of stored energy is shown in Figure 13. Practically all of the 200° peak is absent if the irradiation is carried out at 111°.

An important special aspect of the thermal resistance change has recently been discussed in some detail by Carter.[43] If, as is often done, the graphite moderator is allowed to operate at elevated temperatures, but the fuel is cooled to considerably lower temperatures, then a relatively thin layer of graphite located close to the cooling channels will suffer much more radiation damage than the bulk of the graphite where the higher temperature reduces the damage. The thermal conductivity of the thin layer becomes rapidly smaller, so that with a given channel temperature the graphite temperature increases still further, resulting in further radiation annealing, etc. Thus the difference between the thin nearly insulating layer and the rest of the graphite becomes more pronounced. Carter calculated the dimensions, after very long exposures to a fast flux of 10^{13} n/cm² sec, of this thin layer as a function of the thickness of graphite slab.

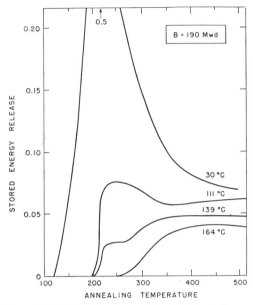

Figure 8.13. Radiation Annealing of Stored Energy

As a typical result, the insulating layer is 0.1 inch if the slab of graphite is 10 in. thick.

Properties which may occasionally become of considerable engineering importance are the chemical properties. Radiation effects on most of these like the peculiar reactions of graphite with halogens or alkali metals, are probably of only academic interest, although they reveal some of the characteristics of the damage mechanism.[44, 45] Very important, however, is the effect of radiation on the burning rate, both in oxygen and in carbon dioxide. This field has not yet been completely explored. It is definitely known that at room temperature a gamma flux will cause oxygen to react measurably with graphite, while it does not so do with carbon dioxide.[46] Furthermore, the efficiency of this effect is quite high: for each ion pair formed in a closed container, one carbon atom is oxidized.

In addition to this instantaneous effect of irradiation a more persistent effect of irradiation has been reported[47] which causes graphite to burn more rapidly in oxygen. Since this effect is not always present in irradiated graphite it may conceivably be due to some active species, possibly a catalytic impurity, introduced by reactor exposure under suitable conditions. A study of graphites irradiated in different atmospheres is apparently required to explain the disagreement. When the effect is present, it seems to indicate a definite decrease of the activation energy for burning from 49 to 36 $kcal$ per mole.

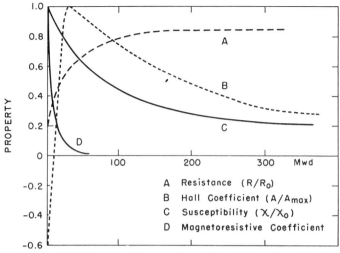

Figure 8.14. Electrical Properties of Bombarded Graphite

The electrical properties of graphite are less important to reactor engineers than the mechanical and thermal properties. They have, however, been invaluable in helping to unravel the mechanism of radiation damage and its annealing.[38] The properties are shown in Figure 14. They confirm the fact, already pointed out earlier that interstitial carbon atoms trap electrons and thus become carbon ions. As a consequence, the graphite conduction bands are left with a deficiency of electrons. This is most conclusively demonstrated by the Hall coefficient which becomes positive after quite short exposures and passes through a maximum with further exposure. This behavior indicates that positive holes gradually replace negative electrons as carriers. Furthermore the band theory of solids predicts, and the Hall measurements confirm, that the total carrier concentration actually increases, when electrons are removed.

Some properties are determined predominantly by the conduction electrons which were originally present. Such properties are the large magnetoresistance and the large diamagnetic susceptibility of graphite. These disappear when the conduction electrons are replaced by positive holes.

The actual number of electrons trapped at interstitials can in principle be estimated from theoretical considerations. However, a much more direct method has been found, which yielded the number 9×10^{-5} electrons trapped per carbon atom per Mwd.[48] This method was based upon observations that precisely measured concentrations of chemical electron traps could be introduced in graphite. By comparing properties like Hall effect or susceptibility of chemically "doped" graphite with those of irradiated graphite, the production rate of traps was determined.

The electrical conductivity of graphite is a measure of the product of the carrier concentration times their mobility. As already described, the carrier concentration increases so that one should expect the resistance to decrease. The resistance is actually found to increase, so that one has to conclude that the mobility decreases very rapidly. This decrease is attributed to scattering by the negatively charged interstitials and vacancies. After heavy bombardments the resistance becomes constant indicating that the mobility decrease just balances the increase in the carrier concentration.

It has always seemed obvious that a comparative study of annealing effects on the many different properties ought to reveal details of the annealing mechanism. Such studies have been quite frustrating. After very short bombardments of 4 Mwd (Figure 15), the thermal and electrical resistance, and stored energy are reduced nearly equally during annealing, while the elastic modulus changes less. This was explained by the assumption that in the 30 to 200° temperature range single interstitial atoms coalesce into carbon molecules C_2 or C_3. At higher temperatures these complexes become mobile and recombine with lattice vacancies or diffuse to crystallite boundaries. The first process coalescing of interstitials, releases energy because new bonds are formed. The effects of annealing temperature on thermal and electrical resistance may also be explained on the basis that these complexes are not very effective electron traps.

If considerable amounts of damage are present, the annealing process

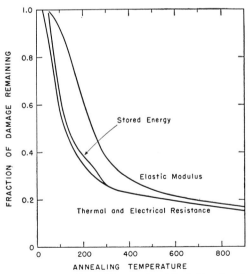

Figure 8.15. Annealing Effects after Weak Bombardment

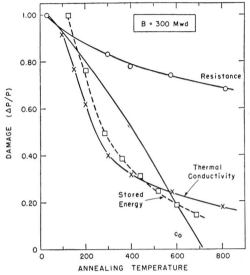

Figure 8.16. Annealing Effects after Heavy Bombardment

becomes very involved as shown in Figure 16, and it may be observed that little correlation exists in the effects of annealing on the above listed properties. There is little doubt that in this particular type of annealing, numerous processes occur simultaneously and obscure one another.

A considerable amount of effort has been devoted to analyze the kinetics of the annealing processes. It is obvious that such an analysis is very complicated after heavy bombardments and yet appreciable damage is necessary to make precise measurements of the annealing behavior. For weakly bombarded graphite many attempts have been made to separate the annealing process into definite reactions with definite activation energies. Neubert[49] and, more recently, Primak[50] have concluded that instead of discrete activation energies a continuous distribution of activation energies characterizes the annealing at least of heavily bombarded graphite. Each damage center requires a different activation energy to anneal, which is determined by its own particular neighborhood, the distribution of other centers in its vicinity, etc. Details of the kinetics of reactions characterized by continuous spectra of activation energies have been explored by Primak[50] and numerous predictions of these kinetics are confirmed by experimental observation. If, however all annealing processes have a wide range of activation energies and particularly if these ranges of activation energies overlap for distinctly separate processes like coalescing of interstitials or annihilation of vacancies, it becomes impossible to resolve the separate processes from the reaction kinetics.

Much information concerning the separate processes which occur during annealing has been obtained from a set of special experiments. Determination of property changes and their annealing at very low temperatures has shown that considerably more damage occurs under these conditions. Irradiations performed at liquid nitrogen temperatures followed by gradual annealing to room temperature have shown that between 50 and 100 per cent more damage is produced at low temperature. It was also shown by Austerman and Hove[51] that not very much additional damage was produced if the bombardment temperature was further lowered to liquid helium temperatures; little annealing occurred below 80°K. These results indicate that practically all the damage which is produced is also retained at liquid nitrogen temperatures. It is, therefore, very instructive to estimate the production rate of displaced atoms. Table 5 shows this quantity as determined from a set of experiments performed either at 80°K or corrected for the measured annealing effect above this temperature. The value estimated from theoretical considerations mentioned earlier is 0.7×10^{-4} per Mwd. A rather precise value can be calculated from the lattice constants if suitable assumptions are made regarding the size of interstitial carbon ions and if relaxation of the vacancies is neglected. Another value for this quantity is obtained from special neutron transmission experiments of Dienes and coworkers,[52] in which the scattering of neutrons from individual displacements was measured. The electrical properties yield a related value, the production rate of electron traps which is 9×10^{-5} per Mwd at room temperature and about 1.4×10^{-4} at low temperatures. There exists fairly good evidence that each interstitial traps one electron and each vacancy two, thus the electrical properties furnish another value for Table 5. Finally a value is obtained from paramagnetic resonance measurements which will be discussed next. All these values agree reasonably well.

It is very fortunate that the interstitial carbon ions produce a distinct paramagnetic resonance absorption which seems to distinguish them from the other damage centers (including close vacancy-interstitial pairs). The intensity of the resonance, its line width, and annealing behavior have therefore yielded precisely the information which is so difficult to extract from kinetic studies such as the temperature range where separation of the clusters of centers occurs, where coalescing of interstitials begins and ends, etc.

Specific information of this nature has also been obtained from radiocarbon tracer experiments.[53] It was found that the interstitial atoms could be tagged with radiocarbon to distinguish them from the normal lattice atoms. The behavior of the interstitials, their reintegration into the lattice,

TABLE 5. PRODUCTION RATE OF INTERSTITIAL-VACANCY PAIRS

Pairs per 10^4 carbon atom per Mwd

Theory	(0.35) to 0.7
Lattice Constant	1.0
Neutron Scattering	0.9
Susceptibility \ Hall Coefficient /	(0.5)
Resonance	(0.4)

and the range of their migrations could then be determined from suitable burning experiments.

A unique damage and annealing mechanism can be selected which is consistent with most of the experimental results which have been described. During neutron or proton bombardment at $-200°C$ nearly all the atoms which have been displaced remain displaced. Roughly one third of the displaced atoms are sufficiently near to vacancies to constitute close pairs; such interstitial atoms are probably not able to trap electrons. The remainder of the displaced atoms are sufficiently far from vacancies that they trap one electron. The vacancies are predominantly single vacancies which trap a pair of electrons and are diamagnetic. On annealing, the process which occurs first is the motion of interstitials. The clustered interstitials will drift apart because of the Coulomb repulsion of their negative charge and the close interstitial vacancy pairs will reintegrate since they do not repel one another.

As the temperature is raised to room temperature, few close pairs remain; their annealing apparently coincides with the next process, recombination of single interstitials into C_2 molecules. This process obviously requires an activation energy sufficiently high to overcome the Coulomb repulsion of the charged interstitials; however this may not be very large because of the dielectric constant of graphite (estimated to be about 6) and also because the charge will leak off at least one of the approaching ions as soon as the repulsion exceeds the effective electron affinity of carbon atoms in a graphite medium. At this critical separation the electron is returned to the graphite conduction band. The combination reaction is probably not complete before a third process begins to occur, reintegration of complexes, predominantly C_2, with vacancies. This process is practically complete near 600°C. Reintegration in this temperature range occurs by motion of C_2. Above 600°C, a few damage centers still remain. Some vacancies are left because a few interstitials will have reacted with surfaces and imperfections. Dislocations are also probably formed during the reintegration process. Furthermore, complete reintegration of interstitials and vacancies may require a higher temperature than trapping of interstitials by vacancies particularly if mismatching has occurred during the annealing, as for instance by combination of C_2 with a single vacancy, of a single carbon atom with a double vacancy, etc. These residual damage centers are required to explain why some properties still anneal at temperatures above 600°C, where no interstitials remain in the lattice if the initial bombardment was short.

Thus far only the annealing of damage centers produced at low temperature has been discussed. If graphite is irradiated at room temperature, the damage process will necessarily be different because the C_1 interstitials are relatively mobile at this temperature. Thus clusters of interstitials will not persist and close interstitial vacancy pairs will immediately recombine.

This mobility of newly formed damage centers may conceivably explain the phenomenon of radiation annealing, although more proof is needed. Newly-formed interstitials may encounter previously formed interstitials and react to form complexes, while the newly-formed atoms are still "hot" atoms, i.e., have not dissipated their recoil energy. This reaction may furthermore be facilitated because the newly-formed interstitial atoms may be temporarily neutral and may not have to overcome the Coulomb repulsion. The barrier potential opposing the transfer of an electron to a newly-formed carbon atom is probably a considerable fraction of the work function of graphite. Transfer probably occurs by tunnelling but may require sufficient time to permit several encounters of this carbon atom with previously formed interstitial ions.

This mechanism would explain why newly formed damage centers react more rapidly at a given temperature with "old" damage centers than these "old" centers can react with each other; this is essentially a restatement of the phenomenon of radiation annealing.

In view of the ability of the postulated mechanism to explain nearly all property changes and their annealing behavior, it is felt that radiation effects are better understood for graphite than for most other solids.

Bibliography

1. O. Sisman and J. C. Wilson, *Nucleonics* 14, 58 (1956); 14, 52 (1956); 13, 51 (1955).
2. W. K. Woods, L. P. Bupp and J. F. Fletcher, International Conference on the Peaceful Uses of Atomic Energy, Geneva, Switzerland, August, 1955, Paper No. 746.
3. R. B. Gallaher and A. S. Kitzer, ORNL-1414 (March 2, 1953).
4. J. O. Henrie, NAA-SR-880 (April 15, 1954).
5. TID-4008 (September 12, 1956).
6. B. T. Price, AERE-R/R-872 (February 28, 1952).
7. Univ. of Chicago Met. Lab. Progress Report CC-648 (May 15, 1943).
8. W. L. Davidson, AECU-1952 (April 1, 1952).
9. Symposium on Hot Laboratories, *Nucleonics* 12, No. 11, 35 (1954).
10. J. Draley and P. Drugas, ANL-4837 (October 28, 1949).

11. W. F. Witzig, WAPD-79 (March, 1953).
12. N. J. Palladino, WAPD-RES-43 (May 24, 1954).
13. P. E. Madsen, AERE-M/R-649 (January 25, 1951).
14. W. J. Sturm and R. J. Jones, ORNL-1540 (November 17, 1953).
15. D. S. Billington, International Conference on the Peaceful Uses of Atomic Energy, Geneva, Switzerland, August, 1955, Paper No. 744.
16. J. C. Wilson, private communication.
17. R. O. Bolt, J. G. Carroll, B. W. Hotten and S. R. Calish, AECU-3148 (June 30, 1956).
18. R. O. Bolt, and J. G. Carroll, International Conference on the Peaceful Uses of Atomic Energy, Geneva, Switzerland, August, 1955, Paper No. 546.
19. H. P. Smith, TID 7007 (January 24, 1957).
20. E. H. Smith, ER-8098 (March, 1956).
21. KAPL-1738 (December 31, 1956).
22. A. O. Allen, International Conference on the Peaceful Uses of Atomic Energy, Geneva, Switzerland, August, 1955, Paper No. 738.
23. C. J. Hochanadel, International Conference on the Peaceful Uses of Atomic Energy, Geneva, Switzerland, August, 1955, Paper No. 739.
24. P. I. Dolin and B. V. Ershler, International Conference on the Peaceful Uses of Atomic Energy, Geneva, Switzerland, August, 1955, Paper No. 679.
25. E. J. Hart, W. R. McDonell and S. Gordon, International Conference on the Peaceful Uses of Atomic Energy, Geneva, Switzerland, August, 1955, Paper No. 839.
26. R. F. S. Robertson, International Conference on the Peaceful Uses of Atomic Energy, Geneva, Switzerland, August, 1955, Paper No. 7.
27. J. R. Humphreys, International Conference on the Peaceful Uses of Atomic Energy, Geneva, Switzerland, August, 1955, Paper No. 740.
28. W. Primak and L. H. Fuchs, *Nucleonics* 13, 38 (1955).
29. J. Wright, J. K. Linacre, W. R. Marsh and T. H. Bates, International Conference on the Peaceful Uses of Atomic Energy, Geneva, Switzerland, August, 1955, Paper No. 445.
30. E. J. Hart and S. Gordon, Abstracts of 131st meeting of American Chemical Society, Miami, April, 1957.
31. S. Siegel, AECD-4045 (June 10, 1947).
32. J. R. Huffman, AECD-3922 (August 4, 1953).
33. H. Z. Schofield, AECD-3486 (May 22, 1951).
34. L. I. Grossweiner and R. L. Seifert, *J. Am. Chem. Soc.* 74, 2701 (1952).
35. D. T. Livey and P. Murray, *J. Nucl. Energy* 2, 202 (1956).
36. O. C. Simpson and J. R. Gilbreath TID-68, 41 (September, 1949).
37. J. H. Crawford and M. C. Wittels, International Conference on the Peaceful Uses of Atomic Energy, Geneva, Switzerland, August, 1955, Paper No. 753.
38. G. R. Hennig and J. E. Hove, International Conference on the Peaceful Uses of Atomic Energy, Geneva, Switzerland, August, 1955, Paper No. 751.
39. D. T. Eggen and W. E. Parkins, NAA-SR-37 (Sept. 12, 1949).
40. F. Seitz and J. S. Koehler, International Conference on the Peaceful Uses of Atomic Energy, Geneva, Switzerland, August, 1955, Paper No. 749; *Discussions Faraday Soc.* 5, 271 (1949).
41. W. S. Snyder and J. Neufeld, *Phys. Rev.* 97, 1636 (1955).
42. C. N. Spalaris, AECD-3679 (November 24, 1954).
43. R. L. Carter, Symposium on Radiation Effects on Materials, A.S.T.M. Paper No. 180, Los Angeles (September 16, 1956).

44. A. Novick, *J. Appl. Phys.* **27**, 572 (1956).
45. L. Quarterman and W. Primak, *J. Am. Chem. Soc.* **74**, 806 (1952).
46. R. E. Woodley, HW-31929 (May 24, 1954).
47. W. L. Kosiba and G. J. Dienes, International Congress on Catalysis, Philadelphia (September 10, 1956).
48. G. R. Hennig, ANL-4765 (February 22, 1952).
49. T. J. Neubert, *et al.*, *J. Appl. Phys.* **27**, 572 (1956).
50. W. Primak, *Phys. Rev.* **100**, 1677 (1955).
51. S. B. Austerman and J. E. Hove, *Phys. Rev.* **100**, 1214 (1955).
52. J. J. Antal, R. J. Weiss and G. J. Dienes, Proceedings of the Conference on Carbon, Buffalo, New York, p. 137 (1956).
53. G. Montet, G. Hennig and A. Kurs, *Nucl. Sci. Engng.* **1**, 33 (1956).

Chapter 9

EXPERIMENTAL TECHNIQUES AND CURRENT CONCEPTS—ORGANIC SUBSTANCES

Milton Burton

Radiation Project*, Department of Chemistry, University of Notre Dame, Notre Dame, Indiana

1. Plan and Scope.—This chapter presents only an overall view of the status of the radiation chemistry of organic compounds. Detailed resumes of the available data have appeared twice[1, 2] in the last few years. In addition, an extensive specialized review of the radiation chemistry of organic liquids[3] presented from a semi-theoretical viewpoint, will appear prior to this paper. The present contribution is intended for those whose background or interest in the effects of high-energy radiation is essentially physical but who wish nevertheless to have a broad view of the chemical situation, as it relates to organic compounds, without the necessity, on the one hand, of reading the details or, on the other, of accepting what they read as incontrovertibly established.

Hardly a facet of the primary effects of high-energy radiation can be presented which does not evoke fundamental questions among physicists and chemists alike. The author presupposes that his readers are generally aware of what is really known and of what is really unknown in that field as well as of what can be conveniently assumed without too much danger. Further, he is secure in the knowledge that he can write didactically because his readers know that didacticism is adopted as a matter of convenience and not as a consequence of an unjustifiable security of feeling. In the physical matters particularly, the reader is cautioned that he is to retain his doubts and to attach them as modifying phrases or clauses to some of the crisper statements he may read herein. The alternative to such a presentation is absolute precision and a much longer article.

2. Varieties of Techniques; Objectives.—The early work[4] on the radiation chemistry of organic compounds stemmed mainly from an interest in the biological effects of high-energy radiation. Thus, a major interest

* Supported in part under Atomic Energy Commission Contract AT(11-1)-38.

persisting up to the present day has been in those compounds which are water soluble.* However, even from the earliest days there has been significant work on pure organic compounds both in the gaseous state (of which the fundamental work of Lind and his collaborators[4] is most notable) and in condensed systems (e.g., the work of Kailan).[4] In the early experiments, natural radioactivity was the principal source of radiation, sometimes as radon alphas and sometimes as betas and gammas from radium and its immediate decay products. Thus, the work was restricted to a few major research centers and to the scientific elite who happed to have access to such rare and very expensive substances. During the 1930's Fricke and his co-workers,[6] in a sense, popularized the use of x-ray sources by their highly successful work not only with aqueous systems but also with occasional organic compounds. Consequently, when radiation chemistry became a matter of great practical importance, as it did from the point of view of atomic energy development in 1942, the scientists concerned were mentally prepared to employ sources of radiation essentially different from those which had been previously used.

At the present time scientists interested in the chemical and physical effects of high-energy radiation cannot restrict their interests to the types of energy associated with radioactivity or with instruments which, from the nuclear physicist's viewpoint, are in the low-energy range. In a symposium of the present nature it is unnecessary to recount reasons for an interest in the particles of extremely high energy. However, it is interesting to note that the development of a new radiation source for purely physical purposes has been generally followed rather closely by its application in essentially chemical work. Examples of such cases are afforded not only by the electron accelerators and x-ray machines (such as Van de Graaff generators, resonance transformers, linear accelerators and betatrons) but also by cyclotrons and by nuclear reactors. The work done with both the latter began in 1942 with the first studies of heavy-particle effects—of deuterons[7, 10] and of neutrons.[7, 8, 11] At present, the groups under Newton and under Garrison particularly are using 32 Mev helium ions from one of the Berkeley cyclotrons in their studies on organic substances.[1] A significant fraction of the recent work on polymerization and on modification of the properties of polymers employs the simple procedure of introducing the substance or mixture of interest directly into the nuclear reactor. While, the early interest in the use of the nuclear reactor in radiation chemistry may have been primarily academic, it is certainly true that many of the more recent experiments have been greatly influenced by the realization of the practical values which might be realizable in the direct use of the reactor in chemical technology.

* For a recent summary of yields cf. A. H. Samuel and M. Burton.[5]

TABLE 1. RANGE, ENERGY AND DISTANCE BETWEEN PRIMARY IONIZATIONS IN A
MEDIUM OF DENSITY 1 g/cm³ FOR VARIOUS IMPINGENT PARTICLES

Particles	Energy	Range (μ)	Energy Dissipation per μ of path kev/μ	Distance Between Primary Ionizations Å
Electrons	100 ev			5.9
	1 kev	0.053		42.8
	50 kev	43	0.67	138
	100 kev	141	0.417	2150
	450 kev	1500	0.21	4600
Protons	1 Mev	23	27.7	25
	10 Mev	1211	4.7	191
Alphas	1 Mev	5.3	264	1.9
	10 Mev	108	56	14

The fact that low-velocity particles transfer energy to the medium through which they pass much more efficiently than do the faster particles is illustrated in Table 1, based on the old data of Lea. This effect is not important in gases, where the primary ionizations are, in all cases, of the order of thousands of angstroms apart. However, in condensed systems, the consequence of this effect (shown in Table 1) is that the electron produced in the primary ionization process, with average energy near 75 ev, does not travel far from the parent ion and dissipates its energy in a spur the average diameter of which probably does not exceed 5Å. In such a spur about 3 ions and perhaps twice as many excited molecules are produced.* When the spurs overlap each other, as they do in liquids under slow particle irradiation, the probability of processes involving interaction of excited or ionized species, or of the decomposition products of such species, is vastly increased. Thus, considerable advantage of interpretation results from experiments in which the same substances are exposed both as gases and in condensed phases to radiations which vary in particle velocity from those typical of slow alphas to the velocities characteristic of high-energy electrons. The latter may be primary particles from a machine, betas from

* This statement is clearly one of those made didactically on a subject of which little is known even in the gaseous state. The Bethe calculation,[13] employed to estimate the relative numbers of ions and excited molecules produced by the movement of a charged particle through a system of hydrogen atoms, gives some theoretical support for this number. Recently D. P. Stevenson (see Section 4.1) has adduced evidence that the maximum energy transferred to a molecule in the ionization process tends to be ca. 2 I and the average energy ca. 1.5 I in many cases, where I is the ionization potential. It can be shown that the ratio of excited molecules to ion production is probably in the range 1.5 to 2 in such cases. According to Fano[14] the value in creases in condensed systems. Much more extensive experimental work (perhaps like that described by Marton and Leder[15] and by Blackstock, Ritchie and Birkhoff,[16] in which energy dissipation is determined for a single collision of an electron traversing a thin film) is required.

radioactive decay processes, or Compton recoils or photoelectrons resulting from interaction of X or gamma rays with matter.

One of the serious difficulties in working with gases is the problem of determination of energy input. This problem has been solved in the past by using alpha radiation, the energy of which may be effectively completely dissipated in a bulb of a few centimeters diameter. In more recent times the same result has been obtained by incorporating C^{14} (156 kv maximum beta ray energy, 5100 y half-life) or tritium (17.9 kv maximum beta ray energy, 12 y half-life) in the gas. Tritium has the advantage of being introduceable in high intensity in elementary form. In neither case are the secondary chemical reactions involving either the radioactive elements or the elementary products of radioactive decay of sufficient magnitude to compete with the processes initiated by the betas themselves.

3. Primary chemical processes.—No matter what type of high-energy radiation is employed, charged particles always result from the interaction of radiation and matter. Conveniently, we may take as our point of initial chemical interest the production of excited molecules and ions which result from the interaction of such charged particles and the molecules through which they pass. What ensues chemically thereafter depends on a number of factors: (a) the compound or compounds involved, (b) the nature of excited states and ions produced, (c) the proximity of such immediate products, (d) the presence and the nature of possible impurities, (e) the state of aggregation.

In our own laboratory we have recently found it convenient to place our observations on a skeleton structure of very simple form

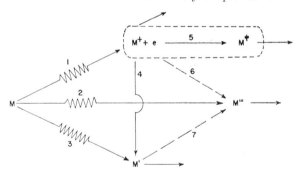

where M is the usual type of molecule, singlet in its ground state.

Reactions 1, 2 and 3 indicate the variety of initial excitation and ionization processes. Reaction 2 is an excitation process to a low-lying triplet level. Electrons with energy inadequate to cause excitation to a singlet level (i.e., by reaction 3) may cause reaction 2 if their energy is in the range described by $E''' < \epsilon < E'$, where E''' and E' are the lowest triplet and singlet levels, respectively. Species M''' represents between 3 and 8 per cent of the total ionized and excited species initially produced. The state represented by M''' is reached with only very low probability in a direct optical process and is consequently metastable. It does not internally convert to the ground state in a rapid process unless strongly perturbed by an external field.

Reaction 1 represents a process in which sufficient energy is imparted to M to ionize it. In the gas phase the number of ions so produced can be and actually have been measured in a number of cases but in the liquid case such measurements are surrounded with difficulty and give results of problematic, if not utterly dubious, significance. The difficulty in liquid phase work resides in the fate of the electron produced in reaction 1.

According to one view, which has been employed successfully to correlate results obtained for radiolysis of water using different types of radiations, the electron from reaction 1 never gets far from the parent ion but is recaptured by it in a time short in comparison with 10^{-13} sec; i.e., by reaction 5.[17, 18]

An opposed view[19] is that the electron actually travels quite far (e.g., about 50 Å) from its parent ion even in the liquid state. The reason cited for this view is summarized in the following terms. Most of the energy of the electron is dissipated very rapidly in resonance transfer processes; i.e., in ionization and excitation. Once the electron is decreased to an energy level below the lowest electron excitation level in the medium through which it is passing (e.g., something below about 3 ev), it can excite only vibrational and rotational energy states. The probability of such processes and energy transference in such processes are both small. In the time required for the electron to be reduced to near ambient temperature it may travel about 50 Å or more from the parent ion. Only when an electron has energy $\leq 4\,kT$ can it be effectively captured.[20, 21]

The fate of the electron in the capture process is the essential matter at issue. According to the view of Samuel and Magee,[17] if the electron reduces to an energy $< 4\,kT$ within 50 Å of the associated positive hole* it is effectively within the field of that hole and is bound to it. According to the Platzman view this picture may be essentially correct in nonpolar liquids such as hydrocarbons but does not necessarily represent the state of affairs in a polar liquid for example. The point maintained by Platzman is that in such a liquid (and in certain other cases) the probability of entrapment by a species other than a parent ion becomes significantly large.

* The point is made that the electron and the associated positive hole may actually move through the liquid as an excitation unit before neutralization occurs. Thus, when the neutralization occurs, the positive ion involved is not necessarily the ion initially produced.

Various types of possible electron traps other than positive ions include (a) a polar molecule which can accept a negative charge, (b) an unsaturated molecule, (c) any molecule with unpaired orbitals, (d) a molecule which can capture an electron in a dissociative process.

Traps of such nature may be presented by impurities, whether adventitious or deliberately added.[21, 22] Two possibilities of electron capture are illustrated by the reactions

$$C_2H_5I + e \rightarrow C_2H_5 + I^- \tag{4}$$

$$O_2 + e \rightarrow O_2^- \tag{4a}$$

When such reactions occur, the neutralization reaction 5 in the skeleton scheme may be replaced by

$$M^+ + N^- \rightarrow M^* + N \tag{5a}$$

where M^* is lower in energy content than $M\ddagger$ by an amount approximately equal to the electron affinity of N.[21, 23] Alternatively, the ion M^+ may itself dissociate before neutralization (cf. the low-pressure reactions in the mass spectrometer) and another realm of possibilities is thereby opened up

$$M^+ \rightarrow A + B^+ \tag{5b}$$

$$M^+ \rightarrow R^+ + X \tag{5c}$$

Reaction 5b is intended to represent a rearrangement process into a molecule and a molecule ion while 5c represents a bond rupture into a free radical and a radical ion. Appearance of $C_2H_4^+$ and $C_2H_5^+$ in the mass spectral pattern of C_2H_6 is attributed to such reactions and, in general, the rearrangement decompositions are believed to be slower than the ruptures. A more complicated compound like C_6H_6 may show a host of successive ruptures and rearrangement decompositions in the gaseous state.[24]

The discussion of the possible alternatives to reaction 5 may be summarized by the statement that we are by no means certain of the duration of existence of ions in the liquid state. They may dissociate before neutralization, they may be neutralized with formation of one or more very energetic species or they may be neutralized with formation of a less energetic species.* In any system each possibility must be considered as it may be affected by the molecular structure of each of the components present. The dotted enclosure around reaction 5 in the skeleton thus represents an aggregate of possibilities which must be carefully examined in order to speculate effectively concerning chemical reactions ensuant on initial ionization.

* Cf. also Section 4.1.

The skeleton shows three reaction paths connecting the primarily produced species. Reaction 4 may represent an internal conversion in which a highly excited electronic state, $M\ddagger$, passes without energy dissipation in one or more steps, but very quickly indeed,[25] to a high vibrational or rotational level of the lowest excited singlet state. According to Kasha, if this process involves only singlet-singlet transitions, it may require only about 10^{-13} sec. On the other hand, if the compendium of states represented by $M\ddagger$ includes high triplet levels*, these may very readily internally-convert to the state M''' but not to the state M'. In such case addition of a species which intercepts step 5 before formation of high-lying triply excited states may greatly modify the course of the reaction and the nature of the products.

The radiation chemistry of M involves then the fates of M^+, $M\ddagger$ (which may represent a compendium of highly excited states), M''' and M'. In many cases it is desired to know exactly what happens in the primary chemical step in the pure compound. This is rarely known from data on the pure compound itself but occasionally some good inferences may be drawn by examining the products from a number of compounds of a single type or by introducing a tracer atom into the compound at a deliberately selected position within the molecular structure. In the following discussion, the order will be to present the chemistry of a few selected cases and then to consider the possible explanations (i.e., suggested mechanisms), as they have been developed by studies of the radiolysis both of the pure compound and of some carefully contrived mixtures.

4. Some illustrative examples.—The cases selected for discussion here are not treated exhaustively. Each case is selected for its illustrative value. Detailed references to the literature are not included but a sufficient number has been given so that the argument can be followed conveniently.

4.1 Hydrocarbons.—By the use of radioactive tracer techniques Gevantman and Williams[26] showed that both CH_3 and CH_2 are intermediate products of the radiolysis of methane. The mass spectrometer pattern of CH_4 includes peaks for CH_3^+, CH_2^+, H^+ and H_2^+. Thus, it may be expected that at least part of the radiolysis occurs via decomposition of vibrationally excited CH_4^+ ions. Recently, Stephenson† has studied mass spectrometer patterns of hydrocarbons as a function of bombarding potential. The results indicate that in several cases the maximum energy transferred in the excitation process is *ca.* 2 I, where I is the ionization potential, and that the average energy is *ca.* 1.5 I. This rule has been found to apply to several

---

* The discussion is simplified by assuming that the state M''' is triplet. More accurately, we should assume that M''' interacts readily with certain states (included in $M\ddagger$) which do not interact readily with the singlet levels of M'. The language here employed is thus a kind of "short-hand".

† Private communication.

hydrocarbons. According to the theory suggested by Rosenstock, Wallenstein, Wahrhaftig and Eyring[27] the resultant mass spectral pattern can be predicted simply by methods akin to those employed in developing the theory of the activated complex; the calculated results agree well with the mass pattern. Free CH_3 and CH_2 radicals, such as those presumably detected by radio-tracer technique, can be produced either by direct decomposition of excited or ionized methane molecules or by neutralization of ions resultant from decomposition of the latter.

It has been customary to assume that C_2H_6 found in the radiolysis of methane results from radical combination. However, recent mass spectrometer studies at pressures exceeding normal operating pressure show peaks such as CH_3^+ and $C_2H_5^+$ which can be attributed to extraordinarily efficient reactions (cross section $ca.$ 150 $\overset{\circ}{A}^2$ with reaction on the first collision) of the type

$$CH_4^+ + CH_4 \rightarrow CH_3 + CH_3^+ + H_2 \tag{6}$$

and

$$CH_3^+ + CH_4 \rightarrow C_2H_5^+ + H_2 \tag{7}$$

Detailed studies of the kinetics of radiolysis of CH_4 by Franklin, Field and Lampe[28] have shown that a free radical mechanism is inadequate to account for the results and that assumption of two-body processes involving an ion increases understanding of the results.

From studies of radiolysis of mixtures of C_6H_6 and C_6D_6, Gordon and Burton[24] concluded that the observed ratios of yields $H_2:D_2:HD$ required mechanisms other than simple bond ruptures (to yield free radicals) or rearrangements (to yield product molecules in a single act) and suggested that cooperative reactions involving two molecules were involved. Recent mass spectrometer results on the simple hydrocarbon molecules suggest that in this case also an ion + molecule reaction may be involved. Such a result has indeed been sought and found by Barker and Lipsky*.

As one of the host of probable ion + molecule reactions which have already been observed. we are now compelled to think seriously of the class of reaction

$$R'H^+ + RH \rightarrow R'R^+ + H_2 \tag{8a}$$

Such a reaction competes, of course, with other reactions involving M^+ and M, which are grouped in the general class

$$M^+ + M \rightarrow Products \tag{8}$$

The relative rate of reaction 8a depends on its activation energy, E_{8a}. If

* Private communication.

$E_{8a} = 0$, only steric (i.e., entropy) factors determine its relative probability*. If E_{8a} has a small positive value, such as may be expected in the general case, its rate becomes temperature sensitive.

One of the great puzzles of cross-linking of polymers has been the mechanism which permits such reactions for polymers like polyethylene but forbids it for polymers like poly*iso*butylene.[29] Also, it has been shown that the cross-linking process proceeds with higher yield at higher temperature. An explanation is inherent in the previous discussion of the relative rates of 8a and 8. For polyethylene we assume merely that the reaction is slightly endothermal and that the positive charge is suitably

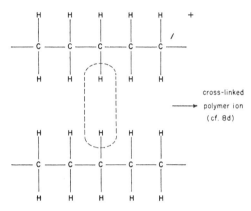

cross-linked
⟶ polymer ion
(cf. 8d)

located for reaction on the first collision; i.e., before the ion can be neutralized by the primarily emitted electron†. On the other hand, it is possible that the situation in poly*iso*butylene and other species which do not crosslink is somewhat different. In the structure

$$\begin{array}{ccccc}
CH_3 & H & CH_3 & H & CH_3 \\
| & | & | & | & | \\
-C & -C-C & -C-C- \\
| & | & | & | & | \\
CH_3 & H & CH_3 & H & CH_3
\end{array}$$

the positive hole may be so localized along the carbon-atom backbone that reactions of type 8a do not have the required cross-section to permit reaction before neutralization by the emitted electron (*cf.* section 3). Also,

---

* The restraints peculiar to the solid state are such that a reaction with $E_a = 0$ is nevertheless prevented by lack of access of molecules to each other. In such an event, the neutralization reaction 5 and its consequences clearly dominate.

† It must be remembered that in the condensed system the molecule ion is constantly in a state of collision. The positive hole belongs, of course, to the molecule in entirety. In a perfect polyethylene molecule, all C atoms are equivalent so that there is no favored "position" for the location of the hole.

purely geometric effects (e.g., proximity of C atoms involved in possible cross-linking) may limit or prevent the bimolecular reactions*. [10, 11]

Although speculation of this type by no means represents a complete theory, it does avoid some of the objections to previously proposed mechanisms and suggests some avenues for future study. One of the more obvious of these is the possibility that suitable substituents in such polymers as poly*iso*butylene may provide sinks for positive holes off the carbon-atom backbone and thus offer a means of cross-linking even in such highly resistant cases.

A variant on reaction 8a as a mechanism of cross-linking, recently suggested by the author meets the objection that, in general, such reactions may be too endothermal. Instead, we write

$$R'H^+ + RH + e \rightarrow R'R + H_2 \qquad (8b)$$

In this reaction note is taken of the fact that the electron is non-localized and is available for capture at the instant of collision of $R'H^+$ and RH. Thus, ion-induced dipole (coulumbic) forces act to increase the cross-section for the collision process and, when $R'H^+$ and RH arrive at the proper configuration, the energy of neutralization becomes effective for completion of the reaction. In a certain sense this view of an ion-molecule-neutralization reaction bears a resemblance to the old ion-cluster mechanism of Lind†.[4]

For improvement of our ideas regarding cross-linking it is interesting to consider the possible influence of substances providing deep electron traps (e.g., alkyl halides) not only on rate of the usual cross-linking processes but also on possible cross-linking in polymers which have been previously found only (or preferentially) to degrade and never (or rarely) to cross-link under the impact of ionizing radiation.

4.2 Protection.—This section is devoted mainly to experiments performed by the author and his colleagues. Yields in radiation chemistry are expressed as G values or 100 ev yields; i.e., $G(H_2)$ in any particular case is the yield of H_2 molecules per 100 ev absorbed in the system. For cyclohexane exposed either to Co^{60} gammas or to 1–2 Mev electrons, $G(H_2) = 5.9$; for benzene $G(H_2) = .038$. In a mixture of the two the yield is much lower than might be expected on application of a simple law of averages.

---

* Collyns, Fowler and Weiss[30] have made similar suggestions regarding mechanism of cross-linking. They did not, however, consider the effect of steric factors or of the "location" of the positive hole.

† Reaction 8b has significance for many reactions other than cross-linking. In liquid water, for example, one can conceive of reactions like $H_2O^+ + H_2O + e \rightarrow H_2 + H_2O_2$ or $2H + H_2O_2$ or $2 OH + H_2$.

The curve of yields is of the form shown in Figure 9.1. Of course, some of the decrease below the expected value can be attributed to addition reactions of the type

$$C_6H_6 + H \rightarrow C_6H_7 \text{ (a free radical)}$$

but such reactions seem inadequate to account for all the results obtained*. It has been suggested that an explanation may lie in the fact that the excitation potentials E_C and E_B and ionization potentials I_C and I_B for cyclohexane and benzene respectively bear the relation

$$E_C > E_B ; \quad I_C > I_B$$

If we let C^* represent the general ionized or excited level produced in cyclohexane by high-energy irradiation, we may expect the general class of reaction

$$C^* + B \rightarrow C + B^* + \text{kinetic energy}$$

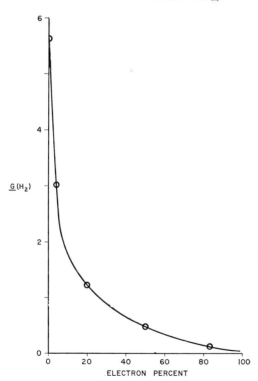

Figure 9.1 Variation of 100 e.v. yield of hydrogen with composition of mixtures of cyclohexane and benzene.

Since B* itself appears rather stable ($G(H_2) = .038$), the energy transfer effectively prevents the reaction. Numerous direct and indirect evidences indicate that such a mechanism does account satisfactorily for the effects observed.

An alternative view which has been suggested is that a reaction like 5a (see Section 3) may be involved; i.e., $C_6H_6 + e \rightarrow C_6H_6^-$ which in turn cuts down the yield of H_2 by causing cyclohexane ion to yield a lower, less productive excited state on neutralization. This view is not supported by experiments on luminescence of benzene solutions containing a scintillator solute. Certain characteristic parameters which appear in the kinetic equations for the luminescence phenomena have the same values for both 2537 Å and Co^{60} gamma induced luminescence. These parameters are characteristic of the solvent and should differ if benzene ions (rather than excited molecules) were involved in the latter case. The conclusion is that $C_6H_6^-$ (with electron affinity <1 ev) has no particular tendency to be produced in high-energy irradiation processes even in those cases in which C_6H_6 is present in high concentration. It would appear that there should be even less probability of its production in cyclohexane + benzene mixtures.

This view of the role of C_6H_6 in protection (i.e., that it taps off excitation energy of a radiation-sensitive species without decomposition) was also used to explain the resistance of aliphatic-substituted benzene compounds to ionizing radiations. It fits extraordinarily well into the subsequent results of the studies of Alexander and Charlesby, who showed that aromatic compounds, whether chemically combined or present as solute, protect polymers and simpler hydrocarbons both against cross-linking and radiolytic degradation.

4.3 Induced decomposition.—A study of the radiolysis of a mixture of benzene-d_6 and propionaldehyde by Patrick and Burton[31] showed (as anticipated) that C_6D_6 does not protect C_2H_5CHO against decomposition. Permitted optical transitions in aldehydes occur at longer wave lengths than for benzene; i.e., the excited singlet states for the former are lower. A similar relationship is perhaps true for the triplet states. Thus, if benzene initially excited to a singlet state internally-converts (i.e. by a radiationless transition) to a long-lived, triplet state, there is a finite probability that the lower state may in turn transfer its energy to neighboring C_2H_5CHO

---

* It has been suggested that absence of HI production in radiolysis of cyclohexane in presence of solute iodine actually speaks against free H atom production in an initial step like $c\text{-}C_6H_{12} \rightarrow c\text{-}C_6H_{11} + H$. This question is considered by the author elsewhere.[3] An explanation (which is admittedly not too satisfactory) may be that the H atoms so produced are hot (*cf.* the work of Hamill and Williams) and that reaction of such atoms occurs on first (or second) collision with the hydrocarbon to the exclusion of possible reaction with iodine, present in relatively low concentration.

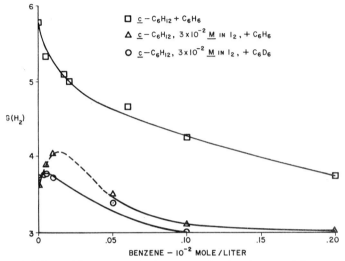

Figure 9.2 Effect of benzene on hydrogen production from cyclohexane containing I_2.

molecules which, in turn, decompose by the reaction

$$C_2H_5CHO \rightarrow C_2H_6 + CO$$

Evidence for such a sequence of reactions has been presented.[31]

Another example of induced decomposition is presented in the case of mixtures of cyclohexane involving iodine. The yield of H_2 from irradiated cyclohexane is reduced by addition of iodine;[32] cf. Section 4.4. The value of $G(H_2)$ approaches 3.6 at iodine concentrations of $3 \times 10^{-2} M$. Addition of either C_6H_6 or C_6D_6 to such a solution gives the results shown in Figure 9.2. It should be particularly noted that, in the latter case, the additional H_2 yield in the hump of the curve is devoid of HD or D_2 content. Clearly, benzene is functioning to induce decomposition of C_6H_{12}, presumably by promoting the rate of a reaction which ultimately yields hydrogen in competition with another reaction which does not. The interpretation, which is presented elsewhere,[33] is that (in the skeleton model of Section 3) the benzene acts to promote reaction 4 in competition with reaction 6.

Another result reported independently by Chang and by Schuler*concerns the reciprocal effect of cyclohexane and alkyl iodides on each other during radiolysis by Co^{60} gamma rays. Chang found that like iodine, methyl, ethyl and cyclohexyl iodides, even when present at concentrations ca. $6 \times 10^{-2} M$, all reduce the $G(H_2)$ from cyclohexane to about 3.7; cf.

* At the Symposium on Radiation Chemistry of Organic Compounds, Miami Meeting of the American Chemical Society, April 8, 1957. Chang's results were reported by Burton, Lipsky and Magee.

Section 4.4. However, the yields of hydrocarbon gas with methyl or ethyl iodides present are increased startlingly; for methyl iodide values of $G(CH_4) \sim 27.8$ have been obtained and for ethyl iodide values of $G(C_2H_6) \sim 8$ were found in preliminary experiments. Here also, promotion of a reaction is observed but, in these cases, the mechanisms appear to be conventional chain reactions and not specially characteristic of radiation chemistry. A rather simplified mechanism is

$$C_6H_{12} \rightarrow C_6H_{11} + H$$

$$H + C_6H_{12} \rightarrow C_6H_{11} + H_2$$

$$C_6H_{11} + RI \rightarrow C_6H_{11}I + R$$

$$R + C_6H_{12} \rightarrow RH + C_6H_{11}$$

Reactions c and d constitute a chain.

Another example of a true induced decomposition is possibly offered by the results of Bakh and Sorokin[34] on the radiolysis of ethanol by high-voltage electrons (0.8–0.9 Mev) and by x-rays (75–80 kvp). They report that $G(H_2)$ in deaerated solution is 6.0 and in oxygenated solutions about twice as great. If this result is correct, it may mean a reaction like

$$M''' \xrightarrow{\quad O_2 \quad} H_2 + \text{residue} \qquad (9)$$

i.e., a rearrangement process

$$C_2H_5OH''' \xrightarrow{\quad O_2 \quad} H_2 + C_2H_4O$$

as an initial step, in which the presence of paramagnetic O_2 induces a forbidden transition to the ground state of the molecular products.

4.4 Quenching.—An electronically excited molecule may lose its energy by degradation into heat, by chemical decomposition (as well as by metathetical reactions), or by emission of light. In some cases the first process, which is an internal conversion, occurs spontaneously to the total or partial exclusion of the other two*. [14] In general, it is possible to subject an excited molecule to stresses which may favor one of these processes in competition with the others. When, by such competition, a process is totally or partially eliminated, it is said to be quenched.

An example of quenching of radiation-induced luminescence is afforded in general by a system of solvents, denoted by S_1 and S_2, scintillator solute X, and quencher Q. In such a system the solute, even in saturated solution, is present in concentration less than 1 per cent. Consequently, the energy from high-energy irradiation is dissipated almost exclusively in the solvent.

* The low value for $G(H_2)$ in benzene and other aromatic compounds indicates the existence of a highly favored mechanism for internal conversion to the ground state.

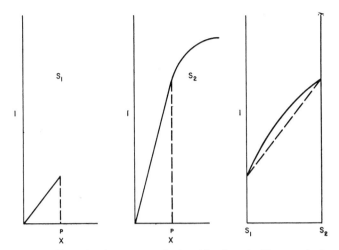

Figure 9.3 Some luminescence relationships in scintillator solutions

In the absence of a scintillator, the resultant luminescence (other than Cerenkov radiation) is trivial. When scintillator solute is present, the energy emitted as luminescence may be 10 times, or more, greater than that which could be primarily absorbed in the solute. Furthermore, the luminescence is characteristic of the solute and not of the solvent. Figure 9.3 shows a diagrammatic relationship between I, intensity of luminescence above the background (at fixed irradiation intensity), and solute concentrations. In 9.3a, I is shown for solvent S_1 at varying scintillator concentration. In 9.3b a similar relationship is shown for solvent S_2, which appears to transfer its luminescence more effectively to the scintillator X. For the illustration selected, I is 3 $\times$ greater at p mole fraction of X in solvent S_2 than in solvent S_1. Figure 9.3c shows the luminescence when the two solutions containing p mole fraction of X are mixed in varying ratios of S_1 to S_2.

When a quencher Q is added to such a scintillator system, the luminescence efficiency is in general decreased. Figure 9.4 shows the rather special experimental results obtained for the system in which S_1 = cyclohexane, S_2 = benzene, X = p-terphenyl, and Q = oxygen. The interesting feature here is the existence of a minimum now shown to be near 1 volume per cent benzene and about 16 per cent below the value for zero benzene at atmospheric pressure of dissolved air and 5.08×10^{-2} mole per cent p-terphenyl. A minimum is found also when X = diphenyl hexatriene, S_2 = toluene, or Q = bromobenzene. Also, it is found when S_1 is cyclohexane containing no more than 90 vol. percent hexane but it has not yet been found for other systems.

An interpretation of Figure 9.4 is that benzene transfers energy efficiently

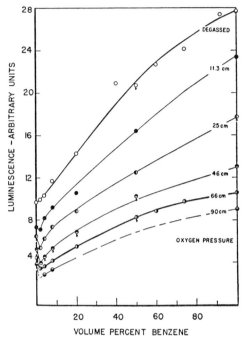

Figure 9.4 Effect of oxygen on gamma-induced luminescence in cyclohexane-benzene solvent.

to p-terphenyl by a virtual photon transfer process involving resonance transfer between several benzene molecules before ultimate transfer to the p-terphenyl. When, in the complex system, there is a sufficient concentration of C_6H_6 molecules well orientated with respect to each other and similarly related to surrounding c-C_6H_{12} molecules, the system is in good resonance for transfer of energy to the p-terphenyl. Such a condition exists except at the lowest C_6H_6 concentrations. Even in the very low concentration C_6H_6 solutions, the C_6H_6 can effectively take energy from c-C_6H_{12} by the reaction

$$C_6H_{12}{}^* + C_6H_6 \rightarrow C_6H_{12} + C_6H_6{}^* + \text{kinetic energy}$$

but the probability of passage of that energy to another C_6H_6 before quenching by oxygen is very low. Thus, the effect of addition of small concentrations of benzene in such an S_1, X, Q system is to reduce its luminescence efficiency. In more precise terms, the rate of transfer of excitation energy to p-terphenyl via a succession of benzene molecules is a non-linear function of some power of the benzene concentration.* In terms of the M-model employed in Section 3, we write for the fate of M'

* A more detailed discussion of such systems will be published later. The results here reported are those of P. J. Berry, of S. Lipsky and of J. M. Nosworthy.

$$M' \xrightarrow{\quad C_6H_6 \quad} M \tag{10}$$

where the benzene causes internal conversion of M from the state M' to its ground state by a very specific process involving excitation of benzene and quenching of the latter.

Various suggestions have been made regarding the mechanism of quenching of benzene by oxygen. One favored by G. O. Schenck[*] involves the intermediate formation of a peroxydyl radical

$$C_6H_6{}^* + O_2 \rightarrow C_6H_6O_2$$

followed by oxidation of cyclohexane or decomposition of the radical. Another is the conventional quenching of an excited state by a paramagnetic molecule (35).

The effect of iodine on cyclohexane (mentioned in Section 4.3) is another case which can be interpreted as a quenching mechanism. In this case the mechanism suggested[33] is

$$M''' \xrightarrow{\quad I_2 \quad} M \tag{11}$$

i.e., an internal conversion to the ground state electrostatically induced by the heavy atom I . In this particular case the reaction which appears to be quenched is the slow rearrangement decomposition

$$C_6H_{12}''' \rightarrow C_6H_{10} + H_2 \tag{12}$$

the G value for which is estimated to be 2.2. Similar quenching of this reaction appears to be afforded also by methyl iodide, ethyl iodide and cyclohexyl iodide.

5. Other processes.—It is not practicable in this short review even to indicate all the various types of processes which can be important in the radiolysis of organic compounds. For such details the reader is referred elsewhere.[3] However, the peculiar significance of low-energy electrons in mixtures must not be ignored. Platzman[19] calls special attention to the electrons which are no longer able to produce excitation in a pure substance; he calls them sub-excitation electrons. When a solute with excitable states lower than those of the solvent is introduced, such states are exclusively excited by sub-excitation electrons and the number of such excited particles so-produced may be out of all proportion to their concentration. The significance of such low-energy electrons has been discussed by Platzman for the radiation chemistry of gases[19] and by the author for that of liquids.[3] It has also been discussed in relation to the chemistry of electric discharge by the author and his colleagues.[36-39]

Literature references

1. B. M. Tolbert and R. M. Lemmon, *Radn. Research*, **3**, 53 (1955)
2. E. Collinson and A. J. Swallow, *Chem. Rev.*, **56**, 473 (1956)

[*] Private communication.

3. M. Burton, "Radiation Chemistry of Organic Liquids", a chapter in "Actions Chimiques et Biologiques des Radiations", edited by M. Haissinsky, Masson et Cie., Paris, Vol. III 1957

4. S. C. Lind, "Chemical Effects of Alpha Particles and Electrons", Reinhold Publishing Co., New York City, 2nd Edition, 1928

5. *Handbook of Biological Data*, Div. of Biol. and Agr., Nat. Acad. Sci., Nat. Research Council, Wright Development Center, 1956, Tables 410 and 411.

6. H. Fricke, Cold Spring Harbor Symp. **3**, 55 (1935); H. Fricke and E. J. Hart, *J. Chem. Phys.* **4**, 418 (1936)

7. M. Burton, *Chem. and Eng. News.* **26**, 1764 (1948)

8. M. Burton, *J. Phys. Colloid Chem.*, **51**, 611 (1947)

9. R. E. Honig and C. W. Sheppard, *J. Phys. Chem.* **50**, 119 (1946)

10. I. A. Breger and V. L. Burton, *J. Am. Chem. Soc.*, **68**, 1639 (1946)

11. M. Burton and T. J. Neubert, *J. Appl. Phys.*, **27**, 557 (1956)

12. D. E. Lea, "Actions of Radiations on Living Cell", Cambridge University Press, Chapter I, 1947

13. H. Bethe, *Ann. Physik.* **5**, 325 (1930)

14. U. Fano, *Phys. Rev.*, **52**, 44 (1946)

15. L. Marton and L. B. Leder, *Phys. Rev.*, **94**, 203 (1954); **95**, 1345 (1954).

16. A. W. Blackstock, R. H. Ritchie and R. D. Birkhoff, *Phys. Rev.*, **100**, 1087 (1955).

17. A. H. Samuel and J. L. Magee, *J. Chem. Phys.*, **21**, 1080 (1955)

18. M. Burton, J. L. Magee and A. H. Samuel, *J. Chem. Phys.*, **20**, 769 (1952).

19. R. L. Platzman, *Radn. Research*, **2**, 1 (1955)

20. J. L. Magee and M. Burton, *J. Am. Chem. Soc.*, **72**, 1965 (1950)

21. J. L. Magee and M. Burton, *J. Am. Chem. Soc.*, **73**, 523 (1951)

22. R. R. Williams, Jr. and W. H. Hamill, *Radn. Research*, **1**, 158 (1954)

23. J. L. Magee, *Disc. Faraday Soc.*, **12**, 33 (1952)

24. S. Gordon and M. Burton, *Disc. Faraday Soc.*, **12**, 88 (1952)

25. M. Kasha, *Disc. Faraday Soc.*, **9**, 14 (1950)

26. L. H. Gevantman and R. R. Williams, Jr., *J. Phys. Chem.*, **56**, 569 (1952)

27. H. M. Rosenstock, M. B. Wallenstein, A. L. Wahrhaftig and H. Eyring, *Proc. Nat. Acad. Sci.*, **38**, 667 (1952)

28. J. L. Franklin, F. H. Field and F. W. Lampe, *J. Am. Chem. Soc.*, **78**, 5697 (1956)

29. Z. M. Bacq and P. Alexander, "Fundamentals of Radiobiology", Butterworths Scientific Publications, London, 1955

30. B. G. Collyns, J. F. Fowler and J. Weiss, *Chem. and Ind.* No. 3, 74 (1957).

31. W. N. Patrick and M. Burton, *J. Phys. Chem.*, **58**, 424 (1954)

32. M. Burton, J. Chang, S. Lipsky and M. P. Reddy, *J. Chem. Phys.*, **26**, 1337 (1957)

33. M. Burton, J. Chang, S. Lipsky and M. P. Reddy, *Radn. Research*, in press.

34. N. Bakh and Yu. I. Sorokin, *Sbornik Rabot Radiatsionnoi Khim.*, Akad. Nauk S.S.S.R., **1**, 163 (1955); English translation: *Symposium on Radiation Chemistry*, Acad. Sci. USSR **1**, 135 (1955)

35. G. K. Rollefson and M. Burton, Photochemistry and the Mechanism of Chemical Reaction, Prentice-Hall, Inc., New York, 1938

36. H. Wiener and M. Burton, *J. Am. Chem. Soc.*, **75**, 5815 (1953)

37. J. C. Devins and M. Burton, *J. Am. Chem. Soc.*, **76**, 2618 (1954)

38. M. P. Reddy and M. Burton, *J. Am. Chem. Soc.*, **79**, 813 (1957)

39. M. Burton and J. L. Magee, *J. Chem. Phys.*, **23**, 2194, 2195 (1955)

Chapter 10

EFFECT OF RADIATION ON BEHAVIOR AND PROPERTIES OF POLYMERS

A. Charlesby*

Tube Investments, Ltd., Cambridge, England

Introduction

The study of radiation effects on materials can be traced back to the early days following the discovery of radioactivity. The very low radiation intensities available at the time limited the scope of the work to reactions which were exceptionally sensitive to radiation. Biological systems received by far the most attention and the use of radiation for therapeutic treatment has been a routine medical technique for many years. Work was also devoted to the study of radiation effects in gases since the high ionizing power of α radiation gave measurable changes in very small amounts of material. However, it is within the last decade that the subject of radiation-induced changes in solids has advanced most rapidly. This is due in part to the provision of much higher power sources and in part to the discovery of new and potentially useful applications. Moreover, the subject of radiation damage has become of fundamental importance in the formulation of an atomic energy programme. It is therefore necessary to distinguish between those aspects of radiation damage which result in more useful materials, where materials sensitive to radiation are studied, and those aspects where radiation damage is to be avoided, placing resistant materials in a category of major interest. Underlying both these objectives is the fundamental study of radiation mechanisms and means by which the direct radiation effect can be diverted and directed in more useful or less harmful directions.

In the early work use was made both of radiations (α, β and γ) arising from nuclear disintegration of naturally-occurring radioactive isotopes, and of x-rays or fast electrons produced by electrical machines capable of providing high voltages. These two quite distinct sources of radiation are still with us today and the experimental techniques of irradiation fall into two groups;[1] those involving radiations (α, β, γ, neutrons, etc.) produced as

---

* Present address: Royal Military College of Science, Shrivenham, Berks

a result of nuclear changes, as in atomic reactors, spent uranium fuel rods, fission products, radioactive cobalt, etc. and[2] those involving high voltage accelerators such as Van de Graaff machines, linear accelerators, resonant transformers, cyclotrons, etc. In the subject with which we are concerned here, similar effects are produced by each of these sources of radiation and the choice of a radiation source is determined by such considerations as availability, cost, penetration and beam intensity.

It has been repeatedly confirmed that the major reactions in polymers, whether produced by fast electrons, x-rays or gamma rays, or mixed radiation including neutrons from atomic reactors, depend primarily on the total energy absorbed and sometimes on the radiation intensity, but rarely, if ever, on the type of radiation or its source. Although exceptions may eventually be found, there is little doubt that this generalisation is of considerable value, as it enables the results obtained with one source of radiation to be immediately compared with those obtained under very different radiation conditions. For example, in the crosslinking of polyethylene or silicones, the density of crosslinking is found to depend only on the energy absorbed per gram and independent of whether this is due to highly penetrating gamma rays absorbed at a rate of about 1 Mrad a day, to mixed radiation from an atomic reactor providing radiation at an intensity of some 3 Mrads/hour or 2 MeV electrons of low penetration (about 6 mm) at a much higher rate of about 1 Mrad/second. In water, on the other hand, marked differences can arise as between α particle radiation and x-ray or electron radiation due to the much higher ionising density of the former. Ions, radicals or other activated species formed close together may react with each other rather than with the surrounding water molecules so that the products formed may differ markedly from those in which the individual ions are more widely spaced.

In the use of radiation for polymerization, the intensity of the radiation is of considerable importance since the length of the growing polymer chain is determined primarily by the concentration of radicals which is itself dependent on the intensity. In this case, the effect of radiation intensity parallels closely that of catalyst concentration when similar reactions are produced by chemical techniques, but the effect can of course be extended over a much wider region using radiation as a means of producing the primary radicals.

Electronic sources of radiation are particularly suitable for providing very intense beams of electrons concentrated on a small area. Radioactive sources, on the other hand, can be used more conveniently to expose larger areas giving lower intensity sources; the same dose can then be accumulated over a long exposure time, and more material can be irradiated at any one time. Where low penetrations are adequate and the reaction is independent of intensity, electron accelerators appear to be economically more advantageous for large scale work. Where high penetration and/or irradiations of low intensity for long periods are required, gamma-producing fission products may be more convenient.

At present, the cost of high energy radiation is still high. If expressed in terms of dollars per kilowatt hour (allowing for the amortization of the equipment, the manpower backing and equipment replacement), it is at present several hundred times as expensive as electric power obtained from the ordinary mains supply. This high cost restricts the use of radiation to fields in which the irradiated products are of considerable value and to those in which a small amount of radiation causes large changes in chemical or physical properties. Chain reactions, polymeric modifications and irradiation of biological systems (c.f. for sterilization) fall into the latter category. We are still in the early days of the production of high energy radiation on an industrial scale; many of the estimates of cost prepared are based on the use of high voltage equipment designed primarily for research purposes. There are encouraging signs that more high power equipment is becoming available with a greatly decreased cost per kwh. This will immediately extend the field of potential applications into areas where until recently economic considerations have been the limiting factor.

Interaction of Radiation with Matter

In passing through matter, radiation may interact either with the atomic nucleus or with the orbital electrons. Reactions with the nucleus resulting in a nuclear change occur primarily with the slow neutron beams present in atomic reactors. Such reactions depend on the initial nuclear structure; chlorine, for example, has a high absorption cross-section, while atoms of hydrogen, oxygen and carbon are relatively immune. For similar nuclear reactions to occur with electrons and gamma rays, considerable energies are required, greater than those considered here. Except for pile radiations of specimens containing certain elements of high absorption cross-section such as chlorine, nuclear changes are generally ignored.

A direct collision of an incident high energy particle with an atomic nucleus may give it sufficient energy to eject it from its position a crystal in or a molecule. This reaction occurs readily with high energy neutrons, particularly in collisions with hydrogen atoms. With electron or gamma radiation where the ratio of the masses is unfavourable to large interchanges of energy during a simple collision, nuclear displacements are far less frequent.

In metals, nuclear displacements are the primary cause of radiation induced changes. The ejected nucleus subsequently collides with other nuclei and eventually lodges in a more or less stable location, such as an interstitial space. The region in which such nuclear re-arrangements occur is referred to as a thermal spike and its effect on physical properties may in some respects be compared with the introduction of impurity atoms. The efficiency of the process is low; many of the displaced nuclei after losing their excess kinetic energy, fall back into a lattice vacancy so that no permanent change is observed.

Reactions with orbital electrons are far more frequent than with nuclei but in the case of metals lead to no permanent change. In ionic crystals the ejected electrons may be trapped giving color centers and increased conductivity. In organic systems, the various groups constituting the molecule are held together by shared electrons; the removal of a bonding electron could therefore disrupt the stability of the molecule, giving rise to unstable species, which by subsequent interaction, form new chemical systems or structures. It is the permanent character of these changes in organic systems (as well as their large number) which accounts for the considerable interest in such reactions, both as a means of studying the interaction of radiation with matter and of producing beneficial changes by means of radiation. In organic systems, nuclear displacements can also occur but their number is negligible compared with the number of electronic changes.

The interaction of radiation with orbital electrons may either result in the ejection of an electron, leaving a positively charged molecule and a free electron, or it may merely result in raising the electron to a higher energy level. The former process is termed ionization, the latter excitation. In gases, a free electron ejected by ionization is captured by an adjacent molecule to give a negatively charged ion, and the number of ion pairs formed is a measure of the effectiveness of the radiation. In air, for example, one ion pair is produced for approximately every 34 ev of energy absorbed, and this figure remains surprisingly constant over a wide range of energies of the incident radiation. If the initial energy of the incident particles is about 10^6 eV (1 MeV), each of these will give rise to some 30,000 ionizations plus an unknown number of excitations before being stopped. In liquids and solids, the number of ionizations and excitations is not known. Ionization is generally assumed to require about the same amount of energy as may be measured in gases, while excitation is often taken as being about twice as frequent as ionization, but there is no really convincing evidence to fully justify these assumptions.

Excitation can also be produced by ultraviolet (U.V.) radiation and indeed many of the reactions produced by high energy radiation in organic systems are directly parallel to those observed when U.V. radiation is used (allowance being made for resonance effects and for limited penetration of U.V. radiation). On the other hand ionization by radiation, which requires more energy, is best compared with the reactions of ionized molecules in the mass spectrometer. The analogy should not be overdrawn however since the possible reactions following ionization are very different. The mass spectrometer operates at very low gas pressures and the interaction between separate molecules is infrequent, whereas in the irradiation of solids or liquids, such interactions must play a predominant part in the course of the reaction.

Polymers

The physical properties of polymers depend at least as much on the arrangement of the individual units as on their chemical structure. One may divide commonly occurring polymers into two distinct classes—(i) those comprising a long chain of repeating units, each such chain generally being a separate molecule whose molecular weight may exceed 10^6, and these may be considered as one-dimensional molecules and (ii) three-dimensional network polymers in which the whole specimen is essentially one single molecule (since each atom in the specimen is linked by a series of primary bonds to all the others). Examples of long chain molecules are polyethylene, rubber, "Teflon" and cellulose, while examples of a three-dimensional network, in which the size of the individual mesh is small, are urea-formaldehyde, phenol-formaldehyde and (in theory) diamond. Graphite may be considered as a two-dimensional network polymer, while vulcanized rubber is a three-dimensional network with a large size of mesh.

The importance of radiation effects in these materials arises primarily from the very small changes needed to convert a one or two-dimensional polymer into a three-dimensional one. Most of the interesting changes produced by radiation are confined to the effects on simple long chain polymers and their transformation into a three dimensional network. The chemical reactions produced when long chain polymers are subjected to high energy radiation are not basically different from those which occur when simple organic compounds are irradiated. For example, saturated hydrocarbons show an increased degree of unsaturation with radiation dose. The curve shown in Fig. 10.1 indicates this property in low molecular weight paraffins and in polyethylene, which has a similar unit structure but whose molecular weight may be many thousands of times greater. Again, many organic systems evolve gases (mainly hydrogen) on irradiation. The same effects are observed when long chain polymers receive the same amount of radiation. The essential difference between the irradiation of simple organic systems and of long chain polymers resides principally in the considerable physical changes resulting from a small change in the chemical bonds. To change a hydrocarbon molecule containing perhaps 20 chemical bonds necessitates a change of at least one of these per molecule, i.e. a 5 per cent change. In a long chain molecule with perhaps 10^5 bonds, a change of only one bond may double or halve this

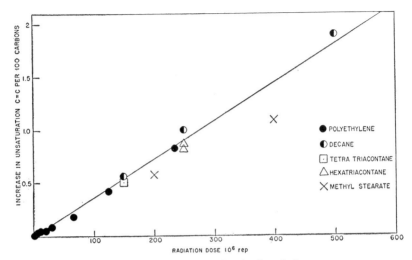

Production of unsaturation by irradiation

Figure 10.1

molecular weight. The chemical change is only 1 in 10^5 or 0.001 per cent, yet this minute chemical change can produce a drastic modification in such physical properties as viscosity, elasticity and solubility.

Many of the properties of long chain polymers can be deduced theoretically from the arrangement of the bonds in the molecule. By studying these changes as a function of radiation dose, it is possible to detect radiation-induced modifications of structure when these are present in only very minute amounts. Fig. 10.2 shows the increase in viscosity of irradiated polyethylene as a function of radiation dose. The doses used amount to a change of only one bond or less in a molecular weight of one million but modification in the flow properties of material above its melting point is very marked.

It is convenient to consider the types of reactions produced by radiation under several headings:

(1) Production of polymers by a chain reaction

(2) The production of graft polymers by radiation

(3) Crosslinking of one-dimensional (long-chain) polymers to produce three-dimensional networks

(4) Degradation of polymers resulting in a reduced molecular weight

(5) Effect of radiation on the crystallinity of certain polymers

(6) The irradiation of polymers in solution

(7) The curing of polyesters

(8) The effect of additives on the course of the reaction

(9) Studies of radiation mechanisms

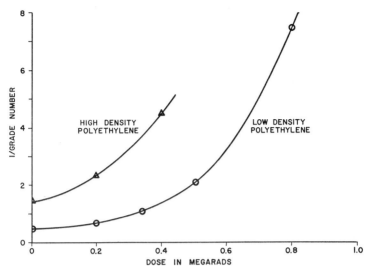

Figure 10.2 Increase in viscosity of polyethylene by crosslinking. (Grade number is rate of flow at 190°).

In most of these areas, work has only been carried out for a few years at the most and the effort available has been limited. Any review of results achieved is therefore likely to reveal more gaps in our knowledge than positive achievements. The success already obtained in certain of the earlier fields, such as polymerization or crosslinking, does, however, greatly encourage us in hoping that with further effort even more valuable information will be obtained.

Chain Reactions and Polymerization

It has been known for a considerable time that many polymers can be produced by irradiation of the monomer in the absence of any catalyst. The reaction proceeds with any form of high energy radiation although most of the experimental work has been confined to gamma radiation. The reaction kinetics of the system have been studied as a function of radiation dose and intensity and, to a lesser extent, of temperature of irradiation. In the two systems most closely studied i.e. methyl methacrylate and styrene, the polymerization kinetics follow closely those observed when the reaction is initiated by chemical catalytic techniques. In the three stages of the process i.e. initiation, propagation and termination, radiation only intervenes in the first step. It is of considerable interest to note that while the primary effects of irradiation are to produce ionization and excitation, the polymerization kinetics follow those associated with a radical initiator rather than an ionic one. It must therefore be concluded that the initial ionization or excitation gives rise to radicals similar to those obtained by chemical methods and that only these radicals initiate the final polymerization observed. Polymerization can also be initiated by ionic methods but so far there is no published information to indicate that this does in fact occur with radiation.

According to the reaction schemes envisaged, chains initiated by radiation will continue to grow until they terminate either by mutual combination or disproportionation with another growing chain, or alternatively, until they react with one of the radicals produced by radiation. Under steady state conditions, these kinetics lead to a dependence on the radiation intensity of the form:

Conversion rate is proportional to (intensity)$^{0.5}$

at low radiation intensities, where termination is due to the interaction of two growing chains. At higher intensities, the yield falls off due to the loss of many primary radicals by combination with growing chains, and this results in a lower molecular weight of the product. At very high intensities, little or no polymerization takes place since the radicals formed by irradiation combine directly with each other. The point at which the square root of dependence ceases to apply depends on the relative reactivities of radicals with each other and with monomers as well as on their concentration.

In certain polymers, notably polyvinyl chloride and polyacrylonitrile, this root intensity relationship is not found to hold even at very low intensities. The cause is not yet clear but appears to be related to non-steady state conditions prevailing during polymerization. For example, the growing polymer chain may be insoluble in the monomer and this will greatly reduce the probability of two such chains being terminated by mutual interaction. Under these conditions, the dependence on the intensity is often found to be of the form:

Conversion rate is proportional to (intensity)$^{0.8}$.

In using radiation to promote polymerization reactions, it is therefore important to work at low intensities to obtain high yields per unit radiation dose and also to obtain high molecular weights.

Radiation initiated polymerization offers various advantages over the more conventional chemical techniques and these include increased purity of the resultant product (it contains no catalytic fragments) and improved temperature control. Using conventional chemical methods, the temperature must be adjusted to obtain decomposition of the catalyst in order to initiate the reaction. The rate of the other stages of the reaction, i.e. propagation and termination, will therefore be largely determined by those required for the initiation step. With radiation, this no longer holds and the most convenient temperature conditions for propagation and termination can be chosen independently of the condition for initiation. At the same time, by altering the radiation intensity enormous variations in the molecular weight of the product can be obtained without the reaction "running away" due to the increase in temperature resulting from the exothermic process.

The absence of temperature limitations can be further extended to allow polymerization in the solid state. Here, the reaction kinetics appear to be quite different to those observed in liquid or in solution and this may permit very different types of polymers to be formed. A theory of such reactions in the solid state is not, however, available and a considerable amount of work can be expected in this new and promising field.

Grafting

The use of radiation has been extended to the production of graft polymers, i.e. long chain polymers in which the backbone consists of monomer units A while the side chain consists largely or predominantly of chains B. Polymers of A and B separately may have very different properties and the combination of the two in one single molecule may give rise to some very useful materials with properties different from either A or B separately, or from a simple mixture. Such graft polymers have been produced by chemical methods but radiation greatly facilitates and extends the possibility of their preparation.

Two techniques have been proposed for producing grafts. The first consists in irradiating the polymer A swollen in the monomer B. Radicals produced on the polymer chain initiate polymerization of the monomer, which forms branches on the polymer backbone.

$$\cdots A\ A\ A\ A\ A\ A\ A\ A\ A \cdots$$
$$B\qquad B$$
$$B\qquad B$$
$$B$$

Difficulties arise due to the formation of homopolymer i.e. chains of B monomers not attached to the backbone A; moreover it is necessary to imbibe adequate quantities of monomer B in the initial polymer A before irradiation. These difficulties can be overcome in part by the irradiation of polymer A in the presence of excess monomer B at intensities sufficiently low to allow further monomer to diffuse into the polymer A as it is being used up.

At very high intensities such as are obtained from electrical accelerators, polymerization in the liquid state usually gives extremely low yields. Experiments have shown that when the monomer is present within a solid polymer, as in a graft, the yield is greatly increased. Once again, this demonstrates that polymerization reactions in a solid or highly viscous medium are very different from those in liquids where rapid diffusion of the reactive entities causes a rapid termination of the reaction. Many polymerization reactions require long exposures because of the very low intensities of radiation needed to obtain high yields and high molecular weights. Experiments have shown that good yields can be obtained with high intensity radiation and short periods of exposure provided that the equilibrium sorption of monomer B in polymer A is high and the reactivity of B is low. Alternatively the radiation dose can be acquired in a series of separate steps between each of which the monomer is allowed to equilibrate within the material already grafted.

As yet, published information on the properties of graft material is relatively scarce; in particular it is not possible to predict readily the properties of a graft material in terms of the properties of the constituents of A and B only. A considerable amount of experimental work therefore remains to be carried out in order to discover which graft systems yield most useful properties. Already a few of these have been obtained and their properties as described briefly in the literature give promise of improved heat stability, better electrical properties, and increased chemical resistance.

Crosslinking and Degradation

Long chain polymers, whether produced by irradiation or by chemical methods can be further modified by exposure to radiation. The chemical changes produced are analogous to those observed when low molecular weight organic molecules are irradiated in the solid state; the main interest arises from the small amount of chemical change required to produce a marked change in the physical properties of most plastic materials.

The changes of most practical importance can be ascribed to two processes—crosslinking and degradation. Crosslinking is a process whereby two separate long chain molecules become linked together by a primary bond, thereby increasing the average molecular weight and viscosity. When sufficient crosslinks are introduced at random in a specimen consisting of long chain molecules, they form a three-dimensional network, the properties of which can be largely deduced on theoretical grounds. For example, while the unirradiated polymer may be soluble in a number of solvents, it is no longer so when transformed in a three-dimensional network consisting largely of closed loops and this may be seen in Fig. 10.3. At the same time, it becomes infusible in that the molecules originally separable by heating now form part of one gigantic molecule which can only be broken up at temperatures sufficient to cause fracture of primary bonds. The point at which the three-dimensional network is first formed from a series of linear or branched molecules can be shown theoretically to correspond to an average of one crosslinked unit per molecule (where all molecules are not of the same size, it is the weight average molecule which must be considered). Below this density of crosslinking, the effect of radiation is simply to increase the viscosity, molecular weight and degree of branching. Above it, it is partly insoluble though it will swell to an extent depending on the density of crosslinks. The elastic properties of a crosslinked network have been previously evaluated in the theory of rubberlike elasticity and this theory applies with a remarkable degree of accuracy to such irradiated polymers. For example, the relationship between stress and strain for a network system could be written in the form

$$f = \rho RT \left(\alpha - \frac{1}{\alpha^2} \right) \bigg/ M_c$$

where f is the applied stress, ρ is the polymer density, R is the gas constant, T the absolute temperature, α is the elongated length divided by its original value and M_c is the average molecular weight between crosslinks.

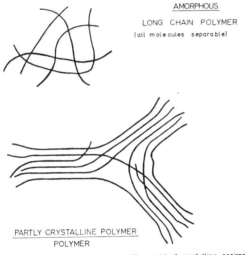

AMORPHOUS

LONG CHAIN POLYMER

(all molecules separable)

PARTLY CRYSTALLINE POLYMER
POLYMER

(all molecules separable above melting point of crystalline regions)

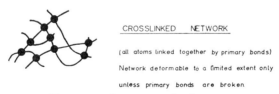

CROSSLINKED   NETWORK

(all atoms linked together by primary bonds)

Network deformable to a limited extent only

unless primary bonds are broken

Figure 10.3 Structures of polymers

(This formula may require correction to allow for the initial finite molecular weight.) Since the average molecular weight between crosslinks M_c is inversely proportional to the radiation dose, it follows that the stress required to produce a given strain is directly proportional to this radiation dose. This is in fact observed over a wide range of radiation doses and can be used to produce elastic materials with any required elastic modulus. If the radiation dose is very high and the resultant crosslinks are sufficiently close together to interfere with one another, rubberlike elasticity is no longer observed and the properties of the irradiated material may become more like those of a glass. Radiation therefore enables us to study quantitatively the change in the physical properties of solid systems over a wide range.

The same type of reaction occurs in low molecular weight systems such as hydrocarbons. These can be used for moderators and coolants in atomic reactors but the effect of radiation is to cause crosslinking, thereby increasing the viscosity up to the point where they are no longer fusible. They then behave as a solid of low elastic modulus. From the work carried out on long chain polymers, it is possible to predict the dose beyond which they cannot be used in the liquid state.

The use of radiation to produce crosslinked materials has already become of commercial importance and crosslinked polyethylene in particular is at present being sold in the form of tape and sheet. Rubber tires have been vulcanized by this process in the absence of sulphur or other additives. Because of the high penetration of gamma radiation, the thickness of rubber is of little importance in the curing process. Silicones offer another useful field in which radiation can be used as a mechanism of crosslinking without introducing catalysts and other impurities.

Degradation may be considered as the opposite reaction to crosslinking insofar as it causes a reduction in the average molecular weight. In theory, a three-dimensional network could be broken down to lower molecular weight constituents but the main emphasis of the work has been on the irradiation of long chain polymers, in which a reduction in average molecular weight can be readily varied. Since degradation causes a reduction in the molecular weight, the mechanical properties of degrading polymers suffer considerably under the effects of radiation. Polyisobutene, butyl rubber, Lucite and Teflon fall into this category and radiation doses of only a few megarads may have a drastic effect on their properties. Teflon, in particular, is very sensitive to radiation and although it may appear undamaged for a short period, on further exposure to radiation it will subsequently lose all its mechanical strength and become powdered. Polymethyl methacrylate (Lucite) is apparently unaffected by radiation at low temperatures although, on subsequent heating or solution, gases are evolved due to the fracture of the side chains. The main chain is reduced in length by random fracture and the mechanical properties suffer accordingly. The exact relationship between radiation dose and degree of degradation has been studied quantitatively and G values (i.e. number of breaks per 100 e.v. of energy absorbed) for the number of main chain breaks have been obtained for various types of radiation, radiation doses and temperatures. These indicate that the electron pile and gamma radiation behave in exactly the same way, and that the G value for fracture is independent of molecular weight. The type of radiation and the fractures occur randomly throughout the molecule. Furthermore the extent of the reaction as measured by the G value does depend on the temperature of irradiation.

It is possible to give a rough guide to those polymers which degrade and those which crosslink. Polymers containing vinyl units of the form:

$$\begin{array}{ccc} H & R_1 \\ | & | \\ -C & -C- \\ | & | \\ H & R_2 \end{array}$$

degrade, whereas those of the form

$$\begin{array}{ccccc} H & H & & H & R \\ | & | & & | & | \\ -C-C- & \text{or} & -C-C- \\ | & | & & | & | \\ H & H & & H & H \end{array}$$

crosslink. It has been confirmed that polymers which show degradation suffer main chain fracture only (no crosslinking) and that the observed reduction in molecular weight is not due to competition between the two processes of crosslinking and degradation, the latter predominating. In the case of crosslinking polymers, it has not yet been discovered whether some degree of degradation also take place. In the case of polyethylene, both effects have been found to occur simultaneously although this may be merely due to the presence of branches which are particularly susceptible to radiation damage. A true comparison would be with unbranched polyethylene but work on this does not yet appear to have been published. In the case of paraffinic hydrocarbons, in addition to crosslinking (or dimerization), degradation also occurs; by extrapolation it may be perhaps assumed that both these reactions take place simultaneously in long chain polymers of the polyethylene type. If, however, degradation occurs predominantly near the ends of a long chain, this argument is then no longer valid for long chain polymers.

Crystallinity

When examined by x-ray or electron diffraction, many polymers show evidence of a crystalline structure (e.g. polyethylene, "Teflon," nylon). The crystals are small and each long chain molecule runs through a number of these taking up an amorphous structure between them. It is the presence of these crystals which is often responsible for giving a polymer its solidity and strength, so that when the temperature is raised above the melting point of the crystals, the molecules are no longer held together, and the polymer is converted to viscous fluid. When the polymer is irradiated, crosslinks may be formed and these crosslinks are able to hold the individual molecules together even in the absence of crystals. It may be said, therefore, that although radiation raises the melting point of polyethylene, it does this without increasing the melting point of the individual

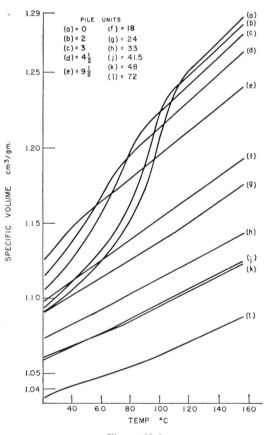

Figure 10.4

crystals. On the other hand, its effect is to convert a material which would flow above the melting point of the crystals into one which shows rubber-like elasticity at the same high temperature.

Evidence is accumulating to show that in addition to causing crosslinking, radiation destroys crystallinity. Polyethylene is available in various grades depending on the regularity of structure and hence the degree of crystallinity at room temperature. Work on all these grades indicates that the crystals are successively destroyed by exposure to radiation, the larger crystals being particularly sensitive in this respect. The dose required to completely destroy crystallinity may be very high, corresponding to perhaps one crosslink per 20 carbon atoms. Accurate measurements of the degree of crystallinity can be made in a number of ways e.g. by determination of the specific volume. Fig. 10.4 shows the specific volume at various temperatures of unirradiated polyethylene and of polyethylene irradiated to varying extents. The radiation used in these experiments was pile radiation and the destruction of the larger crystals is shown by the reduction in temperature of the maximum melting point. The effect can be better shown by translating the same information as given in this figure in terms of "equivalent paraffin" crystal distributions. The melting properties of the polyethylene crystals can be represented by the melting of crystals of simple paraffins of known molecular size. Fig. 10.5 shows that as the radiation dose increases, the average size of these equivalent crystals is decreased.

Experiments indicate that the destruction of crystallinity is particularly evident on exposure to neutrons as is the case of pile radiation. When the same amount of energy is absorbed from an electron beam, the degree of crosslinking is similar but the destruction of crosslinking is far less marked.

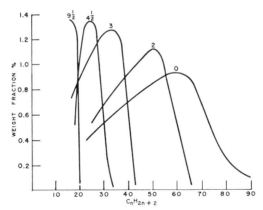

Figure 10.5 Crystal size distribution of irradiated polyethylene. Alkathene 2: Pile irradiation. Figures show radiation dose in pile units.

Curing of Unsaturated Polyesters

Unsaturated polyester molecules are formed as a condensation product of a mixture of unsaturated di-functional acids and alcohols. The molecular weight of these molecules is of the order of 10^3 and each molecule contains one or more sites of unsaturation which give the molecule its reactivity. These polyesters are usually combined with styrene or other monomers and cured by chemical catalysts to give a hard material which is in fact a highly crosslinked three-dimensional network. This cure can also be accomplished by exposure to radiation, the doses required being of the order of one megarad. This low dose, together with the low molecular weight of the material, indicates that the reaction involves a chain mechanism. The course of the reaction can be followed in various ways, e.g. by the heat evolved, by the changes in viscosity or solubility, or by the changes in physical properties following irradiation.

Experiments have been carried out to compare the properties of radiation-cured polyesters with those cured by conventional chemical techniques. Using chemical cures, it is difficult to stop the reaction at any stage since the increase in temperature accompanying the process results in increased radical formation by the catalyst. With radiation, however, the number of initiating centres is directly proportional to the radiation dose and is little, if at all, affected by temperature. A comparison of radiation-induced and chemical curing should therefore indicate not only whether the two reactions produce similar materials but also whether continued irradiation increases the degree of crosslinking of the network above that which can be obtained from a finite amount of chemical catalyst.

Figs. 10.6 and 10.7 indicate a number of the mechanical properties of such irradiated polyesters plotted as a function of radiation dose. This dose was given in the form of an intense electron beam; (1 megarad per second); similar experiments can be carried out using gamma radiation, in which case the required dose is lower. Figs. 6 and 7 show that at low doses the degree of cure falls below that achieved with chemical initiators but tends towards the latter at doses of about 6 megarads. There would therefore appear to be no essential difference between the products obtained by chemical cure and radiation cure. Increasing the dose further (>6 or 7 megarads) has little effect on the resultant product. The properties obtained do not therefore depend on the amount of chains initiated but rather on the properties of the mixture of polyester and monomer. It is useful to note that the cure is complete at about six or seven megarads, irrespective of the mechanism of curing.

* Selection is Pittsburgh Plate Glass Company's trade name for a line of polyester mixtures.

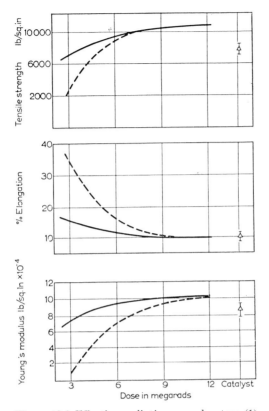

Figure 10.6 Effective radiation on polyesters (1)

Further work (not yet published) indicates that the degree of cure varies as the root of the radiation intensity in conformity with the results obtained for simple polymerization of styrene. The state of cure can furthermore be drastically affected by the incorporation of suitable additives which can either act as protectors against radiation or as inhibitors of the reaction once it has commenced.

An entirely different reaction occurs when the unsaturated polyesters are irradiated without the addition of styrene or other monomer. Here again, a chain reaction occurs and the course of this reaction can be traced either from the rise in viscosity up to the gel point, or from the change in solubility beyond this gel point. When gamma rays are used to initiate the reaction, no variation with radiation intensity is observed over the range 500 to 13000 r/min. Even when an electron beam is used with an intensity of one million r/second, the change in reaction rate is relatively small. The absence of an intensity dependence would indicate that the chain reaction

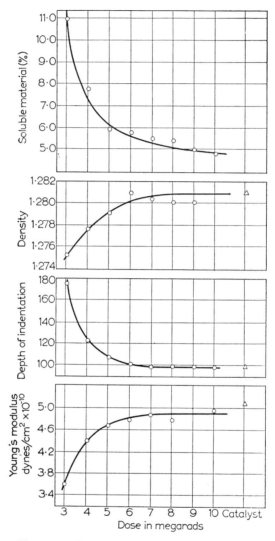

Figure 10.7 Effective radiation on polyesters (2)

does not proceed by the growth of polymer chains which terminate by mutual combination or disproportionation as is the case for conventional polymerization reactions. A mathematical analysis of this type of reaction leads to the conclusion that while each polymerization chain is initiated by the formation of a radical, its termination occurs by some stabilization step intrinsic in the system, such as allylic resonance.

The radiation cure of polyesters which do not incorporate monomers can be modified by the incorporation of additives which increase the radiation dose required to reach the gel point. They do not, however, affect the subsequent decrease in solubility as the radiation dose is increased. It would therefore appear that additives such as quinone react primarily with the radical formed by radiation but not with the growing polymerization chain. A comparison of the inhibiting effect of various additives both on the reaction cure of these polyesters by radiation and by chemical techniques shows that hydroquinone and 8-hydroxyquinoline produce the same degree of inhibition in both cases. Since only radicals are formed in a chemically catalyzed system, this observation shows that a radiation initiated reaction also proceeds via a radical mechanism. When anthracene is used as an additive, it inhibits radiation cure more effectively than it does chemical cure; this difference can be explained in terms of the radiation protection offered by the anthracene molecule.

The Effect of Additives

Although the energy absorbed from a beam of ionizing radiation is captured at random throughout the irradiated specimen, the reactions which take place depend markedly on the chemical structure of the system. In particular, the benzene ring has been shown to offer a considerable degree of radiation protection to molecules of which it forms part. For example, in the case of polystyrene, the energy absorbed per crosslink formed is about 2000 ev whereas for most crosslinking polymers it is only about 20 to 30 ev. Thus, 99 per cent of the energy absorbed in polystyrene is diverted and produces no permanent chemical change. Polyisobutene degrades rapidly under radiation and the energy absorbed per main chain fracture is known. By studying the number of fractures produced in a copolymer of styrene and isobutene, the protection effect of the styrene unit on neighbouring isobutene units can be measured. Similarly, the energy required to crosslink paraffin chains is known; when aromatic side chains are introduced into such paraffin molecules the energy per crosslink is greatly increased. That this protection arises from the resonant nature of the aromatic group can be readily demonstrated by a comparison with similar paraffin chains in which the side group is a cyclic aliphatic group when little or no protection is observed. The extent of protection offered by a single benzene ring appears to extend over a distance of approximately 4–6 carbon atoms along the main chain.

Protection can also be observed when the additive is present as a separate molecule. The degradation of polymethyl methacrylate can be reduced by a factor of about 4 by the addition of a few per cent of additives such as aniline and thiourea. Protection can also be offered against crosslinking of polyethylene. Although the extent of crosslinking is more difficult to measure than the amount of degradation produced by a given radiation dose, the protective effect can be observed in polyethylene by changes in viscosity, by swelling measurements or by changes in the elastic modulus.

Various methods of protection can be considered. In the so-called sponge effect, the energy absorbed by the polymer molecule is transformed by some unspecified mechanism (loosely referred to as energy transfer) to the additive molecule where it is degraded to heat. This form of protection is offered by the benzene ring and results in little or no change in the additive. A second form of protection may arise where the radicals produced by the radiation react with the additive rather than with neighbouring polymer molecules. In this case, protection only occurs until the additive molecule is used up. For higher radiation doses, no protection is offered. A third form of protection may occur, in which the primary damage caused by radiation, e.g. main chain fracture, is repaired by the effect of the additive which links the two broken fragments together again.

Many radiation induced reactions are very dependent on the presence of oxygen during irradiation. Oxygen may be considered as a very reactive form of additive. In many polymers, it attacks the primary polymer chain to produce peroxides which may subsequently cause degradation of the polymer chain. Many studies on radiation effects in polymers carried out in the presence of air lead to misleading results due to this degrading effect of oxygen.

Irradiation of Polymers in Solution

Little work appears to have been done on the reactions occurring when long chain polymers are irradiated in a solvent. Much of the earlier work arises in the field of radiobiology where the polymer concentrations are low. In studying such reactions, it is necessary to distinguish changes arising from the direct effect, when the incident energy is captured directly by the polymer, and the indirect effect where incident radiation causes changes in the solvent. In the latter case, the radicals or ions produced subsequently react with the polymer.

When long chain polymers, such as polyvinyl alcohol or polyvinyl pyrrolidone are irradiated in solution, there is only a slight change in viscosity up to a critical dose, beyond which the solution gels. In this form, the polymers are crosslinked and insoluble in the water but owing to the high degree of swelling the water is imbibed within the gelled polymer network, which it swells. Subsequent irradiation of the system produces a more close-knit network, unable to swell adequately to imbibe all the water. For such high degrees of crosslinking, the gel formed contracts and exudes excess water.

A plot of the minimum dose for gel formation against concentration is shown in Fig. 10.8. It is seen that as the polymer concentration decreases (i.e. polymer molecules are further apart), the minimum dose for gelation decreases. This apparent contradiction arises from the indirect effect; the total energy absorbed per gram of solution varies only slightly with polymer concentration so that the total energy is unaltered. With a decreased number of polymer molecules per gram of solution, the ratio of indirect to direct effect can increase and most of the crosslinking observed at low concentrations is in fact due to the indirect effect.

A sudden change in the reaction occurs at concentrations of the order of 1 per cent. Below this value, the minimum gelation dose increases very rapidly and below about ½ per cent concentration no gel formation can take place. Two explanations have been advanced to account for this drastic change in behaviour with concentration. The first hypothesis assumes that radiation produces (directly or indirectly) reactive sites on the polymer molecule. These will eventually cause the polymer molecule to degrade. If, however, a second polymer molecule is in the vicinity a crosslink may be formed instead. Thus the occurrence of a crosslink or a fracture is dependent upon the concentration. A mathematical analysis shows that the required concentration dependence is a reasonable one.

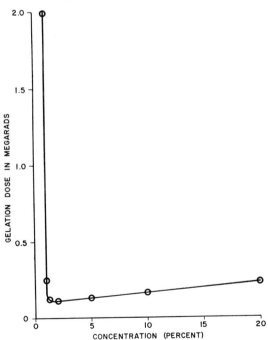

Figure 10.8 Gelation dose of solutions of Polyvinyl Pyrrolidone

A second explanation involves competition between crosslinking and internal linking. Each radical can link itself to another unit either on the same chain or on another chain; the probability of the link occurring being formed between two separate molecules will depend on the relative concentrations c_i (internal concentration) and c (external concentration) of monomer units about the activated group. The probability of a crosslink occurring between units in two separate molecules is $c/(c + c_i)$ and this decreases with concentration c. The internal concentration, c_i, initially depends only on the shape of a long chain polymer molecule in solution. As internal links are formed, each polymer molecule is tied more closely together and takes up a less extended arrangement. Increases in c_i and the probability of further external links are reduced. The transition at about 1 per cent concentration is therefore related to the ratio c/c_i, and its evaluation provides information on the state of polymer molecules in solution.

Radiation Mechanism

The mechanism by which radiation affects polymers, causing crosslinking, degradation, unsaturation, etc., is by no means clearly understood. One of the features of these reactions is that they are independent of radiation intensity. While this can be readily understood for polymers which degrade, the absence of an intensity effect for crosslinking (which involves the reaction of two adjacent molecules) is less easy to explain. The many mechanisms which have been suggested to account for this reaction can be considered as falling into several groups:

(1) Radiation causes ionization, excitation or radical production on one molecule and this species can then attack and combine with an adjacent polymer molecule which is itself not affected by radiation.

(2) Radiation causes the loss of a hydrogen atom which abstracts the hydrogen atom from a neighbouring molecule. Two radicals are thereby formed in close proximity by a single ionization or excitation and these can combine to form a crosslink.

(3) It is assumed that radicals formed by radiation are mobile and can wander through an irradiated specimen until they meet up in pairs to form a crosslink. In this mechanism, two independently formed radicals are required per crosslink.

(4) It has been suggested that unsaturation forms an essential step in the formation of crosslinks but details of the suggested mechanism have not yet been published.

(5) Hydrocarbons are known to suffer main chain fracture and a mechanism of linking has been suggested involving the attack of a fractured molecule on a neighbouring neutral molecule forming a trifunctional link or branch. The statistics for this process (termed endlinking) are not sub-

stantially different from those deduced for the more conventional crosslinking process.

There appear to be serious objections to most of these mechanisms. The crosslinking of polymers in solution, the effect of temperature, the independence of intensity and of type of radiation are all phenomena which must be explained by any useful theory of crosslinking and degradation. There remain a number of essential experiments to be carried out before any convincing mechanisms can be generally accepted.

Conclusion

Although the irradiation of long-chain polymers is a subject of relatively recent growth, the amount of scientific effort devoted to it in the last few years is very considerable. This may be considered to arise from the widespread use which such information can provide in a number of fields. The study of radiation mechanisms and the possibility of carrying out reactions in the solid state provide information of general validity in radiation chemistry. The radiation of polymers offers the further possibility of studying the effect of additives on the reactions and the results of such work can be of considerable interest in the field of radiobiology.

Useful applications have already arisen as a result of this work and many more are to be expected in the near future. There is, however, a danger in over emphasizing the scope of application at this stage. It cannot be too strongly emphasized that the subject is extremely novel and far more basic research on radiation reactions remains to be done before its full possibilities as a new industrial tool can be adequately described.

Literature References

Ballantine, D. S., "The Initiation of Chemical Reactions by Gamma and other ionizing radiations," Atomic Energy Comm. Report TID-8005 (1956).

Alexander, P., and Charlesby, A., "Energy Transfer in Macromolecules to ionizing radiations," *Nature*, **173**, 578 (1954).

Alexander, P. and Charlesby, A., "Radiation protection in copolymers of isobutylene and styrene," *Proc. Roy. Soc.*, **230**, 136 (1955).

Alexander, P., Charlesby, A. and Ross, M., "Degradation of solid polymethyl methacrylate by ionizing radiation," *Proc. Roy. Soc.*, **223**, 1154, 392 (1954).

Alexander, P., Black, R. M. and Charlesby, A., "Radiation induced changes in the structure of polyisobutylene," *Proc. Roy. Soc.*, **A232**, 31–48, (1955).

Bakh, N. A., "Radiolytic oxidation of organic compounds," Intntl. Conf. on Peaceful Uses of Atomic Energy P/683., Geneva, 1955, Vol. 7, p. 538.

Ballantine, D. and Manowitz, B., "The polymerization of vinyl monomers by intense gamma radiation," Atomic Energy Comm. Report BNL-229, Part 5.

Ballantine, D. S., et al, "Evaluation of polyethylene crosslinked by ionizing radiation," *J. Polymer Sci.*, **13**, 410 (1954).

Ballantine, D. S., et al, "Gamma ray initiated polymerization of styrene and methyl methacrylate," Intntl. Congress on Nuclear Eng., 61, June 20, 1954.

Ballantine, D. S., et al, "Fission Products Utilization. IX. Studies on radiation induced graft copolymerization and solid state polymerization," Atomic Energy Comm. Report BNL-414 (1956).

Baskett, A. C. and Miller, C. W., "Electron Irradiation of Polythene," *Nature*, **174**, 364–5, (1954).

Berstein, I. A., et al, "Studies on the gamma radiation-induced polymerization of acrylonitrile," *J. Chem. Phys.*, **21**, 1303 (1953).

Bopp, C. D. and Sisman, O., "How radiation changes polymer mechanical properties," *Nucleonics*, **13** (10), 51 (1955).

Bopp, C. D. and Sisman, O., "Radiation Stability of plastics and elastomers," *Nucleonics*, **13** (7), 28–33 (1955); see also AEC Report ORNL-1373 (1953).

Breger, I. A., "Transformation of Organic Substances by Alpha particles and deuterons," *J. Phys. Colloid Chem.*, **52**, 551 (1948).

Burr, J. G. and Garrison, W. M., "Effect of radiation on physical properties of plastics," Atomic Energy Comm. Report AECD 2078 (1948).

Byrne, J., et al, "Evolution of Halides from halogenated plastics exposed to γ-radiation," *Ind. Eng. Chem.*, **45**, 2549 (1953); see also AEC Report K-981 (1952).

Chapiro, A., "Effect of γ-radiation on polymers of the solid state I. Reticulation of polyethylene," *J. Chim. Phys.*, **52**, 246–58 (1955); (in French).

Chapiro, A., "Polymerization with the aid of gamma rays," *Compt. rend.*, **228**, 1490–2 (1949).

Chapiro, A., "Polymerization by gamma rays," *Compt rend.*, **229**, 827 (1949).

Chapiro, A., "On the polymerization of vinylic compounds initiated by γ-rays; I and II" *J. chim. Phys.*, **47**, 747 and 764 (1950).

Chapiro, A., et al, "Radiochemical polymerization of vinyl monomers," *J. chim. Phys.*, **52**, 689–98 (1955); (in French).

Charlesby, A., "Crosslinking of polyethylene by pile radiation," *Proc. Roy. Soc.*, **A215**, 187–214 (1952).

Charlesby, A., "The crosslinking of rubber by pile radiation," *Atomics*, **5**, 12, 27 (1954).

Charlesby, A., "Crosslinking and degradation of paraffin chains by high energy radiation," *Proc. Roy. Soc.*, **222**, 60 (1954).

Charlesby, A., "Decomposition and polymerization of polytetrafluoroethylene by pile radiation," AERE-M/R 978 (1952).

Charlesby, A., "Effect of high energy radiation on long chain polymers," *Nature*, **171**, 167 (1953).

Charlesby, A., "Effect of high energy radiation on polymers," *Bull. Am. Phys. Soc.*, **29** (3), 14 (1954).

Charlesby, A., "How radiation affects long chain polymers," *Nucleonics*, **12** (6), 18 (1954).

Charlesby, A., "How radiation affects materials: Beneficial effects on polymers," *Nucleonics*, **14** (9), 82 (1956).

Charlesby, A., "Solubility and molecular size distribution of crosslinked polystyrene," *J. Polymer Sci.*, **11**, 513 (1953): see also AERE-M/R 1034 (1952).

Charlesby, A., "Swelling properties of polystyrene crosslinked by high energy radiation," *J. Polymer Sci.*, **11**, 521 (1953): see also AERE-M/R-1051 (1952).

Charlesby, A. and Hancock, N. H., "Effect of crosslinking on the elastic modulus of polythene," *Proc. Roy. Soc.*, **A218**, 245 (1953): see also AERE-M/R 1060 (1952).

Charlesby, A. and Ross, M., "Breakdown of methyl methacrylate polymer by high energy radiation," *Nature*, **171**, 1153 (1953).

Charlesby, A. and Ross, M., "Effect of crosslinking on the density and melting of polythene," *Proc. Roy. Soc.*, A217, 122 (1953).

Charlesby, A., "Changes in silicone polymeric fluids," *Proc. Roy. Soc.*, 230, 120 (1955).

Charlesby, A. and Wycherley, V., "The irradiation of unsaturated polyester resins," *Int. J. Appl. Rad. Isotopes* 2, 26 (1957).

Charlesby, A. and Davison, W. H. T., "Temperature effects in the irradiation of polymers," *Chem. & Ind.*, 232 (1957).

Colichman, E. L. and Fish, R. F., "Resistance of terphenyls to heat and radiation," *Nucleonics*, 15 (2), 72–75 (1957).

Colichman, E. L. and Gercke, R. H. J., "Radiation stability of polyphenyls," *Nucleonics*, 14 (7), 50–4 (1956).

Collins, C. G. and Calkins, V. P., "Radiation damage to elastomers, organic liquids and plastics," Atomic Energy Comm. Report APEX 261 (1956).

Dole, M. and Keeling, C. D., "Pile irradiation of polyethylene," *J. Am. Chem. Soc.*, 76, 4304–11 (1954).

Dole, M., et al, "The pile irradiation of polyethylene," *J. Am. Chem. Soc.*, 76, 4304 (1954).

Eisler, S. L., "Evaluation of rubber for ordnance use. High radiation of polymers. A literature review," Atomic Energy Comm. Report AD-24914. (1953).

Farmer, F. T., "Electrical Properties of polystyrene," *Nature*, 150, 521 (1942).

Feng, P. Y. H. and Kennedy, J. W., "Electrical and chemical effects of beta radiation in polystyrene," *J. Am. Chem. Soc.* 77, 847 (1955).

Fowler, J. F. and Farmer, F. T., "Conductivity induced in insulating materials by X-rays," *Nature*, 173, 317 (1954).

Harrington, R., "How radiation affects materials: Damaging effects on plastics and elastomers," *Nucleonics*, 14 (9), 70 (1956).

Henley, E. J. and Miller, A., "Gamma ray dosimetry with polyvinyl chloride films," *Nucleonics*, 9 (6), Dec. 1951.

Landler, I. and Magat, M., "On the polymerization of styrene induced by slow neutrons," *Compt. rend.*, 226, 1720 (1948).

Lawton, E. J., et al, "Properties of irradiated polyethylene—effect of initial molecular weight," *Ind. Eng. Chem.*, 46, 1703 (1954).

Lawton, E. J., et al, "Some effects of high velocity electrons on wood," *Science*, 113, 380 (1951).

Lawton, E. J., et al, "Irradiation of polymers by high energy electrons," *Nature*, 172, 76 (1953).

Lind, S. C., "The Chemical Effects of Alpha Particle and Electrons" (Book), Chem. Catalog. Co., Inc., New York 1928 (2nd ed.).

Little, K., "Irradiation of linear high polymers," *Nature*, 170, 1075 (1952).

Mesrobian, R. B. and Ander, P., "Gamma ray polymerization of acrylamide in the solid state," *J. Chem. Phys.*, 22, 565 (1954).

Meyer, R. A., et al, "Radiation induced conductivity in polyethylene and teflon," *J. Appl. Phys.*, 27, 1012–18 (1956).

Mund, W., "Radio chemical polymerization of vinyl chloride at constant pressure," *Bull Soc. Chim. Belges*, 62, 109 (1953).

Mund, W. et al, "Polymerization of vinyl chloride under the action of rays," *Bull. Classe Sci. Acad. Roy. Belg.*, 35, 656 (1949).

Ross, M. and Charlesby, A., "Effect of pile radiation on polymethyl methacrylate ('Perspex')," *Atomics*, 4, 189 (1953).

Ryan, J. W., "Effect of gamma radiation on certain rubbers and plastics," *Nucleonics*, 11 (8), 13 (1953).

Ryan, J. W., "Radiation of polytetrafluoroethylene," *Modern Plastics*, 31, 152 (1953).

Saeman, J. F., et al, "Effect of high energy cathode rays on cellulose," *Ind. Eng. Chem.*, 44, 2848 (1952).

Schneider, E. E., "Paramagnetic resonance of X-rayed Teflon," *J. Chem. Phys.*, 23, 978 (1955).

Schmitz, J. V. and Lawton, E. J., "Initiation of vinyl polymerization by means of high energy electrons," *Science*, 113, 718 (1951).

Seitzer, W. H., et al, "β-ray initiation of polymerization of styrene and methyl methacrylate," *J. Am. Chem. Soc.*, 75, 755 (1953).

Sisman, O. and Bopp, C. D., "Effect of radiation on the physical properties of plastics," Atomic Energy Comm. Report AECD 2078 (1943).

Sisman, O. and Bopp, C. D., "Physical properties of irradiated plastics," Atomic Energy Comm. Report ORNL-928 (1951).

Stech, B., "Structural changes in crystals by bombardment with alpha particles," *Z. Naturforsch.*, 7a, 175 (1952); (in German).

Sun, K. H. "Effects of atomic radiation on high polymers," *Modern Plastics*, 32, 141–50, 229–39 (1954).

Todd, A., "Pile irradiation of polyethylene terephthalate," *Nature*, 174, 613 (1954)

Wall, L. A. and Magat, M., "Effects of atomic radiation on polymers," *Modern Plastics*, 30, 111–12, 114, 116, 176, 178 (1953).

Warrick, E. L., "Effects of radiations on organopolysiloxanes," *Ind. Eng. Chem.*, 47, 2388–93 (1955).

Chapter 11

RADIATION INDUCED GRAFT COPOLYMERIZATION

A. J. Restaino

The Martin Company, Baltimore, Maryland.

A graft copolymer may be defined as a chemical combination of polymers in which some of the branches off the main chain are polymer units other than the reference polymer. The reference polymer may be a copolymer or homopolymer. If the homopolymer is composed of units of "A", then the graft copolymer of "B" to "A" may be represented by the structure

$$
\begin{array}{c}
\text{B} \\
\text{B} \\
\text{B} \\
-\text{A A A A A A A}- \\
\text{B} \\
\text{B} \\
\text{B}
\end{array}
$$

Since the polymer to be grafted may be a vinyl or condensation polymer, graft copolymerization reactions may be initiated by free radical producing chemical catalysts, by heat, by acids and bases in the case of condensation polymers and by ionizing radiation in either case.

Neutron, proton, electron, alpha, X- and gamma radiation are generally referred to as ionizing radiation. Because of historical development and present trends the discussion of radiation induced graft copolymerization will be limited to X-radiation produced from Van de Graaff generators and gamma-rays from Cobalt-60.

Cobalt-60 liberates in cascade two gamma-rays of energy 1.17 Mev and 1.33 Mev and upon interaction with matter, Compton scattering is the predominant effect. Interactions of gamma-rays with matter produces ions, free radicals and excited molecules.

The following reaction scheme has been proposed as a working hypothesis to describe the formation of the reactive species when gamma radiation interacts with a vinyl monomer, M.

$$(1) \quad M + \gamma \rightarrow M^+ + e$$

$$(2) \ \mathrm{M} + \mathrm{e} \to \mathrm{M}*$$

$$(3) \ \mathrm{M}^+ + \mathrm{e} \to \mathrm{M}*$$

$$(4) \ \mathrm{M}^+ \to \mathrm{R} \cdot + \mathrm{H}^+$$

$$(5) \ \mathrm{M}* \to 2\mathrm{R} \cdot$$

Reactions (1) and (2) represent direct ionization and direct excitation, respectively. In addition, an excited electronic state in the monomer molecule may be formed by electron absorption (3) Bond rupture of either the ion or excited molecule may result in the formation of free radicals (4, 5). A similar mechanism may be written to demonstrate that gamma-rays produce free radicals in the polymer[1] as well as in the monomer.

There is evidence that radiation induced polymerizations in gaseous,[2] liquid[3, 4] and solid state[5, 6] are free radical processes. The polymerization of equimolar mixtures of liquid methyl methacrylate and styrene using β-rays from $\mathrm{S_r}^{90}$ and Y^{90} has been studied by Tobolsky and Seitzer.[4] Analysis indicates a one to one mole ratio of methyl methacrylate to styrene in the copolymer demonstrating that although ions may be formed, the polymerization process proceeds essentially via a free radical mechanism.[7] Similar results using gamma-rays as the initiation source have been observed by Ballantine et al.[8] Free radical concentrations as high as 10^{-4} molal have been observed from the paramagnetic resonance response of gamma irradiated acrylamide at liquid nitrogen temperatures.[5] Radiation-induced crosslinking reactions investigated by Charlesby[9] and Dole et al.[10] have been assigned a free radical mechanism.*

The feasibility of a given graft copolymerization reaction will depend upon the relative ability of a polymer (A) and a monomer (B) to form free radicals when subjected to ionizing radiation. For example, if the rate of free radical production is larger in the monomer to be grafted than in the polymer, the quantity of homopolymer formed may be large compared to the amount grafted, making the process wasteful. The efficiency of a graft copolymerization reaction may adequately be described by considering the radiation yield of free radicals for a given polymer when compared with the monomer to be grafted. For example the relatively larger G-value for methyl methacrylate compared to that of styrene suggests that the irradiation of polymethyl methacrylate dissolved in styrene should produce graft copolymers. It is assumed here that the radiation susceptibility of polymethyl methacrylate does not decrease significantly from that of the monomer.

* Mechanisms proposed more recently by Burton suggest cross-linking (e.g., in polyethylene) may be produced by ion-molecule interaction of two polymer chains.

Kinetics

Recently G-values* for free radical formation were calculated[11] based on gamma-ray initiated polymerization studies reported by Ballantine et al.,[12] and the results were compared with other radiation initiated polymerizations. Kinetic studies on the gamma induced homopolymerization of methyl methacrylate and monostyrene demonstrate that the rate of polymerization is proportional to the square root of the gamma-ray intensity in the range 40,000 to 300,000 rep/hr. Rate and molecular weight data support the mechanism suggested below:

$$M + \phi \xrightarrow{k_i} R\cdot$$

$$R\cdot + M \xrightarrow{k_p} R_x\cdot$$

$$R_x\cdot + R_y\cdot \xrightarrow{k_t} P$$

where M represents the monomer, ϕ the gamma-ray intensity, $R\cdot$ the free radical, P the polymer, and k_i, k_p, k_t, the rate constants for initiation, propagation and termination respectively. Assuming biradical termination in the case of styrene[13a, b] and methyl methacrylate[14] polymerization, and applying the steady state condition, the following equation results,

$$\frac{d(R\cdot)}{dt} = R_i - 2k_t(R\cdot)^2 = 0 \tag{1}$$

where R_i represents the rate of initiation in moles/liter/sec. and $(R\cdot)$ the free radical concentration. Since the rate of polymerization or propagation rate, R_p, is $k_p (R\cdot) (M)$, substitution of $(R\cdot)$ in the steady state equation above yields,

$$R_i = \frac{2k_t R_p^2}{k_p^2 (M)^2} = \frac{2A'}{(M)^2} R_p^2 \tag{2}$$

where (M) represents the monomer concentration, and A' is the ratio of rate constants k_t/k_p^2. Reported values of A' are:

$$A' = 5.68 \times 10^{-6} \exp (12.46 \text{ kcal/RT}) \text{ for styrene[15]}$$

$$A' = 5.02 \times 10^{-5} \exp (9.35 \text{ kcal/RT}) \text{ for methyl methacrylate.[16]}$$

By means of this equation it has been possible to calculate the G-values for radical formation in the gamma-initiated polymerization of methyl

* G-values reported throughout this chapter are the number of free radicals formed per 100 e.v. of energy absorbed in a material of unit density.

methacrylate and styrene. Equation(2) may be put in a form where G-values can be calculated directly,

$$\frac{G(\text{radicals})}{100 \text{ e.v.}} = R_i \frac{(\text{moles})}{1. \text{ sec.}} \times \frac{1}{d \frac{(\text{gms})}{\text{c.c.}}} \times \frac{11}{10^3 \text{c.c.}} \times 6.02$$

$$\times 10^{23} \frac{\text{radicals}}{\text{mole}} \times \frac{1}{\phi \frac{(\text{rep})}{\text{hr.}}} \times 3.6 \times 10^3 \frac{\text{sec.}}{\text{hr.}} \tag{3a}$$

$$\times 1 \frac{\text{gm. rep.}}{93 \text{ ergs}} \times 1.6 \times 10^{-10} \frac{(\text{ergs})}{100 \text{ e.v.}}$$

$$G = 3.73 \times 10^{12} \frac{R_i}{d\phi} \tag{3b}$$

where the units of density, d, the radiation intensity, ϕ, etc., are represented in equation (3a). Equation (3b) may be extended to G-value calculations for the polymer if it is assumed that the radiation susceptibility of the polymer is not significantly different from that of the monomer.

Table 1 gives a comparison of G-values calculated by Mesrobian et al.

TABLE 1. G-VALUES OF STYRENE AND METHYL METHACRYLATE POLYMERIZATIONS AT SEVERAL TEMPERATURES

Temp., °C.	Field Intensity, Rep/hr.	Polymerization Rate[a] (m./l./sec) $\times 10^5$	Monomer Conc.[b] (moles)/ liter	Rate of Initiation (m./l./sec.) $\times 10^8$	G-Value[c] (Radicals/ 100 e.v.)	G-Value, Ref. 17	G-Value Ref. 18
			Data for Styrene				
72	245,000	5.84	8.25	4.40	0.78		
25	190,000	1.01	8.67	2.08	0.46	0.22 at	1.6 at
−18	265,000	0.24	9.05	2.74	0.56	30.5°C	15°C
			Data for Methyl Methacrylate				
70	245,000	49.9	8.85	28.4	4.88		
25	250,000	21.1	9.37	36.0	5.74	3.14 at	27.5 at
−18	265,000	7.25	9.86	53.8	7.68	30.5°C	15°C

[a] Data of Ballantine et al., reference 12.

[b] Concentration of pure monomer at each temperature calculated from density values. For styrene see "Styrene, Its Polymers, Copolymers and Derivatives", R. H. Boundy and R. F. Boyer, Reinhold, N. Y., 1952, p. 54. Density values for methyl methacrylate were provided by Dr. W. R. Conn of the Rohm and Haas Co.

[c] G-Value calculations are based upon 1 rep being equivalent to the absorption of 93 ergs per gram by material of unit density.

Reprinted from J. Poly. Sci. 19, 220 (1956)

by means of equation (3b) with G-values obtained from β-ray initiated polymerization reactions[17] and gamma-rays[18] at several temperatures.

It may be noted from Table 1 that there is no significant temperature coefficient for the G-values of the two monomers between −18°C and 72°C. This is not surprising since the initiation activation energy for radiation-induced vinyl polymerizations is zero. The less than two-fold variation in G-values may be attributed to errors in rate measurements or experimental errors in A′. Comparison of G-values determined by Mesrobian et al. with those obtained by Seitzer and Tobolsky demonstrate that there is no significant difference in the efficiency of radical production from the two monomers when the initiating source is gamma or beta radiation.

Since the ability of different monomers to swell certain polymer films may vary considerably, graft copolymers produced by ionizing radiation may be classified as surface graft or matrix graft copolymers, based on whether the bulk of grafted monomer is on the polymer film surface or in the polymer film matrix. The classification is, of course, one of convenience and in the case of matrix graft copolymers some of the grafted monomer is at the surface. Studies indicate that the G-values for monomer and polymer as well as the swelling ratios determine whether or not a certain monomer-polymer combination will produce a preponderance of surface or matrix grafting when the system is irradiated.

Surface Graft Copolymers

The inability of most monomers to swell polytetrafluoroethylene films tends to limit the radiation induced graft copolymerization reaction to the surface. The graft copolymerization of monomers such as acrylic acid[6] and vinyl acetate[18] which homopolymerize very rapidly on exposure to gamma irradiation are not wholly inefficient because after initial grafting the polymerized monomer, whose G-value is probably larger than polytetrafluoroethylene, acts as the locus for further grafting. Surface graft copolymers of polytetrafluoroethylene have been prepared with acrylonitrile, acrylic acid, styrene and vinyl acetate. The salient features of the kinetics of the radiation induced graft copolymerization of vinyl acetate to polytetrafluoroethylene have been described recently at the symposium[19].

Polytetrafluoroethylene Vinyl Acetate

The irradiation of films of polytetrafluoroethylene in vinyl acetate containing as much as 0.1 weight percent hydroquinone indicate that the graft copolymerization as well as the homopolymerization of vinyl acetate is affected by hydroquinone, demonstrating that the radiation induced graft copolymerization as well as the homopolymerization are free radical processes. A study of the effect of polytetrafluoroethylene film thickness (3, 5,

TABLE 2. EFFECT OF TEMPERATURE, FIELD INTENSITY AND MONOMER CONCENTRATION
ON THE RATE OF GRAFTING VINYL ACETATE TO 3 MIL
POLYTETRAFLUOROETHYLENE FILMS

Field Intensity (rep/h.) $\times 10^{-4}$	Molar Conc. Vinyl Acetate in Ethyl Acetate	Temperature (°C)	Initial Rate % Graft/min.	Rate $\times 10^4$ (Intensity)$^{1/2}$	$\dfrac{\text{Rate}}{(\text{Monomer})^{3/2}} \times 10^3$
A. Effect of Intensity					
1.5	7	20	0.042	3.4	
7.0	7	20	0.133	5.0	
15.9	7	20	0.185	4.7	
27.0	7	20	0.256	4.8	
46.0	7	20	0.475	5.4	
B. Effect of Temperature					
27.0	10.8	5	0.156		
27.0	10.8	20	0.310		
27.0	10.8	40	0.385		
27.0	10.8	59	0.500		
C. Effect of Monomer Concentration					
27.0	10.8	20	0.310		8.8
27.0	7.0	20	0.256		7.3
27.0	5.0	20	0.105		9.3
27.0	3.0	20	0.050		9.6
27.0	2.0	20	0.022		7.5

and 10 mils) and surface area on the rate of grafting indicates that the weight of vinyl acetate grafted is independent of the film thickness and directly proportional to the surface area. Initial rate studies demonstrate that the rate of grafting* is proportional to the three-halves power of the monomer concentration from 2.0 to 10.8 molar vinyl acetate in ethyl acetate, and to the one-half power of the intensity in the range investigated from 15,000 to 460,000 rep/hr. The activation energy has been found to be 4.6 ± 0.4 kcal/mole. Table 2 summarizes the effects of intensity temperature and monomer concentration on the grafting rate.

The addition of as much as 15 grams per deciliter of high molecular weight polyvinyl acetate to the copolymerization mixture has no effect on the initial rate of grafting. The absence of a "Trommsdorf effect" indicates that the termination step is either unimolecular or by chain transfer to monomer. The latter appears to be more probable.[20a, b]

* The rate of grafting is defined as the weight gained per unit time divided by the final weight multiplied by 100.

If chain transfer to monomer is the principle mode of termination in the graft copolymerization of vinyl acetate to polytetrafluoroethylene, a unique situation arises. The chain transfer to monomer could decrease the rate of grafting, if the monomer radical, which results from chain transfer, initiates homopolymerization instead of further chain transfer with a grafted chain of polyvinyl acetate.

In order to determine whether chain transfer reactions of this type could affect the graft copolymerization rate of vinyl acetate to polytetrafluoroethylene the grafting reactions were carried out in the presence of a "strong" chain transfer agent, carbon tetrachloride. Gamma irradiated solutions of as little as 0.016 molar carbon tetrachloride in vinyl acetate-polytetrafluoroethylene resulted in more than a three-fold decrease in the initial grafting rate. The radiation stabilization of certain organic systems by chlorinated solvents has been reported by Chapiro.[21] It may be that the three-fold decrease in the initial rate of grafting is due to excitation transfer prior to bond change from excited polytetrafluoroethylene molecules to carbon tetrachloride or to the fact that alkyl halides serve as efficient electron traps. The net effect would be to reduce the number of radicals capable of initiating the graft copolymerization, thus reducing the rate. Based on a 600:1 mole ratio of vinyl acetate to carbon tetrachloride it may be concluded that if the effect is due to either process the reaction must be amazingly efficient. However similar studies using benzene instead of carbon tetrachloride indicate that carbon tetrachloride reduces the grafting rate more efficiently than benzene. It is difficult to reconcile this observation with reported results[22] which indicate generally that benzene is a more efficient "protecting agent" than carbon tetrachloride. The alternative view that chain transfer is responsible for the decreased rate of grafting in the presence of carbon tetrachloride is supported by studies[19] of the gamma induced polymerization of vinyl acetate in the presence of carbon tetrachloride. As the concentration of carbon tetrachloride increases the molecular weight decreases. It is difficult to account for this observation on the basis of an energy transfer or electron trap mechanism alone.

Graft copolymers of polytetrafluoroethylene styrene and polytetrafluoroethylene-N-vinylpyrollidone have been prepared by gamma irradiation of polymer films immersed in pure styrene and in 20 per cent aqueous N-vinylpyrollidone.[23] In the case of styrene the weight grafted is observed to be independent of film thickness indicating that the graft copolymerization occurs principally at the film surface. The graft copolymerization of N-vinylpyrollidone to polytetrafluoroethylene exhibits an autocatalytic effect after 2 per cent grafting. A similar observation has been reported[19] for the graft copolymerization of vinyl acetate to polytetrafluoroethylene. These results

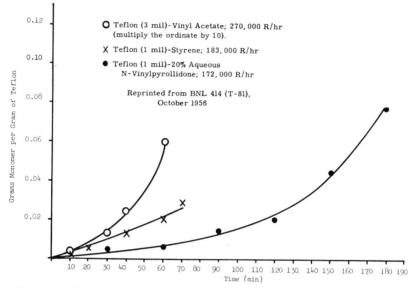

Figure 11.1 Graft copolymerization of some vinyl monomers to teflon initiated by cobalt-60 gamma-rays.

are compared with the graft copolymerization of polytetrafluoroethylene styrene and are represented in Figure 1.

The presence of an autocatalytic effect such as is observed in the radiation-induced graft copolymerization of N-vinylpyrollidone and vinyl acetate to polytetrafluoroethylene will be discussed subsequently in detail. At present it suffices to say that any of three factors may be responsible for the increased grafting rate after initial grafting, namely a "Trommsdorf Effect", an increase in monomer absorption in the grafted polymer or an increase in G-value due to the grafted monomer.

Poylethylene-Acrylonitrile

The gamma induced graft copolymerization of acrylonitrile to polyethylene has been studied by Ballantine et al.[23] in distilled monomer, in dimethylformamide and in aqueous solutions of acrylonitrile. In no case is the equilibrium weight absorbed of acrylonitrile at 25°C. into a one gram polyethylene film of 10 mil thickness greater than 0.4 weight per cent. The diffusion rate of pure acrylonitrile into the 10 mil film is 2.5 × 10⁻⁶ g. per g. of film per cm² per minute.* The rate of diffusion of monomer into the polyethylene film is considerably less than the rate of grafting in all cases studied. These observations are supporting evidence for the fact that

* A. Restaino, W. Reed and R. Hornbeck (unpublished work).

the gamma-ray initiated graft copolymerization of acrylonitrile to polyethylene films is predominantly a surface copolymerization.

Matrix Graft Copolymers.

Polyethylene-Styrene. The synthesis of homogeneous graft copolymers of the matrix type presupposes a careful control of monomer diffusion into the polymer during the course of radiation. Charlesby reports[24] that homogeneous matrix graft copolymers of polyethylene and styrene may be prepared by intermittent irradiation of high intensity from a Van de Graaff accelerator using finely powdered polymers and allowing the monomer time to re-establish equilibrium swelling with the polymer during the irradiations. Ballantine et al.[23] have studied the graft copolymerization of styrene to polyethylene films under continuous irradiation and have observed that the grafted styrene appears as strata within the polyethylene matrix.

Three techniques have been employed successfully in preparing graft copolymers of styrene to polyethylene films; (1) irradiation of the dry film, followed by immersion in monomer, (2) irradiation of the film swollen with monomer and (3) irradiation of the film immersed in monomer.

A gain in weight has been observed when dry polyethylene films are irradiated and then immersed in monomer. The phenomena is referred to as post-polymerization. Although the process is slow, samples of irradiated polyethylene exhibit a gain in weight over a period of ten days when immersed in monostyrene. It appears unlikely that this effect is due solely to thermal decomposition of hydroperoxides formed when polyethylene is irradiated in air.[25] Ballantine reports[23] that gamma irradiation of polyethylene films to 5 Mrep. in the presence of nitrogen results in the formation of a 55 per cent graft copolymer of styrene to polyethylene when the irradiated film is immersed in the monomer for ten days.

The irradiation of polythylene films swollen with styrene results in a decrease of the overall grafting rate due to the limitations of absorbed monomer by the film. It is established that the kinetic dependence of the grafting rate on styrene monomer is not *zero* order.

For these reasons the synthesis of graft copolymers by irradiation of films immersed in monomer has received much wider attention than either of the other techniques.

Kinetic data reported[23] on the gamma induced graft copolymerization of styrene to polyethylene demonstrates that the grafting rate is independent of gamma intensity in the range of 20,000 rep/hr to 300,000 rep/hr. These results would tend to indicate that the process is controlled by the rate of diffusion of monomer into the film. On the other hand, the rate of grafting on 10-mil films of polyethylene is approximately twice as fast as that on 4-mil films. It is difficult to reconcile this result with a diffusion

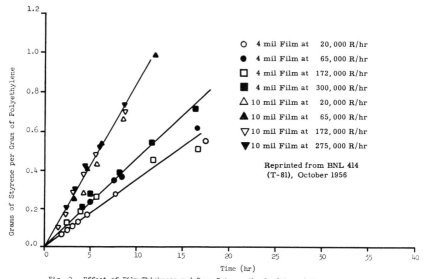

Fig. 2. Effect of Film Thickness and Dose Rate on the Grafting of Styrene to Polyethylene

Figure 11.2 Effect of film thickness and dose rate on the grafting of styrene to polyethylene.

controlled mechanism. The effect of gamma intensity and film thickness on the rate of grafting styrene to polyethylene is represented in Figure 2.

Matrix vs. Surface Grafting

Polyethylene-Methyl Methacrylate. Figure 3 represents the rate of grafting at three intensities when 4-mil polyethylene films are immersed in methyl methacrylate. The observed autocatalytic effect indicates that the grafted methyl methacrylate, which is capable of greater swelling with its monomer than is polyethylene*, may act as a locus for further grafting. The greater radiation susceptibility of polymethyl methacrylate, compared with that of polyethylene,[26] may also be responsible for the increase in the rate of grafting at higher per cent grafts.

Table 3 summarizes the effect of gamma-ray intensity on the initial rate of grafting methyl methacrylate to polyethylene and demonstrates that the initial grafting rate is proportional to the square root of the intensity in the range of 2×10^4 rep/hr. to 1.6×10^5 rep/hr. At higher grafting per cents the dependence of the grafting rate on the intensity falls below the square root dependence and appears to approach zero. A similar result has been observed in the graft copolymerization of vinyl acetate to polytetrafluoroethylene.[19]

* The equilibrium swelling of polyethylene films immersed in pure methyl methacrylate at 25°C. is less than 4 per cent by weight (unpublished).

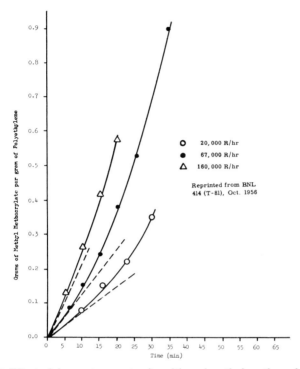

Figure 11.3 Effect of dose rate on rate of grafting of methyl methacrylate to 4-mil polyethylene.

These results demonstrate that the initial grafting takes place predominantly at the surface but as the copolymerization proceeds, the grafted polymer serves as the matrix for further grafting. Evidence for this conclusion is supported by the fact that the grafted monomer will imbibe methyl methacrylate more readily than the initial polyethylene and furthermore, the G-value for polymethyl methacrylate is greater than for polyethylene.

The question arises as to why the gamma induced graft copolymerization

TABLE 3. EFFECT OF DOSE RATE ON THE RATE OF GRAFTING METHYL METHACRYLATE TO 4-MIL POLYETHYLENE

Initial Rate $\times 10^2$ (g. Monomer per g. film per min.)	Dose Rate $\times 10^{-4}$ (R/hr)	$\dfrac{\text{Initial Rate}}{(\text{dose rate})^{1/2}}$
0.75	2.00	5.3
1.3	6.70	5.1
2.2	16.0	5.6

Reprinted from BNL *414* (T-81), Oct., 1956.

of polyethylene films immersed in styrene results in the formation of a matrix graft copolymer whereas similar studies in methyl methacrylate result in the predominant formation of a surface graft. Similarly, an acceptable mechanism must be capable of describing the independence of the grafting rate on the intensity in the former case and the eventual decrease in the dependence of the grafting rate on intensity below one-half order in the case of methyl methacrylate-polyethylene.

Due to the greater concentration of monomer at the surface than in the film, the assumption is made that in the very early stages of grafting, copolymerization occurs at the surface as well as within the matrix of the film. Since polyethylene films will imbibe 2½ times more styrene than methyl methacrylate, based on swelling measurements alone, one would anticipate a greater proportion of matrix to surface grafting in the case of styrene. Once the surface becomes sufficiently grafted with monomer, and in order to maintain the same ratio of matrix to surface grafting, the monomer must diffuse through the grafted surface into the matrix of the polyethylene film. However, since the G-value for polymethyl methacrylate (methyl methacrylate) is large, the monomer becomes grafted to the already grafted methyl methacrylate before it can diffuse into the polyethylene matrix. In the case of styrene the G-value is less than methyl methacrylate by a factor of 20. Because of the smaller G-value and the greater film swelling by styrene, the probability of styrene diffusion through the grafted surface and into the polyethylene matrix is much greater than 20 times that for methyl methacrylate. The situation may be summarized by saying that the surface of grafted methyl methacrylate is a far more efficient shield in preventing the monomer from reaching the matrix of the polyethylene film.

The rapid rate of graft copolymerization of vinyl acetate-polytetrafluoroethylene, acrylonitrile-polyethylene and methyl methacrylate-polyethylene has already been noted. After relatively short periods of irradiation at intensities above 20,000 rep/hr., the thickness of polymer film is observed to increase significantly indicating that the film surface contains substantial amounts of grafted monomer. When this occurs the system may be considered as a matrix grafting of the monomer in films of its own polymer. The reaction is therefore controlled by the diffusion of monomer into its own matrix. This interpretation appears consistent with observations in methyl methacrylate-polyethylene and vinyl acetate-polytetrafluoroethylene that the grafting rate becomes independent of the intensity at higher per cent grafts. Although there is a lack of kinetic data for acrylonitrile-polyethylene one might assume that since the monomer is not imbibed by the grafted acrylonitrile polymer, the grafting always takes place on the surface of the grafted film and not within the matrix of the grafted monomer. Other effects being negligible, one would not aticipate a decrease of the grafting rate dependence on the intensity to zero. Indeed, no such decrease is observed within the grafting per cents reported.[23]

Other Graft Copolymers

In addition to the graft-copolymers of "Teflon" and polyethylene with vinyl monomers already reported, a variety of graft copolymers of cellulose, hevea rubber, "Kel-F," "Mylar," "Nylon," polypropylene, polyvinyl alcohol and polyvinyl chloride have also been synthesized by gamma irradiation of the polymer films immersed in certain vinyl moners. The weight per cent of monomer grafted for various monomer-polymer combinations of specific film thicknesses and gamma-ray intensities is presented in Table 4.

Evidence for the fact that the polymer systems represented in Table 4 are truly graft copolymers has, for the most part, been determined by the solubility characteristics of the grafted films. For example, after grafting polyvinyl acetate and polystyrene to polytetrafluoroethylene, they could not be removed from the surface after 24 hours in boiling benzene.

Evidence for graft copolymer formation in the case of polymethyl methacrylate-styrene (not reported in Table 4) was firmly established by a titration technique developed for this system.[27]

Mesrobian has recently reported[28] that the irradiation of an unsaturated polymer such as Natural Rubber in the presence of para-chlorostyrene not only produces a graft copolymer but also produces the radiation dose required to crosslink the polymer. As the weight percent para-chlorostyrene increases from 0 to approximately 17 percent this simultaneous vulcanization-grafting reduces the radiation dose required for crosslinking by a factor greater than 30, the insoluble gel fraction representing about 95% of the total polymer at 1.05 megarads and 17 initial weight percent monomer. This effect has been attributed to the propagation of para-chlorostyrene to the polymer via several copolymerization steps of growing radicals with the double bonds of the rubber chain. It is of interest to note that at increased concentrations of monomer above 17 weight percent the radiation dose required to produce crosslinking increases markedly. A comparison of the physical properties of these vulcanizites with those obtained by conventional curing agents has not yet been reported.

The various techniques involved in the synthesis of graft and block copolymers have been reviewed by Mark and Immergut[29] and Hart[30]. In the present discussion irradiation of monomer-polymer combinations results in the formation of graft copolymers only if the radicals formed on the polymer chains propagate monomer prior to dismutation. However, if the polymer chain radicals dismute prior to interaction with monomer, propagation will lead to the formation of block copolymers.

TABLE 4. SOME RADIATION PRODUCED GRAFT COPOLYMERS

Polymer	Monomer Grafted	Intensity (rep/hr) $\times 10^5$	Total Dose $\times$ 10^5 rep	Film Thickness (Mils)	Wt. Per cent Monomer Grafted
Cellulose (Cellophane)	Methyl Methacrylate	3	3.00	1	57.0
Cellulose (filter paper)	Methyl Methacrylate	3	3.00	10	86.0
Cellulose (filter paper)	Styrene	3	48.0	10	32.2
Hevea Rubber*	Acrylonitrile 25% by volume in Dimethylformamide	—	6.3	—	100.0
Hevea Rubber*	Styrene		27.0		10.5
Kel-F	Acrylic Acid	3	0.75	9.6	6.0
Kel-F	Acrylonitrite	3	0.75	10.5	1.0
Kel-F	Styrene	3	72.0	10.5	3.4
Kel-F	Vinyl Acetate (undistilled)	3	3.0	10.5	11.0
Mylar*	Styrene		135.0		8.8
Nylon*	Styrene		311.0		10.5
Polyethylene	Acrylic Acid	3	0.75	3	37.0
Polyethylene*	Acrylonitrile 25% by volume in dimethylformamide	3	9.0	4	16.6
Polyethylene*	Methyl methacrylate	1.6	0.4	4	29.5
Polyethylene*	Styrene	2.75	27.0	10	44.5
Polyethylene*	Styrene	2.5	20.0	10	35.0
Polyethylene	Vinyl Carbazole 1.5 M in xylene	2.5	47.5	10	20.0
Polyethylene*	4-Vinyl Pyridine (undistilled)	1.72	1.72	4	33.3
Polyethylene*	Vinyl Stearate 60% in Benzene		28.0		7.2
Polypropylene	Styrene		35.0		43.4
Polyvinyl Alcohol 80% Acetylated	Acrylonitrile undistilled	3.0	2.25	10	99.0
Polyvinyl Alcohol	Acrylamide (saturated solu. in cold H_2O)	3.0	3.0	6	19.8
Polyvinyl Alcohol	Acrylonitrile 6% solu. in cold H_2O	3.0	15.0	6	9.7
Polyvinyl Alcohol	Styrene	3.0	114.0	5.5	2.95
Polyvinyl Alcohol	Vinyl Acetate undistilled	3.0	3.0	5.5	1.9
Polytetrafluoroethylene	Acrylic Acid undistilled	3.0	3.29	3.0	16.0
Polytetrafluoroethylene*	Acrylonitrile		0.63		1.3
Polytetrafluoroethylene*	Styrene	1.83	1.83	1	24.4
Polytetrafluoroethylene*	Styrene	3.0	12.0	3	17.9
Polytetrafluoroethylene	Vinyl Acetate	3.0	2.5	3	61.0
Polyvinyl Chloride	Acrylonitrile (undistilled)	3.0	7.5	40	25.0

Unless otherwise noted monomers are pure and distilled.

* Results reported BNL 414 (T-81) October, 1956.

Otherwise A. J. Restaino, W. N. Reed, The Martin Company, Radiation Effects Unit, Progress Report II ER8519, 13–19 (1956).

TABLE 5. SOME PROPERTIES OF VARIOUS GRAFT COPOLYMERS OF A 4 MIL
POLYETHYLENE FILM BASE

Monomer	% Graft	Dose Rate (rep/hr)	Dose (rep)	Crystal Melting Pt. (°C)	Density (g/cc.)	Ultimate Elong. (%)	Tensile† Strength (psi)	20% Offset Yield Strength (psi)	Tensile Elastic Modulus (psi)
None	—	—	0	111.7	0.9092	860	1930	889	14,700
Acryloni-trile	12.2	300,000	180,000	111.2	0.9334	518	2460	1305	21,870
Acryloni-trile	18.1	180,000	225,000	113.7	0.9328	580	2310	1300	23,500
Styrene	5.3	172,000	224,000	113.0	0.9161	816	2070	942	17,200
Styrene*	21.6	180,000	1,530,000	−‡	0.9371	467	1610	1324	38,300
Styrene	35.5	172,000	2,838,000	−‡	0.9552	100	1382	1446	46,500
Styrene	60.0	180,000	7,110,000	−‡	0.9860	14	1155	1191	56,000
4-Vinyl-pyridine	28.0	172,000	143,000	−‡	0.9860	490	2240	1058	23,400

* Styrene contained inhibitor.
† Tensile properties were determined according to ASTM testing (D882-54)
Method A.
‡ Did not exhibit crystal melting point up to 200°C.
Reprinted from BNL 414 (T-81), October, 1956.

Although sufficient physical property data is unavailable to distinguish
between graft and block copolymers for those systems reported in Table 4,
the difference between radiation produced graft and block copolymers would
be very slight. For example assuming a G-value for radical formation of
unity and a total dose of 1 megarep, less than 10 % of the polymer molecules
of average molecular weight 100,000 form radicals during the course of
irradiation. Assuming the validity of reactions (4) and (5) presented on the
first page of the present chapter, on the average about one sequence of "B"
copolymer units will appear per initial polymer radical propagated. Unless
the irradiated polymer is linear the differentiation between a one stage
graft and a one stage block copolymer has little meaning.

Physical Properties

Physical property studies of some graft copolymers of polyethylene have
been reported by Ballantine et al.[23] The results are reproduced in part in
Table 5.

A slight increase in the crystal melting point of grafted polyethylene is
observed at low radiation doses. At higher doses no melting point* is observed due to the destruction of crystallites in the polyethylene by irradia-

* Melting point determinations are based on birefringence studies in specimens
heated at the rate of 1 to 2°C/min.

tion. In the case of the acrylonitrile graft copolymer, the decrease in ultimate elongation and the increases in tensile strength and elastic modulus indicate that cross-linking is the predominant effect. Likewise, in the styrene-polyethylene graft copolymer, the tensile elastic modulus increases and ultimate elongation decreases with radiation dose. However, the tensile strength of the graft copolymers containing more than 6 per cent styrene decreases with radiation dose indicating that molecular scission with the formation of low molecular weight fragments also occurs. In no case does the effect of radiation in the graft copolymers reported above differ significantly from the effects of radiation on polyethylene in the absence of monomer.[31] It is noteworthy that the refractive index of the 28 per cent graft copolymer of 4-vinylpyridine and polyethylene is 1.571, an increase substantial enough to be attributed to the grafted 4-vinylpyridine and not to the radiation effects on polyethylene alone.

Preliminary studies of the adhesive properties of the graft copolymers of vinyl acetate to polytetrafluoroethylene and styrene to polytetrafluoroethylene indicate an improvement in the adhesive properties of polytetrafluoroethylene. At approximately ten per cent graft in either case the adhesive properties become identical with the homopolymers. The graft copolymer of acrylonitrile to dimethylsiloxane is superior to the silicone rubber in solvent resistance as determined by swelling studies in toluene and heptane. The sulfonated graft copolymer of styrene to polyethylene has properties which make it competitive with other ion-exchange membranes. The graft copolymer of vinyl carbazole to polyethylene has improved dielectric loss properties over polyethylene while the graft copolymer is not as brittle as polyvinyl carbazole. Certain graft copolymers in which metals are chemically bound have tensile strengths above 3,000 psi with elongations less than 4%. The radiation stability of these metal-organic polymers as determined by tensile studies is comparable to polystyrene but the softening point and solvent resistance is substantially superior to polystyrene. Physical properties and applications of some of these graft copolymers have been described elsewhere.[32, 33, 34]

For the most part those polymers which undergo marked changes in physical properties upon irradiation serve as the most efficient base materials for grafting. Some of these materials such as polytetrafluoroethylene are not easily oxidized so that thermal synthesis of graft copolymers of polytetrafluoroethylene is extremely difficult. On the other hand certain substituted polystyrenes which are not very susceptible to change upon irradiation and hence difficult to graft, can be oxidized and graft copolymers may be produced thermally.[35] It is to be noted that there are significant systems in which graft copolymers can be made efficiently by either one of these techniques but not by both. From a commercial point of view radiation-induced graft copolymerization may be considered a supplement to other techniques of grafting through which a broader range of graft copolymers may be synthesized.

Experimental

As is the case with free radical vinyl polmerizations, the removal of oxygen in the preparation of samples for graft copolymerization is essential to eliminate the induction period which inevitably results when oxygen is present. Ordinary degassing of the monomer system or purging with purified nitrogen has proved effective. Either of these techniques is effective in the preparation of samples for polytetrafluoroethylene grafting of pure vinyl monomers. However in some cases; e.g., polymethyl methacrylate-styrene, the high viscosity of the medium makes ordinary degassing ineffective and purging the system with purified nitrogen is preferred. In general the latter procedure is to be recommended since it is simple and more widely applicable.

In a typical preparation a weighed sample of the polymer film is immersed in distilled monomer contained in a glass tube fitted with a ground glass stopper. The system is degassed or purged with nitrogen and irradiated. After the irradiation the polymer film is removed, washed in a solvent to remove monomer and homopolymerized monomer, dried in vacuo and weighed. The increase in weight divided by the final weight multiplied by 100 defines the per cent graft.

Literature References

1. A. Charlesby, Proc. Roy. Soc., A215, 187 (1952).
2. J. C. Hayward, Jr., Polymerization of Ethylene Initiated by Gamma Radiation, doctoral dissertation presented to the Faculty of the Yale School of Engineering. Report No. NYO-3313 under contract AT (30-1)-1173, New Haven, Conn., June 1955.
3. A. Chapiro, C. H. Cousin, Y. Landler and M. Magat, Rec. Trav. Chim. 68, 1037 (1949).
4. W. H. Seitzer, R. H. Goeckermann and A. V. Tobolsky, J. Am. Chem. Soc. 75, 755-6 (1953).
5. A. J. Restaino, R. B. Mesrobian, H. Morawetz, D. S. Ballantine, G. J. Dienes and D. J. Metz, J. Am. Chem. Soc. 78, 2939 (1956).
6. A. J. Restaino, R. B. Mesrobian, D. S. Ballantine, G. J. Dienes, Consiglio Nazionale Delle Ricerche 25, 1, (1955).
7. C. Walling, E. R. Briggs, W. Cummings and F. K. Mayo, J. Am. Chem. Soc. 72, 48 (1950).
8. D. Ballantine, B. Manowitz, A. Glines, P. Colombo, S. Ballanca, BNL (T-35) March 1953.
9. A. Charlesby, Proc. Roy. Soc. (London) 222A, 73 (1954).
10. M. Dole, C. D. Keeling and D. G. Rose, J. Am. Chem. Soc. 76, 4311 (1954).
11. J. Behr, R. B. Mesrobian, A. J. Restaino, D. S. Ballantine, A. Glines, and D. J. Metz, J. Polymer Sci. 19, 219 (1956).

12. D. S. Ballantine, P. Colombo, A. Glines and B. Manowitz, *Chem. Eng. Prog. Symp. Series*, **50**, No. 11, 267 (1954).
13(a.) J. H. Baxendale, M. G. Evans and G. S. Park, *Trans. Faraday Soc.*, **42**, 155 (1946); J. H. Baxendale, S. Bywater, and M. G. Evans, *J. Polymer Sci.*, **1**, 237 (1946).
  (b.) M. G. Evans, *J. Chem. Soc.* 1947, 266–74.
14. L. M. Arnett and J. H. Peterson, *J. Am. Chem. Soc.* **74**, 2031 (1952).
15. A. V. Tobolsky and J. Offenbach, *J. Polymer Sci.* **16**, 311 (1955).
16. A. V. Tobolsky and B. Baysal, *J. Polymer Sci.* **11**, 471, (1953).
17. W. H. Seitzer and A. V. Tobolsky, *J. Am. Chem. Soc.* **77**, 2687 (1955).
18. A. Prévost-Bernas, A. Chapiro, C. Cousin, Y. Landler, and M. Magat, *Discussions of the Faraday Society (Rad. Chem.)* **12**, 98–109 (1952).
19. A. J. Restaino and W. N. Reed, "Kinetics of the Gamma Induced Graft Copolymerization of Vinyl Acetate to Polytetrafluoroethylene", (to be published).
20(a.) M. S. Matheson, E. E. Auer, E. B. Bevilacqua, and E. J. Hart, *J. Am. Chem. Soc.* **71**, 2610 (1949).
  (b.) C. H. Bamford, and M. J. Dewar *Nature* **157**, 845 (1946); *Proc. Roy. Soc.* **A192**, 309 (1947).
21. A. Chapiro, *J. Chim. Phys.* **47**, 775 (1950).
22. M. Haissinsky, "Actions Chimiques et Biologiques des Radiation", Masson et Cie, Paris (1955).
23. D. S. Ballantine, P. Colombo, A. Glines, B. Manowitz, D. J. Metz, BNL **414**, (T-81), 3–8 Oct. (1956).
24. A. Charlesby, private communication.
25. A Chapiro, *J. Chem. Phys.* **52**, 246 (1955).
26. O Sisman and C. D. Bopp, ORNL 928, June 1951; O. Sisman and C. D. Bopp, ORNL 1373, July 1953.
27(a.) G. Smets and M. Claesson, *J. Polymer Sci.* **8**, 289 (1952).
  (b.) D. J. Metz and R. B. Mesrobian, *ibid.*, **16**, 345 (1955).
28. R. B. Mesrobain, paper presented at the 132nd Meeting of the American Chemical Society, New York City, September, 1957.
29. E. Immergut and H. Mark, Makromol. Chem. *18/19*, 322 (1956).
30. R. Hart, Ind. Chim. Belge *21*, 1053, 1193, 1309 (1956); *22*, 39 (1957).
31. E. J. Lawton, J. S. Balwit and A. M. Bueche, *Ind. Eng. Chem.* **46**, 1703 (1954).
32. W. K. Chen, R. B. Mesrobian, D. S. Ballantine, D. J. Metz and A. Glines, *J. Polymer Sci.* **23**, 903 (1957).
33. A. J. Restaino, *Product Engineering* **28**, 173 (1957).
34. A. J. Restaino, *Nucleonics* **15**, 189 (1957).
35. D. J. Metz and R. B. Mesrobian, *J. Polymer Sci.* **16**, 345 (1955).

Bibliography: Effect of Irradiation on Solids

HELEN C. FRIEDEMANN

A. Theories on Irradiation Effects in Solids

1. Anon., What are the Effects of Radiation on Electronic Components? Nucleonics *14* (7), 33–5 July 1956.
2. Anon., How Radiation Affects Materials. Nucleonics Special Report, Sept. 1956, p. 53–88.
3. Anon., Proceedings of the International Conference on the Peaceful Uses of Atomic Energy, Nuclear Chemistry and Effects of Irradiation. Vol. VII (1956), 691 p. United Nations, N Y.
4. Allen, A. O., Effects of Radiation on Materials, PBL-7899 and MDDC-962 (AEC reports).
5. Army Chemical Center, Md. Symposium—Chemistry and Physics of Radiation Dosimetry, Atomic Energy Comm. Report NP-3237 (Sept. 1950).
6. Averbach, B. L. et al., Survey of Effects of Radiation on Materials, Atomic Energy Comm. Report AEC-500, Sept. 1949.
7. Ballantine, D. S., The Initiation of Chemical Reactions by Gamma and other Ionizing Radiations, Atomic Energy Comm. Report TID-8005 (1956).
8. Berggren, R. et al., Mechanics of Testing Irradiated Materials, Delivered at ASTM, Los Angeles, Calif., 9/20/56.
9. Billington, D. C., Radiation Damage in Reactors, Atomic Energy Comm. Report P-744.
10. Billington, D. C., How Radiation Affects Materials: Basic Mechanisms, Nucleonics *14* (9), 54 (1956).
11. Bonfiglioli, G. et al., The Interest of the Study of Radiation Effects on Solids, Ric. scient. *25* 11, 3011–24 (1955), (in Italian).
12. Bopp, C. D. and O. Sisman, How to Calculate Gamma Radiation Induced in Reactor Materials, Nucleonics *14* (1), 46 (1956).
13. Brauer, R. W., Problems of the Delayed Effects of Ionizing Radiation, Atomic Energy Comm. Report USNRDL-TR-80 (1956).
14. Brinkman, J. A., The Production of Atomic Displacements by High Energy Particles, Atomic Energy Comm. Report NAA-SR-1459 (1955).
15. Brown, F. W., Studies on Nuclear Reactors. 4. Theory of Ionization and Atomic Displacement Produced by Fast Particle in Graphite. I. Preliminary Considerations, Atomic Energy Comm. Report NAA-SR-4 (1948).
16. Brown, F. W. and F. E. Faris, Theory of Ionization and Atomic Displacements Produced by Fast Particles in Graphite. II. Analysis of Resistivity Range Measurements, Atomic Energy Comm. Report NAA-SR-20 (1951).
17. Brown, W. L. and R. C. Fletcher, Annealing of Bombardment Damage in Germanium: Theoretical, Phys. Rev. (2) *91*, 237 (1953).
18. Brown, W. L. et al., Annealing of Bombardment Damage in Solids, Phys. Rev. (2) *90*, 709–10 (1953).
19. Burton, M., Radiation Chemistry; The Chemical Effects of Radiation on Matter; Training Program Notes, Atomic Energy Comm. Report AECD 2977 (1950).
20. Buser, W. and P. Grav, Behavior of γ-Recoil Atoms in Solids, Helv. Phys. Acta *28*, 458–60 (1955).
21. Chang, R., Fundamental Studies of the Mechanism of Radiation Damage, Atomic Energy Comm. Report NYO-7298 (1955).

22. Dienes, G. J., Displaced Atoms in Solids—Comparison Between Theory and Experiment, Delivered at ASTM, Los Angeles, Calif., 9/20/56.
23. Dienes, G. J., Effect of Radiation on Elastic Constants, Atomic Energy Comm. Report BNL-1200 (1952).
24. Dienes, G. J., Radiation Effects in Solids, Ann. Rev. Nucl. Sci. *2*, 187–220 (1953).
25. Dienes, G. J., A Program for the Study of Radiation Effects on Mechanical Properties, Atomic Energy Comm. Report NAA-SR-71.
26. Dienes, G. J., Effects of Nuclear Radiations on the Mechanical Properties of Solids, J. Appl. Phys. *24*, (6) 666–74 (1953); see also Report BNL-1340
27. Dienes, G. J., Theoretical Aspects of Radiation Damage in Metals, Intntl. Conf. on Peaceful Uses of Atomic Energy, P/750.
28. Dienes, G. J., Variable Activation Energy and the Motion of Lattice Defects, Phys. Rev. (2) *91*, 1283–4 (1953).
29. Duhamel, F. et al., A New Method for Studying Certain Physicochemical Effects of Irradiation in Piles. Measurement of Electromagnetic Absorption of Solids, Compt. rend. *237*, 1684–5 (1953) (in French).
30. Eggen, D. T. and W. E. Parkins, Preliminary Experiments on Radiation Damage Due to Electron Bombardment, Atomic Energy Comm. Report NAA-SR-37 (1956).
31. Faris, F. E., Compendium of Radiation Effects on Solids, Vol. II Atomic Energy Comm. Report NAA-SR-241 (1953).
32. Fletcher, R. C. and W. L. Brown, Annealing of Bombardment Damage in a Diamond-Type Lattice, Phys. Rev. (2) *92*, 585–90 (1953).
33. Fowler, G. N. and G. M. D. B. Jones, On the Ionization Loss of a Fast Particle in a Dielectric Medium, Proc. Phys. Soc. (London) *A66*, 597–600 (1953).
34. Gilbert, W. S. and A. Andrew, The Use of Cyclotron Irradiation in the Study of Radiation Effects of Materials, Atomic Energy Comm. Report NAA-SR-1477 (1956).
35. Glocker, H., On the Fundamental Law of the Physical Effects of X-Radiation of Different Wave Lengths, Z. Physik *136*, 352–66 (1953) (in German).
36. Hanle, W., Physical and Chemical Effects of Strong Radiation, Angew. Chem. *65*, 225–30 (1953) (in German).
37. Harris, E. G., The Disordering of Polyatomic Solids by Neutrons, Off. of Tech. Serv. Report PB 121202 (1956).
38. Harrison, W. A. and F. Seitz, On the Theory of Radiation Damage, Bull. Am. Phys. Soc. *30* (2), 7 (1955).
39. Hausner, H. H., Solid Materials as Affected by Irradiation, to be published in "Encyclopedia of Chemical Technology", Interscience, New York.
40. Hausner, H. H., Effects of Irradiation on Solid Materials, Schweiz. arch. angew. Wissenschaft u. Tech., Sept. 1956 (in German).
41. Hausner, H. H., Effects of Irradiation on Solid Materials, in 4th Annual Conference—"Atomic Energy in Industry", Nat. Ind. Conf. Board, New York, Oct. 1955, p. 231.
42. Hehemias, J. V. et al., Problems Encountered in Routine Use of 10-Kilocurie, Gamma-Radiation Source, Am. J. Phys. *22*, 511–16 (1954).
43. Hittman, F. and O. A. Kuhl, High Temperature Underwater Irradiation Facility, Nucleonics *13* (5), 60 (1955).
44. Huntington, H. B., Creation of Displacements in Radiation Damage, Phys. Rev. (2) *93*, 1414–15 (1954).
45. Jech, C., Change of Surface Property by α-Radiation, Z. Physik. Chem. (Leipzig) *203*, 309–11 (1954) (in German).

46. Jelley, J. V., Cerenkov Radiation and Its Applications, Brit. J. Appl. Phys. *6*, 227–32 (1955).

47. Jones, S. S., How Radiation Affects Important Materials, Gen. Elec. Rev. *57* (4), 6–11 (1954).

48. Jones, S. S., Nuclear Radiations: Their Effects Upon Organic Materials, Can. Chem. Processing *39*, 36–46 (1955).

49. Kinchin, G. W. and R. S. Pease, The Displacement of Atoms in Solids by Radiation, Rep. Prog. Phys. (Inst. of Phys.) *18*, 1–51, (1955).

50. Kurti, N. and F. E. Simon, On the Use of γ-Rays in Low Temperature Calorimetry, Phil. Mag. (7) *44*, 501–3 (1953).

51. Lomer, W., The Direct Conversion of β-Irradiation Energy into Low Voltage Electrical Energy, AERE-T/M-108 (1954).

52. Mannal, C. et al., Atomic Radiations Change Materials, Power *99* (7), 94–6, 196–8, 200–3 (1955).

53. Martin, A. B., and M. M. Mills, Application of Particle Accelerators to the Study of Radiation Damage, Atomic Energy Comm. Report NAA-SR-56 (1949).

54. Marx, J. W., Radiation Damage and Rate Processes, Phys. Rev. (2) *91*, 1564–5 (1953).

55. Mills, M. M., Theory of Atomic Displacements Produced by Fast Electrons, Atomic Energy Comm. Report NAA-SR-38 (1950).

56. Mincher, E. L. and R. M. Lichtenstein, Utilization of Gross Fission Products, Atomic Energy Comm. Report GEL-67.

57. Nabarro, F. R. N., Deformation of Crystals by the Motion of Single Ions, Phys. Soc. Report (1948) of the 1947 Bristol Conf. on Strength of Solids, p. 75–90.

58. Naval Research Laboratory, Conference on Effects of Radiation on Dielectric Materials, Office of Nav. Res. Symposium Report ACR-2.

59. Nuclear Development Corp., Disagreeability of the Elements After Neutron Bombardment, Report to International Nickel Co., Sept. 1, 1955.

60. Oak Ridge National Laboratory, Radiation Damage Conference, Mar. 24, 1953.

61. Palladino, N. J., Information Pertaining to the Use of Thermocouples in High Neutron Flux, Atomic Energy Comm. Report WAPD-RES-13 (1954).

62. Pearlstein, E. A. et al., Energy Dependence of Irradiation Effects in Solids, Bull. Am. Phys. Soc. *30*, (2), 7 (1955).

63. Platzman, R. L., On the Heating Resulting From the Absorption of Gamma Rays at Extremely Low Temperatures, Phil. Mag. (7) *44*, 497–500 (1953).

64. Primak, W., Experimental Evidence for Thermal Spikes in Radiation Damage, Phys. Rev. *98*, 1854–5 (1955).

65. Riezler, W., Effects of Radiations on Materials, Stahl u. Eisen *76* (1), 14–17 (Jan. 12, 1956).

66. Schwed, P. C. and G. Groetzinger, Considerations Regarding the Distribution of Radiation Damage in Matter Bombarded by Light Ions and a Method of Making it Uniform, J. Appl. Phys. *23*, 234–6 (1952).

67. Seigle, L. L. and A. J. Opinsky, Mechanism of Dimensional Instability, Atomic Energy Comm. Report SEP-160 (1954).

68. Seitz, F., Radiation Effects in Solids, Physics Today *5* (6), 6–9 (1952).

69. Seitz, F., On the Disordering of Solids by Action of Fast Massive Particles, Disc. Faraday Soc. *5*, 271 (1949).

70. Seitz, F. and J. S. Koehler, The Theory of Lattice Displacements Produced During Irradiation, Intntl. Conf. on Peaceful Uses of Atomic Energy, P/749.

71. Seitz, F. and J. S. Koehler, Radiation Disarrangement of Crystals, in "Impurities and Imperfections", Am. Soc. Metals, Cleveland, 1955, p. 213.

72. Seitz, F. and J. S. Koehler, Displacement of Atoms During Irradiation, in "Solid State Physics", Vol. 2, Academic Press, 1956, p. 305–442.

73. Seitz, F. and E. P. Wigner, Effects of Radiation on Solids, Scientific Am. *195*, 76 + 5 pages. Aug. 1956.

74. Sherrard, G. R., Transcript Summary of Various Irradiation Damage Reports on Electrical and Thermal Insulating Materials, Atomic Energy Comm. Report AECD 4218 (1956).

75. Sisman, O. and J. C. Wilson, How Radiation Affects Materials: Engineering Use of Damage Data, Nucleonics *14* (9), 58 (1956).

76. Slater, J. C., The Effects of Radiation on Materials, J. Appl. Phys. *22* (3), 237–56 (1951); see also report AEC-500 (1949).

77. Smoluchowski, R., Effect of Nuclear Irradiation on Ionic Crystals, Intntl. Conf. on Peaceful Uses of Atomic Energy, P/748.

78. Smoluchowski, R., Radiation Effects in Solids Produced by Nuclear Disintegration, Bull. Am. Phys. Soc. *30* (2), 7 (1955).

79. Smoluchowski, R. et al., Radiation Effects in Solids, Atomic Energy Comm. Report NYO-7379 (1955).

80. Snyder, W. S. and J. Neufeld, On the Disordering of Solids by Heavy Corpuscular Radiations, Phys. Rev. (2) *94*, 760 (1954).

81. Snyder, W. S. and J. Neufeld, Disordering of Solids by Neutron Radiation, Phys. Rev. *97*, 1636 (1955).

82. Snyder, W. S. and J. Neufeld, Vacancies and Displacements in a Solid Resulting From Heavy Corpuscular Radiation, Phys. Rev. *103*, 862–4 (1956).

83. Surosky, A. E., The Nuclear Jungle (Environment and Radiation Effects), Environmental Quarterly *2* (3), 7 (July 1956).

84. Truell, Rohn, Radiation Damage in Solids as Observed by Ultrasonic Attenuation and Velocity Measurements, Atomic Energy Comm. Report NYO-7292 (1956).

85. Tucker, C. W. and P. Senio, On the Nature of Thermal Spikes, J. Appl. Phys. *27*, 207–9 (1956).

86. Warren, B. E., X-Ray Study of Radiation Damage, Atomic Energy Comm. Reports NYO-767 (1951); NYO-3731 (1952); NYO-3732 (1952); NYO-3734 (1953) and NYO-6508 (1954).

87. Wilson, J. C. and D. S. Billington, Effect of Nuclear Radiation on Structural Materials, J. Metals *8* (5), 665 (1956).

88. Woodard, A. S. and F. R. Long, A Bibliography on Radiation Effects on Solids, Atomic Energy Comm. Report NAA-SR-1420 (1955).

89. Wruck, D. A., Crystal Structure as a Factor in Irradiation Damage, Thesis, University of Illinois, 1954.

90. Wruck, D. and C. Wert, Crystal Structure as a Factor in Radiation Damage, Bull. Am. Phys. Soc. *29* (3), 19 (1953); see also Acta Met. *3*, 115 (1955).

91. Yockey, H. P. The Use of Cyclotron Irradiation in the Study of Radiation Effects on Materials, Atomic Energy Comm. Report NAA-SR-186 (1952).

92. Yockey, H. P., Use of Thermocouples in a Radiation Field, Phys. Rev. *101*, 1426 (1956).

93. Yockey, H. P., Cyclotron Techniques in Studies of Radiation Effects, Atomic Energy Comm. Report NAA-SR-21, 1948.

94 Yockey, H. P. et al., Cyclotron Techniques for Radiation Damage Studies Rev. Sci. Instr. *25*, 1011–19 (1954.)

95. Zakharov, A. I., Effect of Radiation on the Physical Properties and Structure of a Solid, Uspekhi fiz. nauk *57* (4), 525–76 (1955).

96. Zhukhovitskii, A. A. and V. A. Geodakyan, Determination of Diffusion Coefficients on the Basis of β-Radiation Absorption, Dokl. Akad. Nauk SSSR *102*, 301–5 (1955) (in Russian).

B. *IRRADIATION EFFECTS ON METALS*

97. Adam, J. et al., An Effect of Electron Bombardment on Order in Cu₃Au Alloy, Phil. Mag. (7) *43*, 1216 (1953).
98. Andrade, A. N. da C., Effect of Alpha-Ray Bombardment on Glide in Metal Single Crystals, Nature *156*, 113–14 (1951).
99. Andrade, E. N. da C., The Effect of Surface Conditions on the Mechanical Properties of Metals, Mainly Single Crystals, Inst. Metals Monograph and Report Series No. 13, p. 133–43 (1953).
100. Andrew, A. and C. R. Davidson, Induced Thermoelectric Potential from Radiation Damage, Phys. Rev. (2) *89*, 876–7 (1953).
101. Andrew, A. et al., Effect of Cyclotron Irradiation on Some Thermocouple Materials, Phys. Rev. (2) *86*, 643 (1952).
102. Aronin, L. R., Effects of Fast Neutron Irradiation on Order-Disorder in Ni-Mn Alloys, Atomic Energy Comm. Report MIT-1107 (1955).
103. Aronin, L. R., Radiation Damage Effects on Order-Disorder in Ni-Mn Alloys, J. Appl. Phys. *25*, 344 (1954), see also AEC Report AECU-2634 (1953).
104. Baldwin, E. E., Effects of Neutron Radiation Upon the Tensile and Impact Properties of ASTM-A-302-B Steel, Paper No. 56-A-107, Am. Soc. Mech. Eng., 11/26/56, New York.
105. Baldwin, E. E., Effects of Temperature and Radiation on the Tensile and Impact Properties of ASTM-A-302-B Mn-Mo Steel, Atomic Energy Comm. Report KAPL-1416 (1955).
106. Barile, S., Study of X-Ray Induced Optical Absorption Bands in CaF₂, J. Chem. Phys. *20*, 297 (1952).
107. Barnes, R. S., and M. J. Makin, On the Mechanism of Irradiation Annealing, J. Nuclear Energy *2*, 291–8 (1956).
108. Beaver, R. J., Irradiation Experiments on Uranium Dioxide-Aluminum Powder Fuel Plates, Atomic Energy Comm. Report CF-55-6-13 (1955).
109. Beaver, R. J., Irradiation Experiments on Aluminum Fuel Plates Containing 48 w/o U, 52 w/o Al Alloy, With a 20% Enrichment in the U-235 Isotope, Atomic Energy Comm. Report CF-56-6-148 (1956).
110. Becker, M. et al., Infrared Absorption of Nucleon Bombarded Silicon. I., Phys. Rev. (2) *85*, 730 (1952).
111. Bentley, W. C. et al., The Formation of Higher Isotopes and Higher Elements by Reactor Irradiation of Pu-239; Some Nuclear Properties of the Heavier Isotopes, Intntl. Conf. on Peaceful Uses of Atomic Energy, P/809.
112. Billington, D. S., Radiation Damage in Reactor Materials, ibid. P/744.
113. Billington, D. S. and S. Siegel, Effect of Nuclear Radiation on Metal, Metal Progress *58*, 847 (1950); see also AEC Report 2810 (1950).
114. Billington, D. S., Irradiation Effects in Reactor Materials, in "Nuclear Metallurgy", V. III, IMD Spec. Report Series No. 3, AIME (1956), p. 31.
115. Binnie, W. P. and A. M. Liebschutz, An X-Ray and Electron Diffraction Study of Radiation Damage in Single Crystals, Atomic Energy Comm. Report AECU-2225 (1952), p. 4–13.
116. Binnie, W. P. and A. M. Liebschutz, An X-Ray Study of Radiation Damage in Single Crystals, Atomic Energy Comm. Report COO-104 (1953), p. 41–89.

117. Binnie, W. P. and A. M. Liebschutz, An X-Ray and Electron Diffraction Study of Radiation Damage in Single Crystals of Germanium and Silicon, Atomic Energy Comm. Report COO-102 (1953) p. 15–21.

118. Binnie, W. P. and A. M. Liebschutz, The Elastic Constants of Silicon Before and After Neutron Bombardment From X-Ray Diffuse Scattering, Bull. Am. Phys. Soc. *29* (3), 12 (1954).

119. Bleiberg, M. L., Phase Changes in Pile Irradiated Uranium Base Alloys, Atomic Energy Comm. Report WAPD-T-300.

120. Bleiberg, M. L., Effect of Neutron Bombardment Upon the Properties of ASTM Type SA212B Steel, Atomic Energy Comm. Report WAPD-T-206 (1955).

121. Blet, G., The Constants of Selenium Photopiles, Exposed to Radiation for Long Periods, J. Phys. Radium *17* (5), 430–9 (1956).

122. Blewitt, T. H. and R. R. Coltman, Radiation Ordering in Cu_3Au, Acta Met. *2*, 549 (1954).

123. Blewitt, T. H. and R. R. Coltman, The Effect of Reactor Irradiation on the Stress Strain Curve of Copper, Atomic Energy Comm. Report AECD 3095 (1951).

124. Blewitt, T. H. and R. R. Coltman, The Effect of Neutron Irradiation on Metallic Diffusion, Phys. Rev. *85*, 384 (1952).

125. Blewitt, T. H. and R. R. Coltman, The Effect of Pile Irradiation on the Stress Strain Curve of Copper, Phys. Rev. *82*, 769 (1951); see also AEC Report TID-5015.

126. Blewitt, T. H. et al., Very Low Temperature Irradiation of Metals. Energy Released at 35°K, Bull. Am. Phys. Soc. (II) *1*, 130 (1956).

127. Boas, W. and R. W. K. Honeycombe, The Anisotropy of Thermal Expansion as a Cause of Deformation in Metals and Alloys, Proc. Roy. Soc. *A188*, 427 (1947).

128. Boltax, A. M., Effects of Irradiation on a Precipitation Hardening Alloy of Copper-Iron, Delivered at ASTM, Los Angeles, Calif., 9/20/56.

129. Bowen, D., Survey of Radiation Effects on Fuel Materials, Delivered at ASTM, Los Angeles, Calif., 9/20/56.

130. Bowen, D. and G. W. Rodeback, The Influence of Cold Work and Radiation Damage on the Debye Temperature of Copper, Acta Met. *1*, 649–53 (1953); see also AEC Report NAA-SR-254 (1953).

131. Bowen, D. B. and G. W. Rodeback, The Influence of Cold Work and Radiation Damage on the Vibrational Spectra of Copper, Phys. Rev. (2) *92*, 531 (1953).

132. Bowman, F. E. et al., Cyclotron Irradiation Damage of Thorium, Stainless Steel and Zirconium, Atomic Energy Comm. Report NAA-SR-287 (1955).

133. Brattain, W. H. and G. L. Pearson, Changes in Conductivity of Germanium Produced by α-Particle Bombardment, Phys. Rev. (2) *80*, 846–50 (1950).

134. Brinkman, J. A., On the Nature of Radiation Damage in Metals, J. Appl. Phys. *25*, 961 (1954); see also AEC Report NAA-SR-198 (1952).

135. Brinkman, J. A. and W. S. Gilbert, Effects of Fission Fragments on Radiation Damaged Metals, Atomic Energy Comm. Report NAA-SR-262 (1953).

136. Brooks, F. C., Displaced Atom Densities in Cyclotron Irradiated Metals, Atomic Energy Comm. Report AECD 3341 (1952).

137. Broser, I. and R. Warminsky, Modifications Produced by α-Particle Irradiations in CdS Crystals, Z. Naturforsch. *6a*, 85–102 (1951) (in German).

138. Brown, W. L. et al., Annealing of Bombardment Damage in Germanium: Experimental, Phys. Rev. (2) *92*, 591–6 (1953).

139. Brown, W. L. et al., Traps Produced by the Electron Bombardment of Germanium at Low Temperature, Bull. Am. Phys. Soc. *29* (5) 23 (1954).

140. Bruch, C. A. et al., Embrittlement of Molybdenum by Neutron Radiation, Trans. AIME *203*, 281 (1955).

141. Bruch, C. A. et al., Variations in Radiation Damage to Metals, Presented at Nucl. Eng. and Sci. Congress, Cleveland, Dec. 1955.

142. Burnham, J. B. and M. H. Bartz, Dimensional Stability of Irradiated Thorium, Atomic Energy Comm. Report IDO-16162 (1954).

143. Callendine, G. W. Jr., et al., Diffusion Effects of Cobalt When Bombarded with Neutrons, Phys. Rev. (2) *86*, 642 (1952).

144. Carlsen, K. et al., Notes on the Stability of Uranium Fuel Elements, Intntl. Conf. on Peaceful Uses of Atomic Energy, P/885.

145. Cashin, W. M. and C. W. Tucker, Jr., X-Ray Diffraction Effects to be Expected from Irradiated Uranium, Atomic Energy Comm. Report KAPL-1158 (1954).

146. Castleman, L., Survey of Effects of Neutron Bombardment on Structural Materials, Delivered at ASTM Los Angeles, Calif. 9/20/56.

147. Cauchois, Y., Preliminary Investigation on the X-Ray Spectrum of Copper Alloys Irradiated with Fast Neutrons, Compt. rend. *241*, (15), 942–4 (1955).

148. Charlesby, A., Effects of Atomic Pile Radiation on the Elastic Modulus of an Austenitic Steel, AERE M/R 1434, see also J. Nucl. Energy *1*, 264–73 (1955).

149. Chiswik, H. H. and L. R. Kelman, Thermal Cycling Effects in Uranium, Intntl. Conf. on Peaceful Uses of Atomic Energy, P/557.

150. Cleland, J. W. and J. H. Crawford, Jr., Radiation Effects in Indium Antimonide, Phys. Rev. (2) *93*, 894–5 (1954).

151. Cleland, J. W. and J. H. Crawford, Jr., Neutron Irradiated Indium Antimonide, Phys. Rev. *95*, 1177 (1954).

152. Cleland, J. W. and J. H. Crawford, Jr., Fast Neutron Bombardment of GaSb, Phys. Rev. *100*, 1614 (1955).

153. Cleland, J. W. et al., Effects of Gamma Radiation on Germanium, Phys. Rev. *102* (2), 722–4 (1956).

154. Cleland, J. W. et al., Evidence for Production of Hole Traps in Germanium by Fast Neutron Bombardment, Phys. Rev. (2) *84*, 861–2 (1951).

155. Cleland, J. W. et al., Fast Neutron Bombardment of n-Type Germanium, Phys. Rev. *98*, 1742–50 (1955).

156. Cleland, J. W. et al., Fast Neutron Bombardment of p-Type Germanium, Phys. Rev. *99*, 1170–81 (1955).

157. Cleland, J. W. et al., The Effect of Fast Neutron Bombardment on the Conductivity of p-Type Ge, Phys. Rev. (2) *82*, 763 (1951).

158. Cleland, J. W. et al., The Effect of Fast Nuetron Bombardment on the Electrical Properties of Ge, Phys. Rev. *83*, 312 (1951).

159. Cleland, J. W. et al., Low Temperature Fast Neutron Bombardment of Copper-Beryllium Alloy, Phys. Rev. *91*, 238 (1953).

160. Clifford, C. and T. Arnette, Lead Storage Battery Radiation Damage Tests, Atomic Energy Comm. Report ORNL-106.

161. Coltman, R. R. and T. H. Blewitt, The Effect of Fast Neutron Bombardment on Diffusion in Cu₃Au, Phys. Rev. (2) *91*, 236 (1953).

162. Coltman, R. R. and T. H. Blewitt, The Effect of Neutron Irradiation on Metallic Diffusion, Phys. Rev. (2) *86*, 641–2 (1952).

163. Cook, H. C., Irradiation Effects on 2S Aluminum, Atomic Energy Comm. Report BNL-1365 (1951).

164. Cook, L. G. and R. L. Cushing, The Effects of Neutron Irradiation in the NRX Reactor on the Order-Disorder Alloy Cu₃Au, Acta Met. *1*, 539–48 and 549-51 (1953).

165. Cooper, E. P. and M. M. Mills, The Possibility of "Freezing-In" Radiation Damage Effects in Simple Metals, Atomic Energy Comm. Report AECD 3796 (1950).

166. Cooper, H. G. et al., Resistivity Changes in Cu, Ag and Au Produced by Deuteron Irradiation Near 10°K, Phys. Rev. (2) 94, 496 (1954).

167. Cooper, H. G. et al., Irradiation Effects in Cu, Ag and Au Near 10°K, Phys. Rev. (2) 97, 599–607 (1955).

168. Corbett, J. W. et al., Electron Irradiation of Copper Below 10°K, Phys. Rev. 104, 851–2 (1956).

169. Crawford, J. H., Jr. et al., Evidence of Hole Traps in Germanium Produced by Fast Neutron Bombardment, Phys. Rev. (2) 85, 730 (1952).

170. Crawford, J. H., Jr. and K. Lark-Horovitz, Fast Neutron Bombardment Effects in Germanium, Phys. Rev. (2) 78, 815–6 (1950).

171. Crawford, J. H., Jr. et al., Thermally Unstable Disorder in p-Type Germanium Produced by Fast Neutron Bombardment, Phys. Rev. (2) 91, 243 (1953).

172. Crawford, J. H., Jr. and K. Lark-Horovitz, Thermal Equilibrium in Neutron Irradiated-Semiconductors, Phys. Rev. (2) 79, 889–90 (1950).

173. Damask, A. C., Some Resistivity Effects of Short Range Order in Brass, J. Appl. Phys. 27, 610–16 (1956).

174. Dienes, G. J., A Theoretical Estimate of the Effect of Radiation on Elastic Constants of Simple Metals, Phys. Rev. (2) 86, 228–34 (1952).

174a. Davis, R. E. et al., Neutron-Bombarded Semiconductors, Phys. Rev. (2) 74, 1255 (1948); see also AEC Report AECD 2054 (1948).

175. Debiesse, J. et al., Influence of Radioactivity on the Thermoelectronic Emission of Cathodes, Compt. rend. 232, 2015–6 (1951) (in French).

176. Denney, J. M., Radiation Damage Energy Threshold in a Face-Centered Cubic Alloy, Phys. Rev. (2) 92, 531 (1953).

177. Denney, J. M., Experimental Evidence for Melted Regions in Metal Crystals Resulting from Particle Bombardment, Bull. Am. Phys. Soc. 29 (3), 19–20 (1954).

178. Dieckamp, H. and E. C. Crittenden, Jr., Shear Modulus of Irradiated Copper, Bull. Am. Phys. Soc. 29 (3), 20 (1954).

179. Dienes, G. J., Effect of Radiation on Elastic Constants, Phys. Rev. (2) 87, 666 (1952).

180. Dienes, G. J., A Theoretical Estimate of the Effect of Radiation on Elastic Constants of Simple Metals, Phys. Rev. (2) 86, 228–34 (1952).

181. Dixon, C. E. and C. J. Meechan, Hardness Change in Copper Irradiated with 1.25 mev Electrons, Phys. Rev. (2) 91, 237–8 (1953).

182. Dixon, C. E. et al., Bombardment of Ordered Cu₃Au by 1 mev Electrons, Phil. Mag. (7) 44, 449–50 (1953); see also AEC Report AECU-2346.

183. Dufour, C. et al., Direct Evidence for the Conductivity of a Thin Dielectric Subjected to an Electron Bombardment, J. Phys. radium 12, 887–8 (1951) (in French).

184. Dugdale, R. A., Recent Experiments at Harwell in Irradiation Effects in Crystalline Solids, in "Defects in Crystalline Solids", Phys. Soc. London, 1955, p. 246.

185. Dugdale, R. A., The Extra Electrical Resistance Due to Cold Work and Neutron Irradiation of Pt, Phil. Mag. (7) 43, 912–4 (1952).

186. Duwez, Pol, Proposed Experiments for Studying the Influence of Irradiation on Intermetallic Diffusion, Atomic Energy Comm. Report NAA-SR-58 (1950).

187. Duwez, Pol and R. D. Johnson, The Effect of Irradiation on Diffusion in Cu-Au

and Cu-Ni Powder Compacts, Atomic Energy Comm. Report NAA-SR-168 (1952).

188. Eggen, D. T. and M. J. Laubenstein, Displacement Energy of Radiation Damage in Copper, Phys. Rev. (2) *91*, 238 (1953).

189. Eggleston, R. R., The Annealing of Copper after Radiation Damage at Low Temperatures, Acta Met. *1*, 679–83 (1953).

190. Eggleston, R. R., Annealing of Radiation Damage Effects in Copper, Phys. Rev. (2) *92*, 531 (1953).

191. Eggleston, R. R. and F. E. Bowman, Radiation Damage of Beta Brass, J. Appl. Phys. *24*, 229–30 (1953).

192. Ellis, W. C. and E. S. Greiner, Production of Acceptor Centers in Ge and Si by Plastic Deformation, Phys. Rev. (2) *92*, 1061–2 (1953).

193. Fairbrother, F., Jr., and J. S. Foster, Jr., Sputtering of Stainless Steel by Protons in the 30–80 kev Range, Atomic Energy Comm. Report UCRL-4169 (1953).

194. Fan, H. Y., Infrared Absorption of Nucleon-Bombarded Silicon. II, Phys. Rev. (2) *85*, 730 (1952).

195. Fan, H. Y. and K. Lark-Horovitz, Fast Particle Irradiation of Germanium Semiconductors, in "Defects in Crystalline Solids", Phys. Soc. London, 1955, p. 232.

196. Faris, F. E., The Effects of Irradiation on Structural Materials, Intntl. Conf. on Peaceful Uses of Atomic Energy, P/747.

197. Feldman, M. H., Radiation Decomposition of Reactor Materials in the NAA-NPR, Atomic Energy Comm. Report NAA-SR-95 (1951).

198. Fillnow, R. H. et al., X-Ray and Metallurgical Studies on Neutron Irradiated Cu_3Au, Phys. Rev. (2) *91*, 236 (1953).

199. Fleeman, J. and G. J. Dienes, Effect of Reactor Irradiation on the White-to-Grey Tin Transformation, J. Appl. Phys. *26* (6), 652–4 (1955).

200. Fleeman, J., Effect of Neutron Irradiation on the Phase Change in Tin, Phys. Rev. (2) *91*, 237 (1953).

201. Fletcher, R. C. et al., The Absence of Bombardment Annealing in the Electron Bombardment of Ge, Bull. Am. Phys. Soc. *29* (5), 22–3 (1954).

202. Florida, C. D. et al., Irradiation of Transistors, Nature *173*, 397–8 (1954).

203. Foote, F. G. et al., Irradiation Effects in Uranium and Its Alloys, Intntl. Conf. on Peaceful Uses of Atomic Energy, P/745.

204. Foreman, A. J. E., Calculations on the Rate of Swelling of Gas Bubbles in Uranium, Brit. AERE report—to be published.

205. Forster, H. J. et al., Deuteron Irradiation of Germanium Near Liquid Nitrogen Temperature, Phys. Rev. (2) *91*, 229–30 (1953).

206. Forster, J. H. et al., Conductivity of Deuteron Irradiated Germanium and Silicon, Phys. Rev. (2) *86*, 643 (1952).

207. Frankel, J. P. and G. W. Brown, An Alternative "Mechanism" of the Dimensional Instability of Uranium, Atomic Energy Comm. Report LWS-24552 (1952).

208. Frohmeyer, G. et al., The Wave Length Dependence of the Electric Conductivity of CdS Single Crystals on Radiation with X- and γ-Rays, Z. Physik *137*, 117–25 (1954) (in German).

209. Frohmeyer, G. et al., The Wave Length Dependence of the Conductivity of CdS Crystals Irradiated with X- and γ-Rays, Naturwissenschaften *40*, 338 (1953) (in German).

210. Geib, I. G. and R. E. Grace, Hardness of Deuteron Irradiated Molybdenum,

Phys. Rev. (2) *86*, 643 (1952); Erratum Phys. Rev. (2) *86*, 638 (1952); see also AEC Report AECU 2225, p. 34–6 (1952).

211. Gerthsen, C. and W. Kolb, The "Differential Ionization" by α-Radiation in CdS Crystals, Z. Naturforsch. *A8*, 315–17 (1953) (in German).

212. Girshfeld, S. V., The Study of Delayed Neutrons Emitted by U-233 as a Result of Irradiation by Thermal Neutrons, Intntl. Conf. on Peaceful Uses of Atomic Energy, P/648.

213. Glen, J. W., A Survey of Radiation Effects in Metals, AERE M/TN 27 (1954); see also Adv. in Phys. *4*, 381–478 (1955).

214. Glick, H. L. et al., The Resistivity of Cu₃Au During Neutron Irradiation, Phys. Rev. (2) *87*, 1074 (1952); see also AEC Report WAPD-T7 (1952).

215. Glick, H. L. and W. F. Witzig, Additional Data on the Resistivity of Cu₃Au During Neutron Irradiation, Phys. Rev. (2) *91*, 236 (1953).

216. Gregory, J. N. and S. Moorbath, Effect of Pile Radiation on the Emanating Power of Alumina, AERE CM/129.

217. Gresky, A. T. and E. D. Arnold, Products Produced in Continuous Neutron Irradiation of Thorium, Atomic Energy Comm. Report ORNL-1817 (1956).

218. Grimshaw, L. C., Effects of Irradiation and Corrosion on Stainless Steel Welded Joints in Pressurized Water Reactors, WAPD-AD(P)-987 (1955).

219. Haldar, B. C., Chemical Consequences of the (n, γ) Reaction on Platinum Complexes, J. Am. Chem. Soc. *76*, 4229–33 (1954).

220. Hanson, G. H., Irradiation of Thorium 230 in MTR, Atomic Energy Comm. Report IDO-16065 (1953).

221. Harmon, T. C. et al., Hardness Measurements of Molybdenum Before and After Bombardment, Atomic Energy Comm. Report COO-102, (1953) p. 1–7.

222. Harmon, T. C. et al., Hardness of Deuteron Irradiated Molybdenum, Atomic Energy Comm. Report COO-104 (1953) p. 17–40.

223. Hausner, H. H. and M. C. Kells, Powder Metallurgy—Its Role in the Design of Nuclear-Power Reactors, Mech. Eng. *77*, 665 (1955).

224. Henderson, J. W. et al., Analysis of the Resistivity Changes Produced by Deuteron Irradiation of Copper, Silver and Gold, Phys. Rev. (2) *86*, 642–3 (1952).

225. Hiller, D. M. and D. S. Martin, Jr., Radio Chemical Studies on the Photofission of Thorium, Atomic Energy Comm. Report ISC-227 (1952).

226. Hittman, F. and O. A. Kuhl, Initial Studies on the Effect of High Level γ-Radiation on Corrosion of Metals, Atomic Energy Comm. Report BNL-2257 (1954).

227. Holden, A. N. and F. W. Kunz, A Model For Radiation Damaged Ductile Metals, Atomic Energy Comm. Reports AECD 3616 (1954) and KAPL-929.

228. Holland, H. D. and D. Gottfried, Effect of Nuclear Radiation on the Structure of Zircon, Acta Cryst. *8*, 291–300 (1955); see also Dept. of Comm. Report PB 118328.

229. Howe, J. P., Problems in Materials in Nuclear Power, in "Symposium on Nuclear Metallurgy", Am. Inst. Mining Met. Engrs., 1955, p. 9–28.

230. Hurley, P. M. and H. W. Fairburn, Alpha Radiation Damage in Zircon, J. Appl. Phys. *23*, 1408 (1952).

231. Hutchinson, W. R., Effect of Irradiation on Weldability of ASTM A 212, Grade B, Atomic Energy Comm. Report WAPD-153 (1956).

232. James, H. M. and K. Lark-Horovitz, Localized Electronic States in Bombarded Semiconductors, Z. physik. Chem. *198*, 107–26 (1951); see also AEC Report TID-5011.

233. Jamison, R. E. and T. H. Blewitt, Slip Lines in Pile Irradiated Copper Single Crystals, Phys. Rev. (2) *86*, 641 (1952).

234. Jamison, R. E. and T. H. Blewitt, Behavior of Two Types of Thermocouple Under Pile Irradiation at Low Temps., Rev. Sci. Instr. *24*, 474 (1953).

235. Jamison, R. E. and T. H. Blewitt, Some Deformation Characteristics of Reactor Irradiated Copper Single Crystals at 78°K and 300°K, Phys. Rev. (2) *91*, 237 (1953).

236. Jeppson, M. R. et al., Creep of Aluminum Under Cyclotron Irradiation, J. Appl. Phys. *26*, 365 (1935).

237. Jeppson, M. R. et al., Effect of Cyclotron Irradiation on Creep of Aluminum, Atomic Energy Comm. Report AECD 3631.

238. Johnson, W. E. and K. Lark-Horovitz, Neutron Irradiated Semiconductors, Phys. Rev. (2) *76*, 442–3 (1949).

239. Johnson, R. D. and A. B. Martin, The Effect of Cyclotron Bombardment on Self Diffusion in Silver, J. Appl. Phys. *23* (11), 1245–54 (1952).

240. Jones, E R W. et al., The Creep of Aluminum in the NRX Pile, AERE M/R 795 (1951).

241. Jones E. R. W. et al., The Creep of Aluminum During Neutron Irradiation, J. Nuclear Energy *1*, 76–86 (1954).

242. Jordan, P., Physicochemical Phenomena Accompanying Nuclear Reactions in Finely Pulverized Solids Irradiated with Neutrons, Helv, Chim. Acta *34*, 715–22 (1951) (in French).

243. Keating, D. T., Diffraction Studies of Possible Ordering in Alpha Brass, Bull. Am. Phys. Soc. *29* (3), 31 (1954).

244. Keesom, P. H. et al., The Influence of Neutron Bombardment on the Low Temperature Atomic Heat of Si, Phys. Rev. (2) *89*, 900 (1952). Science *116*, 630–1 (1952).

245. Kelly, E. M., Electron Microscope Study of Slip Bands in Radiation Damaged Al Crystals, Atomic Energy Comm. Report NAA-SR-261 (1954).

246. Kemper, R. S., Jr., and W. S. Kelly, The Effect of Irradiation on the Mechanical Properties of Arc Melted Bureau of Mines Zr with Various Degrees of Cold Work, Atomic Energy Comm. Report HW-38079 (1955). Also presented at meeting ASTM, June 1956.

247. Kenworthy, H. M. and H. H. Neely, Threshold Displacement Energy in Nickel, Atomic Energy Comm. Report NAA-SR-1580 (1956).

248. Kernohan, R. H. et al., Effect of Neutron Irradiation on the Precipitation Hardening Reaction in Alloys Containing Beryllium, J. Appl. Phys. *27*, 40–2 (1956).

249. Kimura, K. and K. Ohira, Electron Bombardment Conductivity of (BaSr)O, Bull. Inst. Chem. Res. Kyoto Univ. *23*, 53–4 (1950).

250. Kinchin, G. H. and R. S. Pease, The Mechanism of the Irradiation Disordering of Alloys, J. Nuclear Energy *1*, 200–2 (1955).

251. Kittel, J. H., Preliminary Investigation of Effects of γ-Radiation on Age Hardening of an Al-Cu Alloy, NACA RM E7E12 (declassified) (1947).

252. Kittel, J. H., Preliminary Investigations of Effects of α-Particle Bombardment on the Creep Rate of Aluminum, NACA RM E7E13 (declassified) (1947).

253. Kittel, J. H., How Radiation Affects Materials: Damaging Effects on Solid Reactor Materials, Nucleonics *14* (9), 63 (1956).

254. Kittel, J. H. and S. H. Paine, Effects of Irradiation on Some Alloys of U-Zr, Delivered at ASTM, Los Angeles, Calif., 9/20/56.

255. Klein, J. L. and W. B. Nowak, Effect of Irradiation on the X-Ray Line Shape of 2S Aluminum from a Hanford Water Cooling Tube, Atomic Energy Comm. Report MIT-1085.

256. Klein, J. S. and W. B. Nowak, Radiation Damage in 99.0% Aluminum, Atomic Energy Comm. Report MIT-1091.
257. Kloepper, R. M., Influence of Gamma Radiation on RG 8/U Cable, Atomic Energy Comm. Report LAMS-1973 (1955).
258. Klontz, E. E., Electron Bombardment of Germanium, Atomic Energy Comm. Report COO-102 (1953) p. 28.
259. Klontz, E. E., Resistance Changes in Germanium Single Crystals during Electron Bombardment, Atomic Energy Comm. Report COO-104 (1953); p. 131–6.
260. Klontz, E. E., Production of Lattice Defects in Germanium by Electron Bombardment, Atomic Energy Comm. Report AECU-2267 (1952). AECU-2664 (1952).
261. Klontz, E. E. and K. Lark-Horovitz, Electron Bombardment of Germanium, Phys. Rev. (2) 82, 763 (1951).
262. Klontz, E. E. and K. Lark-Horovitz, Electron Bombardment of Semiconductors; Irradiation of Materials with Charged Particles from the Purdue Cyclotron, Atomic Energy Comm. Report AECU-2225 (1952), p. 56–65.
263. Klontz, E. E. and K. Lark-Horovitz, Displacements Produced by Electron Bombardment of Germanium, Phys. Rev. (2) 86, 643 (1952).
264. Klontz, E. E. et al., Electrical Properties of Electron-Bombarded Germanium, Bull. Am. Phys. Soc. 30 (2), 12 (1955).
265. Koehler, J. S., Radiation Damage and Recovery in Cu, Ag, Au, Ni and Ta, Atomic Energy Comm. Report COO-199 (1954).
266. Koehler, J. S., Radiation Damage and Recovery in Copper, Atomic Energy Comm. Report COO-197 (1953).
267. Koehler, J. S. and F. Seitz, Radiation Disarrangement of Crystals, Z. Physik 138, 238–45 (1954). See also "Defects in Crystalline Solids," Phys. Soc. London (1955), p. 222–31.
268. Kohn, W., Bombardment Damage of Germanium Crystals By Fast Electrons, Bull. Am. Phys. Soc. 29 (3), 11 (1954).
269. Kohn, A. and J. Doumerc, Study of Some Phenomena Observed in Metallic Samples Irradiated in Air by Deuterons of About 3 mev, J. Phys. Radium 16, 649–53 (1955) (in French).
270. Kolb, W., On the Differential Conductivity-Excitation of CdS Crystals by α-Particles, Ann. Physik 14, 397–411 (1954) (in German).
271. Konobeevsky, S. T., On the Question of the Nature of Radiation Damage in Fissionable Materials, Soviet J. Atomic Energy No. 2, 208–18 (1956).
272. Konobeevsky, S. T. et al., Effect of Irradiation on Structure and Properties of Fissionable Materials, Intntl. Conf. on Peaceful Uses of Atomic Energy, P/681.
273. Konobeevsky, S. T. et al., Effect of Irradiation on the Structure and Properties of the Structural Materials, ibid. P/680.
274. Kunz, F. W. and A. N. Holden, Effect of Short-Time Moderate Flux Neutron Irradiations on the Mechanical Properties of Some Metals, Acta Met. 2, 816 (1954); see also AEC Report KAPL-1066 (1954).
275. Lark-Horovitz, K., Nucleon Bombarded Semiconductors, in "Semiconducting Materials", Butterworths' Scient. Pub., London (1951) p. 47.
276. Lark-Horovitz, K., Problems of the Irradiation Physics of Semiconductors, Intntl. Conf. on Peaceful Uses of Atomic Energy P/753.
277. Lark-Horovitz, K. et al., Nucleon Bombarded Silicon, Phys. Rev. (2) 78, 334 (1950).

278. Lark-Horovitz, K. et al., Deuteron Bombarded Semiconductors, Phys. Rev. (2) *73*, 1256 (1948).

279. Leeser, D. O., How Atomic Radiation Affects Engineering Materials, Materials and Methods *36*, 75 (1952).

280. Leeser, D. O., How Nuclear Radiation Affects Engineering Materials, Materials and Methods *40*, 109 (1954).

281. Leeser, D. O., Radiation Effects on Welds and Notches in Plain Carbon Steels, Stainless Steels and Nonferrous Alloys, Delivered at ASTM, Los Angeles, Calif. 9/20/56.

282. Leeser, D. O. and G. J. Deily, Effect of Irradiation on the Notched-Bar Impact Properties of Some Plain Carbon Steels, Delivered at ASTM, Los Angeles, Calif., 9/20/56.

283. Lewis, W. B., Calculated Reactivity Changes in the Long Irradiation of Natural Uranium, Canad. Chalk River Report DR–28 (1955).

284. Lewis, W. B., Reactivity Changes Expected and Observed in Long Irradiation of Natural Uranium in the NRX Reactor, Canad. Chalk River Report DR-21 (1955).

285. Li, C. Y. and A. S. Nowick, Atomic Mobility in a Cu-Al Alloy after Quenching and Neutron Irradiation, Phys. Rev. *103*, 294–303 (1956).

286. Lillie, D. W., Metallurgy in Nuclear Energy, Metal Progress *68*, 82–4, Sept. 1955.

287. Lloyd, L. T. and H. H. Chiswik, Deformation Mechanisms of Alpha Uranium Single Crystals, Atomic Energy Comm. Reports ANL-FGF-2 (1955); ANL-5367 (1954); see also Trans. AIME *203*, (11) 1206–14 (1955).

288. Loferski, J. J. and P. Rappaport, Electron Voltaic Study of Electron Bombardment Damage and its Thresholds in Ge and Si, Phys. Rev. *98*, 1861 (1955).

289. Lomer, W. M., The Direct Conversion of Beta Irradiation Energy into Low Voltage Electrical Energy, AERE-T/M 108 (1954).

290. Lomer, W. M., Diffusion Coefficients in Copper under Fast Neutron Irradiation, AERE-T/R 1540 (1955).

291. McDonnell, W. R. and H. A. Kierstead, Expansion of Copper Bombarded by 21-mev Deuterons, Phys. Rev. (2) *93*, 247 (1954).

292. McKay, K. G., Electron Hole Production in Germanium by Alpha Particles, Phys. Rev. *84*, 829–32 (1951).

293. McReynolds, A. W. et al., Neutron Irradiation Effects in Copper and Aluminum at 80°K, Phys. Rev. *98*, 418 (1955).

294. Makin, M. J., The Effect of α-Particle Bombardment on the Creep of Cd Single Crystals, J. Nuclear Energy *1*, 181–93 (1955); see also Nature *174*, 4433, 752–3 (1954).

295. Makin, M. J., Radiation Damage to Metals and Associated Problems, J. Inst. Metals *84*, 101–3 (1955–6).

296. Makin, M. J. and F. J. Minter, The Effect of Neutron Irradiation on the Mechanical Properties of Metals. Part I. Titanium and Zirconium, AERE-M/R 2009 (1956).

297. Martin, A. B. et al., The Effects of Cyclotron Bombardment on the Physical Properties of Metals, Phys. Rev. (2) *81*, 664 (1951).

298. Martinez, J. O., Measurement of Diffused Radiation in Aluminum, Inst. del hierro y del acero 8, 41, 782–96, Oct.–Dec. 1955 (in Spanish).

299. Marx, J. et al., Effect of Deuteron Bombardment on the Electrical Resistivity of Cu, Ag and Au Phys. Rev. (2) *86*, 643 (1952).

300. Marx, J. W. et al., Radiation Damage and Recovery in Cu, Ag, Au, Ni and Ta, Phys. Rev. (2) *88*, 106–12 (1952); see also AEC Report AECU 2118 (1952).

301. Meechan, C. J., An Electrical Resistivity Study of Lattice Defects Introduced in Copper by 1.25 mev Electron Irradiation at 80°K, Atomic Energy Comm. Report NAA-SR-1571 (1956).

302. Meyer, R. A., Influence of Deuteron Bombardment and Strain Hardening on Notch Sensitivity of Mild Steel, J. Appl. Phys. *25*, 1369 (1954).

303. Meyer, R. A., Influence of Deuteron Bombardment and Strain Hardening on Mild Steel, Atomic Energy Comm. Report US NRDL-431.

304. Moller, Marx D., Induced Radioactivity of Some Structural Alloys, Atomic Energy Comm. Report ER-6119 (1954).

305. Moller, Marx D., Nuclear Radiation Effects on Aircraft Materials, Aviation Age *21* (1) 20–23, Jan. 1954.

306. Mongini, L., Effects of Nuclear Radiation on the Electrical Resistivity and Hardness of Metals, Energia Nucleare No. 8, 209–20 (1953) (in Italian).

307. Montariol, F. et al., Intergranular and Interdendritic Segregation of Trace Impurities in Aluminum by Irradiation in an Atomic Pile, Compt. rend. *235*, 477–80 (1952).

308. Montariol, F. et al., The Use of Radioelements to Study the Segregation of Impurities in the Grain Boundaries of High Purity Aluminum, Rev. Met. *50*, 768–74 (1953).

309. Moyer, J. W., Irradiation of Germanium by Fast Monoenergetic Neutrons, Atomic Energy Comm. Report KAPL-1455 (1956).

310. Moyer, J. W., Electron Irradiation of Silicon p-n Junctions, Atomic Energy Comm. Report KAPL-1146 (1954).

311. Mueller, P., The Importance of Radioactive Radiation to Materials Science, VDI Z. *97* (5), 138–44 (1955).

312. Murphy, W. F. and S. H. Paine, Fast Neutron Effects on Tensile and Hardness Properties of Stainless Steel, Delivered at ASTM, Los Angeles, Calif., 9/20/56.

313. Murray, G. T. and W. E. Taylor, Effect of Neutron Irradiation on a Super-Saturated Solid Solution of Be in Cu, Acta Met. *2*, 52 (1954), see also AEC Report ORNL-1323 (1953).

314. Murray, G. T. and W. E. Taylor, Neutron Bombardment of a Copper-Beryllium Alloy, Phys. Rev. (2) *86*, 642 (1952).

315. Nabarro, F. R. N., Effect of Radiation on Elastic Constants, Phys. Rev. (2) *87*, 665-6 (1952).

316. Neumann, B. and E. Schmid, Effect of Corpuscular Irradiation on Age Hardenable Alloys, Metall *9*, 349–52 (1955) (in German).

317. Nowak, W. B., Radiation Damage (Internal Friction) in 99.99+% Aluminum, Atomic Energy Comm. Report MIT-1066 (1956).

318. Nowak, W. B., A Recrystallization Study of Radiation Damage in Aluminum, Atomic Energy Comm. Report MIT-1063 (1951).

319. Oak Ridge National Laboratory, Quarterly Progress Report—Physics Division, Atomic Energy Comm. Report ORNL-865 (1951) p. 87—Semiconductor bombardment research; p. 98—Bonded wire resistance strain gages; p. 77—Phase transition on neutron bombardment; p. 106—Effect of pile irradiation on performance of electrical leads.

320. Odencrantz, F. K., Alpha Particle Bombardment of PbS Semiconductors, Phys. Rev. (2) *88*, 166 (1952).

321. Olson (?) et al., Pitting Corrosion Observed on Active and Dummy Fuel Elements from the Bulk Shielding Reactor, AECD-3174 (1954).

322. Orlin, J. J., Electrons Emitted from Metals after Irradiation by 1.5 mev X-Rays, Univ. i Bergen Arbok, Naturvitenskap. Rekke, No. 9, 1–14 (1954) (in English).

323. Overhauser, A. W., Annealing Effects in Irradiated Copper, Phys. Rev. (2) *92*, 530 (1952).

324. Overhauser, A. W., Isothermal Annealing Effects in Irradiated Copper, Phys. Rev. (2) *90*, 393–400 (1953), see also AEC Report AECU-2358 (1952).

325. Overhauser, A. W., Stored Energy Measurements in Irradiated Copper, Phys. Rev. *94*, 155–7 (1954).

326. Paine, S. H. and J. H. Kittel, Irradiation Effects in Uranium and its Alloys, Preprint #94, Nucl. Eng. and Sci. Congress. Cleveland, Dec. 1955; see also Intntl. Conf. on Peaceful Uses of Atomic Energy, P/745.

327. Paine, S. H. et al., Effect of Neutron Bombardment on the Transition Temperature for Ductile-to-Brittle Fracture in Low-Carbon Steels, Delivered at ASTM, Los Angeles, Calif. 9/20/56.

328. Parkins, W. E., Some Effects of Irradiation on Metals, Atomic Energy Comm. Report AECD 3372 (1952).

329. Pasynkov, V. V., The Action of Radiation from Radioactive Substances on a (Se) Photocell, Zhur. Tekh. Fiz. *25*, 1376–85 (1955) (in Russian).

330. Pease, R. S., X-Ray Examination of Irradiation Effects in Boron Compounds, Acta Cryst. *7*, 633 (1954).

331. Pepper, R. et al., Hall and Resistivity Measurements During Electron Bombardment of Ge and InSb, Bull. Am. Phys. Soc. *29* (3), 12 (1954).

332. Pigg, J. C. et al., Pile Irradiation of Semiconducting Cu_2O, Phys. Rev. (2) *82*, 763 (1951).

333. Plail, O. S., Some Experimental Irradiation Tests on Natural Uranium, Brit. AERE report—to be published.

334. Pomerantz, M. A. et al., Electrical Conductivity Induced in MgO Crystals by 1.3 mev Electron Bombardment, Phys. Rev. *99*, 489–90 (1955).

335. Pugh, S. F., Damage Occurring in Uranium during Burn-Up, Intntl. Conf. on Peaceful Uses of Atomic Energy, P/443.

336. Pugh, S. F., The Growth, Wrinkling and Fission Product Damage of Uranium and Its Alloys During Irradiation, Brit. AERE report—to be published.

337. Pugh, S. F., The Growth of Alpha Uranium on Irradiation, Brit. AERE report— to be published.

338. Pugh, S. F., The Mechanism and Kinetics of the Growth and Wrinkling of Uranium on Slow Thermal Cycling in the Alpha Range, Brit. AERE report— to be published.

339. Pugh, S. F., Changes in the Properties of Uranium During Burn-Up, J. Inst. Metals *84*, 105–7 (1955–6).

340. Purdue Research Foundation, Irradiation of Materials with Charged Particles from the Purdue Cyclotron, AECU-2225 (1952).

341. Randolph, B. W., Irradiation Effects in Metals, MA Thesis, Purdue Univ. 1952.

342. Randolph, B., Temperature Dependence of the Resistivity of Deuteron Irradiated and Annealed Molybdenum, Phys. Rev. (2) *85*, 710 (1952).

343. Rappaport, P. and J. J. Loferski, Threshold for Electron Bombardment-Induced Lattice Displacements in Si and Ge, Bull. Am. Phys. Soc. *30* (7), 34 (1955).

344. Rappaport, P., Minority Carrier Lifetime in Semiconductors as a Sensitive Indicator of Radiation Damage, Phys Rev. *94*, 1409–10 (1953); Bull. Am. Phys. Soc. *29* (3), 11–12 (1954).

345. Redman, J. K. et al., Effect of Fast Neutron Irradiation on the Critical Shear Stress of Copper, Bull. Am. Phys. Soc. (II) *1*, 130 (1956).

346. Redman, J. K. et al., The Activation Energy for the Recovery of Reactor Irradiated Copper Crystals, Phys. Rev. (2) *91*, 448 (1953).

347. Reynolds M. B. et al., Study of the Radiation Stability of Austenitic Type 347 Stainless Steel, J. Metals *7*, 555 (1955).

348. Richards, J. T., Effect of Irradiation on Beryllium Copper, Acta Met. *3* (2), 211–2 (1955).

349. Roake, W. E., A Replica Press Attachment for the Precision Mounting Press for Use in Preparing Al Replicas of the Surfaces of Irradiated Materials, Atomic Energy Comm. Report HW-30156 (1953).

350. Rosenblatt, D. B. et al., Radiation Induced Changes in the Electrical Resistance of Alpha Brass, J. Appl. Phys. *26*, 1044–9 (1955).

351. Royal, J., The Effects of Neutron Bombardment on the Electrical Resistance of Aluminum, Beryllium and Tuballoy Uranium, Atomic Energy Comm. Report CC-2319 (1944).

352. Ruther, (?), Corrosion Experiments with 2S Aluminum at 200°C, Atomic Energy Comm. Report ANL-5500 (1956).

353. Saller, H. A., Beneficial Effects of Radiation on Metals, Nucleonics 14 (9), 86–8 (1956).

354. Schettig, J. R., Impact Results on Irradiated Stainless Steels Containing B^{10}, Atomic Energy Comm. Report WAPD-SFR-Fe-303 (1955).

355. Schmid, E. and K. Lintner, Effect of Bombardment of Corpuscular Rays (α-Particles) on the Plasticity of Metallic Crystals, Oesterr. Akad. Wiss. Math-Naturw. Kl., Sitzber. Abt. II, *163* (4) 109–21 (1954).

356. Schmid, E. and K. Lintner, Effects of Electron Bombardment on the Plasticity of Metals, Z. Metallkunde *46*, 71 (1955).

357. Scimar, R., Radiation Damage in Metals, Rev. Universelle des Mines *12*, (9), 185–99 (1956).

358. Seeger, A., Radiation Damage and Diffusion Processes in Noble Metals, Z. Naturforsch. *10a* (3), 251 (1955).

359. Seitz, F., On the Disordering of Alloys during Irradiation, Bull. Am. Phys. Soc. *30* (2), 17 (1955).

360. Shulman, R. G., Hole Trapping in Germanium Bombarded by High Energy Electrons, Phys. Rev. *102*, 1451–5 (1956).

361. Sidhu, S. S. and C. O. Henry, Effect of High Energy Neutron Bombardment on Crystal Lattice of Beryllium, Graphite, Diamond and Aluminum, Phys. Rev. (2) *80*, 123 (1950).

362. Siegel, S., Effects of Pile Radiation on Beryllium Metal, Atomic Energy Comm. Report AECD 4045 (1947); M-3300 (1946).

363. Siegel, S., Radiation Damage as a Metallurgical Research Technique, from "Modern Research Techniques in Physical Metallurgy", ASM (1953) p. 312.

364. Siegel, S., Effects of Neutron Bombardment on Order in the Alloy Cu$_3$Au, Phys. Rev. *75*, 1823 (1949).

365. Siegel, S. and D. S. Billington, Effect of Nuclear Radiation on Metals, Metal Progress *58*, 847 (1950).

366. Simnad, M. and R. Smoluchowski, Effect of Proton Irradiation Upon the Electrode Potential of Tungsten, Phys. Rev. 98, 1530; 99, 1891–2 (1955).

367. Sosin, A., Effect of Electron Irradiation and Quenching on the White-to-Gray Tin Transformation, Atomic Energy Comm. Report NAA-SR-1550 (1956).

368. Sparks, L. N., Nuclear Effects on Machine Tools, Atomic Energy Comm. Report WT-1184 (1956).

369. Spivak, G. V. et al., Nature of Attack of Metals by Ion Bombardment, Dokl. Akad. Nauk SSSR 88, 511–14 (1953) (in Russian).
370. Stech, B., Strukturaenderung an Kristallen Durch Beschuss Mit α-Teilchen, Z. Naturforsch. 7a, 175–85 (1952).
371. Steele, R. V. and W. P. Wallace, Effect of Neutron Flux on the Mechanical Properties of Aluminum Alloys, Atomic Energy Comm. Report LRL-145 (1954).
372. Steele, R. V. and W. P. Wallace, Effect of Neutron Radiation on Aluminum Alloys, Metal Progress 68, 114–5 (1955).
373. Stevens, D. K. et al., Magnetic Susceptibility of Fast Neutron Bombarded Germanium, Bull. Am. Phys. Soc. 29 (3), 11 (1954); see also AEC Report ORNL-1599 (1954).
374. Sutton, G. R. and D. O. Leeser, Radiation Effects on Reactor Materials: Metals, Nucleonics 12 (9), 8, 13–16 (1954).
375. Sutton, G. R. and D. O. Leeser, How Radiation Affects Structural Materials, Iron Age 174 (8), 128; and (9) 97 (1954).
376. Sutton, G. R. and D. O. Leeser, Radiation Effects on Structural Materials, in "Nuclear Engineering, Part II", Am. Inst. Chem. Engrs., Chem. Eng. Progr. Symposium Series 50 (12), 1954, p. 208.
377. Taylor, W. E., Comparison of Thermally Induced Lattice Defects in Germanium and Silicon with Defects Produced by Nucleon Bombardment, Phys. Rev. (2) 86, 642 (1952).
378. Thomas, D. E., Irradiation Effects on Physical Metallurgical Processes, in "Nuclear Metallurgy", V. III, IMD Spec. Report Series No. 3, AIME, (1956) p. 13.
379. Thompson, D. O. and D. K. Holmes, Dependence of Young's Modulus and Internal Friction of Copper Upon Neutron Bombardment, J. Appl. Phys. 27, 191–2 (1956).
380. Thompson, D. O. and D. K. Holmes, Effect of Neutron Irradiation Upon the Young's Modulus and Internal Friction of Copper Single Crystals, J. Appl. Phys. 27, 713–23 (1956).
381. Thompson, D. O. et al., Neutron Irradiation Effects Upon Young's Modulus and Internal Friction of Cu, J. Appl. Phys. 26, 1188 (1955).
382. Tucker, C. W., Jr., and J. B. Sampson, Interstitial Content of Radiation Damaged Metals from Precision X-Ray Lattice Parameter Measurements, Bull. Am. Phys. Soc. 29 (3), 20 (1954); see also AEC Report KAPL-1037 (1954).
383. Varley, J. H. O., Radiation Damage in Ionic Solids, J. Inst. Metals 84, 103–5 (1955–6).
384. Varley, J. H. O., Radiation Damage in Non-Fissile Materials, Intntl. Conf. on Peaceful Uses of Atomic Energy, P/444.
385. Vineyard, G. H., Theory and Mechanism of Radiation Effects in Metals, in "Nuclear Metallurgy", V. III, IMD Spec. Report Series No. 3, AIME (1956) p. 1.
386. Volkenshtein, N. V. and A. N. Orlov, Change of Electrical Conductivity of Certain Ferrites under the Action of γ-Rays, Izvest. Akad. Nauk SSSR Ser. Fiz. 18, 494–50 (1954), AEC-tr-2582.
387. Walton, G. N. et al., The Condition of Fission Product Iodine in Irradiated Uranium Metals Intntl. Conf. on Peaceful Uses of Atomic Energy, P/436.
388. Warren, B. E., X-Ray Study of Radiation Damage, Atomic Energy Comm. Report NYO-6513 (1955).

389. Wheeler, R. G. and W. S. Kelly, Irradiation of Zircaloy-2 Impact Specimens Containing Hydrogen, Atomic Energy Comm. Report HW-39805 (1955).
390. Wilson, J. C. and R. G. Berggren, Effects of Neutron Irradiation in Steels, ASTM Bull. No. 206 (1955).
391. Wilson, J. C. and D. S. Billington, Effect of Nuclear Radiation on Structural Materials, Preprint #91, Nucl. Eng. Sci. Congress, AIChE, Cleveland, Dec. 1955.
392. Witzig, W. F., Creep of Copper Under Deuteron Bombardment, J. Appl. Phys. *23*, 1263–6 (1952); Phys. Rev. (2) *87*, 211 (1952); see also AEC Report AECD 3290, WAPD-43 (1951).
393. Witzig, W. F., WAPD-1 Experiments in the Materials Testing Reactor. 1. Gamma Heating WAPD-1, Atomic Energy Comm. Report WAPD-79 (1953).
394. Wruck, D. and C. Wert, The Role of Crystal Structure on Irradiation Effects on Metals, Acta Met. *3*, 115–20 (1955); see also AEC Report AECU-2906 (1954).
395. Yockey, H. L. et al., Effect of Cyclotron Irradiation on Creep of Aluminum, Atomic Energy Comm. Report NAA-SR-121 (1956).
396. Young, F. W., Jr., On the Effect of Reactor Exposure on the Rate of Oxidation of Copper Single Crystals, Atomic Energy Comm. Report CF-55-3-70 (1955).
397. Zartman, I. F., Effect of Nuclear Reactor Radiation on Structural Materials, Presented at Nuclear Sci. and Eng. Congress, Cleveland, Dec. 1955.
398. Zavoiskii, V. K. and B. V. Ershler, Results of Irradiation Effects on Diffusion of Silver in Lithium, in Proc. Acad. Sci. USSR on Peaceful Uses of Atomic Energy, Div. of Phys.-Math., July 1955 Moscow, p. 362–8.

C. IRRADIATION EFFECTS ON NONMETALS

399. Alexander, P. and A. Charlesby, Energy Transfer in Macromolecules to Ionizing Radiations, Nature *173*, 578–9 (1954).
400. Alexander, P. and A. Charlesby, Radiation Protection in Copolymers of Isobutylene and Styrene, Proc. Roy. Soc. *230*, 136 (1955).
401. Alexander, P. and M. Fox, Polymerization and Depolymerization by X-Rays; Effects of Protective Agents, J. Chim. Phys. *50*, 415 (1953).
402. Alexander, P. et al., Degradation of Solid Polymethylmethacrylate by Ionizing Radiation, Proc. Roy. Soc. *223*, 1154, 392 (1954).
403. Alexander, P. et al., Radiation-Induced Changes in the Structure of Polyisobutylene, Proc. Roy. Soc. *A232*, 31–48 (1955).
404. Allen, A. O. and D. M. Richardson, Effect of Clinton Reactor Radiation on Plastics, Atomic Energy Comm. Report CNL-16 (1948).
405. Anon., Polymers by Radiation, Ind. Eng. Chem. *44*, 11A (1952).
406. Anon., Cross-Linking of Polythene in the Atomic Pile, Brit. Plastics *26*, 79 (1953).
407. Anon., A New Curing Process, Perfected by General Electric, Plastics Newsletter *13*, No. 20 May 1953.
408. Anon., "Atom-Cooked" Plastics, Atomics *4*, 142, June 1953.
409. Anon., Plastics Tailor-Made by Gamma Irradiation, Materials and Methods *44*, 173–4 (1956).
410. Anon.. Polypropertied Polymers, Ind. Eng. Chem. *45*, 11A (1953).
411. Anon., Crosslinked Polyethylene, Chem. Eng. News *32*, 1392 (Apr. 1954).
412. Anon., Irradiated Insulation, Electronic Design *2*, 6 (Apr. 1954).
413. Anon., Irradiated Polyethylene, Modern Plastics *31*, 100 (Apr. 1954).
414. Anon., Effect of Ionizing Radiation on High Polymers, European Scient. Notes No. 8-7, 90 (1954).

415. Anon., What are the Effects of Radiation on Electronic Components? Nucleonics *14* (7), 33–5 (1956).

416. Antonov-Romanovskii V. V. et al., The Dosimetry of Radioactive Radiations by Aid of Flash Phosphors, In Proc. Acad. Sci. USSR on Peaceful Uses of Atomic Energy, Div. of Phys.-Math, July 1955 Moscow, p. 342–61.

417. Armistead, F. C. et al., Conductivity Changes in Dielectrics during 2.5 mev X-Radiation, Atomic Energy Comm. Report MIT-1028 (1955).

418. Asano, S., On the Infrared Sensitive Behaviors of Some Doubly Activated ZnS Phosphors, J. Chem. Soc. Japan *9*, 580–92 (1954).

419. Aten, A. H. W., Jr. and J. B. M. van Berkum, A Thermal Reaction in Neutron Irradiated Permanganate, J. Am. Chem. Soc. *72*, 2373 (1950).

420. Austerman, S. B. and J. E. Howe, Irradiation of Graphite at Liquid Helium Temperatures, Phys. Rev. *100*, 1214–15 (1955).

421. Bakh, N. A., Radiolytic Oxidation of Organic Compounds, Intntl. Conf. on Peaceful Uses of Atomic Energy, P/683.

422. Bakh, N. A., ed., Symposium on Radiation Chemistry, Part II. Action of Radiations on Individual Organic Compounds and High Polymers, Acad. Sci. USSR, Moscow, 1955.

423. Ballantine, D. and B. Manowitz, The Polymerization of Vinyl Monomers by Intense Gamma Radiation, Atomic Energy Comm. Report BNL-229, Part 5.

424. Ballantine, D. S. et al., Evaluation of Polyethylene Cross-Linked by Ionizing Radiation, J. Polymer Sci. *13*, 410 (1954).

425. Ballantine, D. S. et al., Gamma Ray Initiated Polymerization of Styrene and Methyl Methacrylate, Intntl. Congress on Nuclear Eng., 61, June 20, 1954.

426. Ballantine, D. S. et al., The Effects of γ-Radiation on Vinyl Polymer Systems, Atomic Energy Comm. Report BNL-294 (1954).

427. Ballantine, D. S. et al., Fission Products Utilization. IX. Studies on Radiation Induced Graft Copolymerization and Solid State Polymerization, Atomic Energy Comm. Report BNL-414 (1956).

428. Banus, M. D., Gamma Ray Sensitive Alkali Halide Crystals, Atomic Energy Comm. Report AD-11802 (1952).

429. Baskett, A. C. and C. W. Miller, Electron Irradiation of Polythene, Nature *174*, 364–5 (1954).

430. Benda, H., Measurements of the Electrical Conductivity of CdS Crystals by Irradiation with Electrons of Moderate Energy, Ann. Physik (6) *9*, 413–22 (1951) (in German).

431. Benny, A. H. and F. C. Champion, Some Effects of Neutron Irradiation on Diamond, Nature *173*, 1087 (1954).

432. Benny, A. H., and F. C. Champion, Neutron Bombardment on Counting Diamonds, Proc. Roy. Soc. (London) *A234*, 432–40 (1956).

433. Berman, R. et al., Effect of Neutron Irradiation on Thermal Conductivity of a Quartz Crystal at Low Temperature, Nature *166*, 864–6 (1950).

434. Berry, C. R., Change in KCl Lattice by Soft X-Rays, Phys. Rev. *98*, 934–6 (1955).

435. Berstein, I. A. et al., Studies on the Gamma Radiation-Induced Polymerization of Acrylonitrile, J. Chem. Phys. *21*, 1303 (1953).

436. Best, J. V. F., The Coloration of Some Optical Glasses by X- and Gamma-Radiation AERE-C/R 1125 (1953).

437. Binder, D. and W. J. Sturm, On the Equivalence of X-Ray Lattice Parameter and Density Changes in Neutron Irradiated LiF, Phys. Rev. (2) *94* (3), 760 (1954); Phys. Rev. *96*, 1519 (1954).

438. Binder, D. and W. J. Sturm, Annealing Process in Neutron Irradiated LiF, Phys. Rev. 99, 603–4 (1955).

439. Birks, J. B. and F. A. Black, Deterioration of Anthracene Under Alpha Particle Irradiation, Proc. Phys. Soc. (London) 64A, 511–2 (1951).

440. Birks, J. B. and J. W. King, The Luminescence of Air, Glass and Quartz Under α-Particle Irradiation, Proc. Phys. Soc. (London) B66, 81–4 (1953).

441. Bolt, R. O. and J. G. Carroll, Organics as Reactor Moderator-Coolants. Some Aspects of the Thermal and Radiation Stabilities, Intntl. Conf. on Peaceful Uses of Atomic Energy. P/742.

442. Bopp, C. D. and O. Sisman, How Radiation Changes Polymer Mechanical Properties, Nucleonics 13 (10), 51 (1955).

443. Bopp, C. D. and O. Sisman, Stress Strain Curves for Reactor-Irradiated Plastics Nucleonics 14 (3), 52 (1956).

444. Bopp, C. D. and O. Sisman, Radiation Stability of Plastics and Elastomers Nucleonics 13 (7), 28–33 (1955); see also AEC Report ORNL-1373 (1953).

445. Born, J. W., A Study of the Effects of Nuclear Radiations on Elastomeric Compounds and Compounding Materials, Air Force. Report WADC-TR-55-58 (1955).

446. Borrman, B. B. and M. VanHerik, Effect of Radiation on a Lucite Radium Applicator, Nucleonics 14 (4), 96 (1956).

447. Bowen, D., Thermal Conductivity of Irradiated Graphite, Atomic Energy Comm. Report NAA-SR-59 (1950).

448. Bowen, D., Electrical Conductivity of Irradiated Graphite. I. and II. Atomic Energy Comm. Reports NAA-SR-33 (1949) and NAA-SR-39 (1950), resp.

449. Breger, I. A., Transformation of Organic Substances by Alpha Particles and Deuterons, J. Phys. Colloid Chem. 52, 551 (1948).

450. Breger, I. A. and E. B. Brittin, Effects of Radiation on Coals, Presented at 30th Nat. Colloid Symposium, Am. Chem. Soc., Madison, Wis. (1956).

451. Bresee, J. C. et al., Gamma Radiation Damage Studies of Organic Protective Coatings and Gaskets, ORNL-2174 (1956).

452. Bresee, J. C. et al., How Radiation Affects Materials: Damaging Effects on Chemical Materials, Nucleonics 14 (9), 75 (1956).

453. Bretton, R. H. et al. Effect of Gamma Radiation on Chemical Reactions, Atomic Energy Comm. Reports NYO-3307, -3309, -3310, -3311 (1952) and -3312 (1953).

454. Burr, J. G. and W. M. Garrison, Effect of Radiation on Physical Properties of Plastics, Atomic Energy Comm. Report AECD 2078 (1948).

455. Burr, J. G. et al., Behavior of Certain Plastics and Elastomers under Irradiation, Atomic Energy Comm. Report AECD-3634 (1948).

456. Burton, M., Radiation Chemistry, Phys. Colloid Chem. 51, 611 (1947).

457. Burton, M., Effects of High Energy Radiation on Organic Compounds, J. Phys. and Colliod Chem. 51, 786–97 (1947).

458. Burton, M. and W. N. Patrick, Radiation Chemistry of Mixtures, J. Phys. Chem. 58, 421, 424 (1954).

459. Byrne, J. et al., Evolution of Halides from Halogenated Plastics Exposed to γ-Radiation, Ind. Eng. Chem. 45, 2549 (1953), see also AEC Report K-981 (1952).

460. Calkins, V. P., Radiation Effects on Reactor Materials: Nonmetals, Nucleonics 12 (8), 9 (1954).

461. Calkins, V. P., Radiation Damage to Nonmetallic Materials, in "Nuclear Engineering—Part II", AIChE, Chem. Eng. Progr. Symposium Series 50, No. 12, 1954, p. 28, see also AEC Report APEX 167 (1954).

462. Calkins, V. P. et al., Survey and Evaluation Report on Radiation Damage to Plastic Materials, Atomic Energy Comm. Report ANPD-GE-1955.
463. Campbell, J. B., Irradiated Polyethylene, Materials and Methods *40*, 91–5 (1954).
464. Carson, W. N., Jr. and C. W. Michaelson, Effect of Radioactivity on the pH Response of Glass Electrodes, Atomic Energy Comm. Report HW-26763 (1953).
465. Carter, R. L., Measurement of Stored Energy During Quasi-Isothermal Annealing of Irradiated Graphite. I. Method and Preliminary Results, Atomic Energy Comm. Report NAA-SR-288 (1953).
466. Carter, R. L., Radiation Effects on Graphite, Delivered at ASTM, Los Angeles, Calif., 9/20/56.
467. Cathers, G. I., Radiation Damage to Radiochemical Processing Reagents, Preprint #288, Nuclear Eng. and Sci. Congr., AIChE, Cleveland, Dec. 1955; Intntl. Conf. on Peaceful Uses of Atomic Energy, P/743.
468. Champion, F. C. and B. Dale, Variations in the Photoconductivity and in the Electrical Counting Properties of Diamonds, Proc. Roy. Soc. (London) *A234*, 419–32 (1956).
469. Chapiro, A., Effect of γ-Radiation on Polymers of the Solid State. I. Reticulation of Polyethylene, J. chim. Phys. *52*, 246–58 (1955) (in French).
470. Chapiro, A., Polymerization with the Aid of Gamma Rays, Compt. rend. *228*, 1490–2 (1949).
471. Chapiro, A., On the Relative Radiochemical Effectiveness of Mixed Radiation from Atomic Piles and γ-Radiation, Compt. rend. *239*, 703–5 (1954) (in French).
472. Chapiro, A., Polymerization by Gamma Rays, Compt. rend. *229*, 827 (1949).
473. Chapiro, A., On the Polymerization of Vinylic Compounds Inititated by γ-Rays. I and II, J. chim. Phys. *47*, 747 and 764 (1950), resp.
474. Chapiro, A., On the Mechanism of Radiochemical Deterioration of Polymers, J. chim. Phys. *53*, 306–7 (1956) (in French).
475. Chapiro, A. et al., Radiochemical Polymerization of Vinyl Monomers, J. chim. Phys. *52*, 689–98 (1955) (in French).
476. Chapiro, A. et al., Polymerization Initiated by Nuclear Radiation, Rec. Trav. Chim. *68*, 1037 (1949); Science *113*, 718 (1951).
477. Charlesby, A., Comparison of Equations of State for Amorphous Long Chain Polymers, Phil. Mag. *44*, 578 (1953).
478. Charlesby, A., Cross-Linking of Polyethylene by Pile Radiation, Proc. Roy. Soc. *A215*, 187–214 (1952).
479. Charlesby, A., The Cross-Linking of Rubber by Pile Irradiation, Atomics *5*, 12, 27 (1954).
480. Charlesby, A., Crosslinking and Degradation of Paraffin Chains by High Energy Radiation, Proc. Roy. Soc. *222*, 60 (1954).
481. Charlesby, A., Decomposition and Polymerization of Polytetrafluorethylene by Pile Radiation, AERE-M/R 978 (1952).
482. Charlesby, A., Degradation of Cellulose by Ionizing Radiation, J. Polymer Sci. *15*, 263–70 (1955).
483. Charlesby, A., Effect of High Energy Radiation on Long Chain Polymers, Nature 171, 167 (1953).
484. Charlesby, A., Effect of High Energy Radiation on Polymers, Bull. Am. Phys. Soc. *29* (3), 14 (1954).
485. Charlesby, A., Effect of High Energy Radiation on the Solubility and Molecular Weight Distribution of Rubber, AERE-M/R 1185 (1953).

486. Charlesby, A., Effect of Molecular Weight on the Cross Linking of Siloxanes by High Energy Radiation, Nature *173*, 679–80 (1954).
487. Charlesby, A., Gel Formation by Main Chain Fracture of Long Chain Polymers, Proc. Roy. Soc. *231*, 521 (1955).
488. Charlesby, A., High Energy Radiation and Long Chain Polymers, C/R 1231, 111–126 (1953) (Brit. report).
489. Charlesby, A., How Radiation Affects Long Chain Polymers, Nucleonics *12* (6), 18 (1954).
490. Charlesby, A., How Radiation Affects Materials: Beneficial Effects on Polymers, Nucleonics *14* (9), 82 (1956).
491. Charlesby, A., Investigation of Halo Patterns of Amorphous Polymers, J. Polymer Sci. *10*, 201 (1953).
492. Charlesby, A., Irradiation of Long Chain Polymers, Chem. Eng. Progress *51*, 10, 476–8 (1955).
493. Charlesby, A., Recent Developments in the Irradiation of Long Chain Polymers, Intntl. Conf. on Peaceful Uses of Atomic Energy, P/465.
494. Charlesby, A., Solubility and Molecular Size Distribution of Cross Linked Polystyrene, J. Polymer Sci. *11*, 513 (1953); see also AERE-M/R 1034 (1952).
495. Charlesby, A., Swelling Properties of Polystyrene Cross-Linked by High Energy Radiation, J. Polymer Sci. *11*, 521 (1953); see also AERE-M/R-1051 (1952).
496. Charlesby, A., Treatment of Polymeric Substances, Brit. Pat. 749,680, see also Nuclear Eng. *1*, 316 (1956).
497. Charlesby, A. and N. H. Hancock, Effect of Crosslinking on the Elastic Modulus of Polythene, Proc. Roy. Soc. *A218*, 245 (1953); see also AERE-M/R 1060 (1952).
498. Charlesby, A. and M. Ross, Effect of Cross-Linking on the Density and Melting of Polythene, Proc. Roy. Soc. *A217*, 122 (1953).
499. Charlesby, A. and M. Ross, Breakdown of Methyl Methacrylate Polymer by High Energy Radiation, Nature *171*, 1153 (1953).
500. Charlesby, A., and M. Ross, The Effect of Pile Radiation on the Density and Melting of Polythene, AERE-M/R 1003 (1952).
501. Charlesby, A. et al., Degradation of Solid Polymethyl Methacrylate by Ionizing Radiation, AERE-M/R 1269 (1953).
502. Charlesby, A. et al., Modification of Polymers by Irradiation, Gordon Res. Conf. on Radiation Chemistry, July 6, 1954.
503. Chepur, D. V. and V. A. Petrusevich, Additional Conductance of HgI_2 Effected by X-Rays, Zhur. Tekh. Fiz. *25*, 1523-9 (1955) (in Russian).
504. Chipman, D. R. and B. E. Warren, An X-Ray Method for Studying Radiation Damage in Graphite, Atomic Energy Comm. Report KAPL-677 (1952).
505. Chipman, D. L. et al., X-Ray Measurements of Radiation Damage in Black Phosphorus, J. Appl. Phys. *24*, 1251 (1953); see also AEC Report BNL-1479.
506. Clark, C. D. et al., The Absorption Spectra of Irradiated Diamonds after Heat Treatment, Proc. Roy. Soc. (London) *A237*, 75–89 (1956).
507. Cochran, R. G. et al., Reactor Radiations Through Slabs of Graphite, Atomic Energy Comm. Report CF-54-7-105 (1954).
508. Cole, O. P., Effect of Irradiation on Polyethylene Coatings, Gordon Res. Conf. on Organic Coatings, July 15, 1954.
509. Coleman, J. H., Effect of Beta Radiation on the d-c Conductivity of Good Insulators, Annual Report on Electrical Insulation, 1954 Meeting.
510. Coleman, J. H. and D. Bohm, Method for Increasing the Electrical Resistivity of Insulators under Ionizing Radiation, J. Appl. Phys. *24*, 497 (1953).

511. Colichman, E. L. and R. F. Fish, Resistance of Terphenyls to Heat and Radiation, Nucleonics *15* (2), 72–75 (1957).

512. Colichman, E. L. and R. H. J. Gercke, Radiation Stability of Polyphenyls, Nucleonics *14* (7), 50-4 (1956).

513. Collins, C. G. and V. P. Calkins, Radiation Damage to Elastomers, Organic Liquids and Plastics, Atomic Energy Comm. Report APEX 261 (1956).

514. Collinson E. and F. S. Dainton, X-Ray and Gamma-Ray Induced Polymerization of Aqueous Solutions of Acrylonitrile. A General Discussion, Disc. Faraday Soc. No. 12, p. 212 (1952) (Aberdeen Univ. Press, Ltd.).

515. Crawford, J. H., Jr., The Nature of Radiation Damage in Crystalline Solids, Am. Ceram. Soc. Bull. *36*, 95–8, Apr. 1956.

516. Crawford, J. H., Jr. and M. C. Wittels, A Review of Investigations of Radiation Effects in Ionic and Covalent Crystals, Intntl. Conf. on Peaceful Uses of Atomic Energy, P/753.

517. Dainton, F. S., Effect of Gamma and X-Rays on Dilute Aqueous Solutions of Acrylonitrile, Nature *160*, 268 (1947).

518. Dainton, F. S., On Existence of Free Atoms and Radicals in Water and Aqueous Solutions to Ionizing Radiation, J. Phys. Chem. *52*, 490 (1948).

519. Dainton, F. S., Polymerization as a Guide to Tract Distribution, J. chim. Phys. *48*, 182 (1951).

520. Dainton, F. S. and J. Rowbottom, Kinetics of the Coloration and Luminescence of Vitreous Silica Induced by Irradiation with X- and γ-Rays with Observations on Related Phenomena, Trans. Faraday Soc. *50*, 480–93 (1954).

521. Dale, M. and C. D. Keeling, Pile Irradiation of Polyethylene, J. Am. Chem. Soc. *76*, 4304–11 (1954).

522. Davidson, W. L. and I. G. Geib, Effects of Pile Bombardment on Uncured Elastomers, J. Appl. Phys. *19*, 427 (1948); Rubber Chem. and Tech. *22*, 138 (1949).

523. Day, Harold R., Irradiation Induced Photoconductivity in MgO, Phys. Rev. *91*, 822–7 (1953).

524. Day, M. J. and G. Stein, Effects of X-Rays Upon Plastics: Electronic Processes, Nature *168*, 644 (1951).

525. Delbecq, C. J. et al., Optical and Electrical Properties of LiF, X-Irradiated at −190°C, Z. Physik *138*, 266–75 (1954) (in German).

526. Delcroix, J. L. and J. Yvon, Macroscopic Expansion of Graphite on Irradiation, Compt. rend. *242*, 628–30 (1956).

527. Dienes, G. J. and D. A. Kleinman, Nature of Radiation Damage in Diamond, Phys. Rev. (2) *91*, 238 (1953).

528. Dole, M., Effect of Radiation on Colloidal and High Polymeric Substances, Symposium IV. Chem. and Phys. of Radiation Dosimetry, Report Pt. I, (105925), p. 129 (Sept. 1950). Army Chem. Center, Md.

529. Dole, M. and W. H. Howard, Melting Behavior of Irradiated Polyethylene, Presented at 30th Nat. Colloid Symposium, Am. Chem. Soc., Madison, Wis. June 1956.

530. Dole, M. et al., The Pile Irradiation of Polyethylene, J. Am. Chem. Soc. *76*, 4304 (1954).

531. Dole, M. et al., How Polyethylene Cross Links, Chem. Eng. News *32*, 1342 (1954).

532. Eatherly, W. P. and J. J. Donoghue, A New Circuit for Precision Measurement of the Hall and Magneto-Resistive Effects with Results of Observations on Reactor Irradiated Graphite, Atomic Energy Comm. Report NAA-SR-68 (1950).

533. Eatherly, W. P. and N. S. Rasor, The Thermoelectric Power of Graphite Dependence on Temperature, Type and Neutron Irradiation, Atomic Energy Comm. Report NAA-SR-196 (1952).

534. Edgerton, Germeshausen and Grier Inc., Sensitivity of Films to Gamma Radiation, Atomic Energy Comm. Report EGG-1068 (1952).

535. Eidus, T. and K. Puzitskii, Polymerization and Other Transformations of Ethylene and Propylene Under the Influence of Heat, Free Radicals, and Other Active Particles, Uspekki Kim *22*, 838 (1953). (See Chem. Abs. *47*, 11800, Nov. 1953).

536. Eisler, S. L., Evaluation of Rubber for Ordnance Use. High Radiation of Polymers. A Literature Review, Atomic Energy Comm. Report AD-24914 (1953).

537. Estin, R. et al., Radiation Sensitive Glasses, Atomic Energy Comm. Report AD-27424 (1953).

538. Faris, F. E., ed., Radiation Effects Quarterly Progress Report (Graphite), Atomic Energy Comm. Reports NAA-SR-286 (1954); NAA-SR-1152 (1955) and AECD 3928 (1954).

539. Farmer, F. T., Electrical Properties of Polystyrene, Nature *150*, 521 (1942).

540. Feng, P. Y. H. and J. W. Kennedy, Radioactive Charging Through Solid Dielectrics, Atomic Energy Comm. Report AECU-2685 (1953).

541. Feng, P. Y. H. and J. W. Kennedy, Electrical and Chemical Effects of Beta Radiation in Polystyrene, J. Am. Chem. Soc. *77*, 847 (1955).

542. Fields, M., Chemical Systems Sensitive to Radiation, ATI-150188 (1951).

543. Fogelstroem, I. and T. Westermark, Production of P^{33} by Neutron Irradiation of Sulphur, Nucleonics *14* (2), 62 (1956).

544. Fowler, J. F., X-Ray Induced Conductivity in Insulated Materials, Proc. Roy. Soc. (London) *A236*, 464–80 (1956).

545. Fowler, J. F. and F. T. Farmer, Effect of Temperature on the Conductivity Induced in Insulators by X-Rays, Nature *171*, 1020–1 (1953).

546. Fowler, J. F. and F. T. Farmer, Conductivity Induced in Insulating Materials by X-Rays, Nature *173*, 317 (1954).

547. Fowler, J. F. and F. T. Farmer, Conductivity Induced in Polytetrafluorethylene by X-Rays, Nature *174*, 136 (1954).

548. Fowler, J. F. and F. T. Farmer, Conductivity Induced in Mica by X-Rays, Nature *175*, 648 (1955).

549. Fowler, J. F. and F. T. Farmer, Conductivity Induced by X-Rays in Polyethylene Terephthalate. A Possible Insulator for Radiological Apparatus, Nature *175*, 590–1 (1955).

550. Fox. M., Action of Certain Protective Compounds on Gamma Ray Damage to Polymeric Solutions, Compt. rend. *237*, 1682 (1953).

551. Frankl, D. R. and T. A. Read, Effects of F Centers on the Internal Friction of Rocksalt Single Crystals, Phys. Rev. *89*, 663–4 (1953).

552. Gale, A. J. and F. A. Bickford, Radiation Resistant Fused Silica, Nucleonics *11* (8), 848 (1953).

553. Germann, Frank E. E. et al., Energy Transfers in Irradiated Solutions of Mixed Phosphors, Science *120*, 540–2 (1954).

554. Ghormley, J. A. and H. A. Levy, Some Observations of Luminescence of Alkali Halide Crystals Subjected to Ionizing Radiation, J. Phys. Chem. *56*, 548 (1952).

555. Gold, L., Distribution of Radioactivity in Labeled Polymers, Nucleonics *11* (7), 48 (1953).

556. Goode, J. H., How Radiation Affects Organics in Solvent Extraction of Fuel, Nucleonics *15* (2), 68–71 (1957).

557. Gordon, R. B. and A. S. Nowick, Structure Sensitivity of the X-Ray Coloration of NaCl Crystals, Phys. Rev. *101*, 977–83 (1956).

558. Gordon, R. B. and A. S. Nowick, The Pinning of Dislocations by X-Irradiation of Alkali Halide Crystals, Acta Met. *4*, 514 (1956).

559. Gregory, J. N. and S. Moorbath, Effect of Pile Irradiation on the Emanating Power of Alumina, AERE C/M 129 (1952).

560. Grenishin, S. G., Effect of Electrons on Photographic Film, Zhur. Tekh. Fiz. *22*, 33–9 (1952) (in Russian).

561. Griffiths, J. H. E. et al., Paramagnetic Resonance in Neutron Irradiated Diamond and Smoky Quartz, Nature *173*, 439–40 (1954).

562. Hacskaylo, M. and G. Groetzinger, Generation of Color Center Precursors in Alkali Halides by Electrolysis, Phys. Rev. (2) *87*, 789 (1952).

563. Haissinsky, M. and W. Gluzbarg, Action of Ionizing Radiations on Colloidal Solutions, Compt. rend. *233*, 1192–4 (1951) (in French).

564. Haissinsky, M. and M. doCarmo Anta, Reduction of Ceric Salts and Oxidation of Ferrous Sulfate by Polonium α-Particles, Compt. rend. *236*, 1161–3 (1953) (in French).

565. Hanle, W. and K. H. Rau, Light Yield and Dissociation of Phosphors by Electron and Ion Collisions, Z. Physik *133*, 297–308 (1952) (in German).

566. Hardwick, T. J., The Oxidation of Ferrous Sulfate by γ-Rays. The Temperature Coefficient of Air Saturated Solutions, Can. J. Chem. *31*, 881–3 (1953).

567. Hardwick, T. J., The Oxidation of Ferrous Sulfate Solutions by γ-Rays. The Effect of Surface/Volume Ratio of Polystyrene Cells on the Yield, Can. J. Chem. *31*, 512–4 (1953).

568. Harrington, R., How Radiation Affects Materials: Damaging Effects on Plastics and Elastomers, Nucleonics *14* (9), 70 (1956).

569. Haworthy, D. T., Inhibitor Breakdown in Zinc Bromide Shielding Windows, Nucleonics *13* (10), 66 (1955).

570. Hayes, S. and R. Smoluchowski, Small Angle X-Ray Scattering in Proton Irradiated Diamond, Phys. Rev. (2) *91*, 244 (1953).

571. Hayward, J. C., Jr., Polymerization of Ethylene Initiated by Gamma Radiation (Thesis), Atomic Energy Comm. Report NYO-3313 (1955).

572. Hayward, J. C., Jr. and R. H. Bretton, Kinetics of the Ethylene Reaction Initiated by Gamma Radiation, Intntl. Congress on Nuclear Eng. 62, June 1954.

573. Head, H. G., The Chemical Effects of Ionizing Radiation in Solids. II. Atomics *6*, 241–7 (1955).

574. Henley, E. J. and M. Litt, Degradation of Vinyl Iodide Polymer by Gamma Radiation, Presented at 30th Nat. Colloid Symposium, Am. Chem. Soc., Madison, Wis. June 1956.

575. Henley, E. J. and A. Miller, Gamma Ray Dosimetry with Polyvinyl-Chloride Films, Nucleonics *9* (6), Dec. 1951.

576. Hennig, G., A Comparison of the Effects of Oxidation and the Effects of Neutron Irradiation on Graphite, Atomic Energy Comm. Report ANL-4765.

577. Hennig, G. R., A Chemical Model of Radiation Damaged Graphite, Delivered at Am. Nuclear Soc., June 1956, Chicago.

578. Hennig, G. R. and J. E. Hove, Interpretation of Radiation Damage to Graphite, Intntl. Conf. on Peaceful Uses of Atomic Energy, P/751.

330 EFFECTS OF RADIATION ON MATERIALS

579. Hennig, G. et al., The Decomposition of Nitrate Crystals by Ionizing Radiations, J. Chem. Phys. *21*, 664–8 (1953).

580. Hill, J. J. and J. Aron, An Investigation of the Thermoluminescence of Fluorite Colored by X-Ray Irradiation, J. Chem. Phys. *21*, 223–8 (1953).

581. Hill, J. J. and P. Schwed, Experimental Study of the Mechanism of Thermoluminescence in Irradiated Sodium Chloride, J. Chem. Phys. *23*, 652–8 (1955).

582. Hobbs, L. M. et al., Effects of Gamma Radiation on Rubber and Polymerization, Atomic Energy Comm. Report COO-196 (1953) p. 158.

583. Hochanadel, C., Decomposition of Fused Sodium Hydroxide by Fast Electrons, J. Am. Chem. Soc. *76*, 2675 (1954).

584. Javitz, A. E., Impact of High Energy Radiation on Dielectrics, Elec. Mfg. *55* (6), 70 (1955).

585. Kalabukhov, N. P. and V. V. Mumladze, Measurement of the Dark Currents in Colored Crystals of KCl after Bombardment with a Beam of Electrons, Soobshcheniya Akad. Nauk, Cruzinskol SSR *12*, 11 (1951) (in Russian).

586. Karpov, V. L., Action of Nuclear Radiations on Highly Polymerized Substances, in Proc. Acad. Sci. USSR on Peaceful Uses of Atomic Energy, Div. of Chem., July 1955, Moscow, p. 3–21, p. 13–22 (English transl.).

587. Keating, D. T., X-Ray Measurement of Pile Irradiated LiF, Phys. Rev. *97*, 832 (1955).

588. Keating, D. T., X-Ray Measurements on Low Temperature Neutron Irradiated Graphite, Phys. Rev. *98*, 1859–60 (1955).

589. Keller, S. P. and J. J. Clemmons, Thermoluminescence and Fluorescence in Alkali Halide Crystals Induced by Soft X-Ray, J. Chem. Phys. *23*, 586–7 (1955).

590. Kernohan, R. H. and G. M. McCammon, Fading Characteristics of γ-Induced Coloration in High Density Glass, Atomic Energy Comm. Report ORNL-975 (1951).

591. Kinchin, G. H., Changes in the Electrical Properties of Graphite Due to Neutron Irradiation, J. Nuclear Energy *1*, 124–9 (1954).

592. Kinchin, G. H., The Effects of Irradiation on Graphite, Intntl. Conf. on Peaceful Uses of Atomic Energy, P/442.

593. Klein, G. E., Radiodiffractometry and Its Application to the Study of Irradiated Ceramic Specimens, Presented at Am. Ceram. Soc., New York, Apr. 1956.

594. Klein, P. H. and C. Mannal, Effects of High Energy Gamma Radiation on Dielectric Solids. I and II. Insulation *2*, 9–13 (1956); Comm. and Electronics *22*, 723–9 (1956).

595. Klimenkov, V. I. and Y. N. Aleksenko, Change of the Properties of Graphite when Irradiated by Neutrons, in Proc. Acad. Sci. USSR on Peaceful Uses of Atomic Energy, Div. Phys.-Math., July 1955, Moscow, p. 322–41.

596. Kline, G. M., The Year 1953 in Review, Modern Plastics *31*, 117 (1954).

597. Kobayashi, K., Annealing of Some Radiation Effects in Sodium Chloride Irradiated with High Energy Protons, Bull. Am. Phys. Soc. (II) *1*, 32 (1956).

598. Kobayashi, K. et al., Radiation Effects in Alkali Halides Produced by High Energy Protons and Gamma Rays, Intntl. Conf. on Peaceful Uses of Atomic Energy, P/748.

599. Koch, L., Semiconductors and Nuclear Radiations, L'Onde Electrique *35*, 977–80 (1955) (in French).

600. Kosiba, W. L. et al., Some Effects Produced in Graphite by Neutron Irradiation in the BNL Reactor, Preprint ≴93, Nuclear Eng. and Sci. Congress, Cleveland, Dec. 1955.

601. Kratky, O. and G. Porod, X-Ray Investigation of Dissolved Chain Molecules, Rec. Trav. Chim. *68*, 1106 (1949).

602. Kreidl, N. J., Irradiation Damage to Glass, Atomic Energy Comm. Report NYO-3777 (1953); NYO-3780 (1954); NYO-3782 (1955).

603. Kreidl, N. J., Some Effects of High Energy Radiation on Glass, Atomic Energy Comm. Report NYO-3778 (1953).

604. Kreidl, N. J., Some Experiments on the Interaction of Glass with High Energy Radiation, Atomic Energy Comm. Report NYO-3779 (1953).

605. Kreidl, N. J. and J. R. Hensler, Formation of Color Centers in Glasses Exposed to Gamma Radiation, J. Am. Ceram. Soc. *38*, 423–32 (1955).

606. Kuzminsky, A. S. et al., Some Characteristics of Radiation Vulcanization, Soviet J. Atomic Energy No. 3, 431–4 (1956).

607. Landler, I. and M. Magat, On the Polymerization of Styrene Induced by Slow Neutrons, Compt. rend. *226*, 1720 (1948).

608. Landler, I. and M. Magat, Preliminary Results of Styrene Polymerization Initiated by Slow Neutrons, Bull. Soc. Chim. Belges *57*, 381 (1948).

609. Lautout, M., Photostimulation and Coloration of Fused Quartz Irradiated by X- or γ-Radiation, J. Chim. Phys. *52*, 267–71 (1955) (in French).

610. Lautout, M., Absorption Spectrum and Thermoluminescence Curve of Fused Quartz Irradiated by X- and γ-Radiation, J. Chim. Phys. *52*, 259–66 (1955) (in French).

611. Lawton, E. J. et al., Properties of Irradiated Polyethylene, Effect of Initial Molecular Weight, Ind. Eng. Chem. *46*, 1703 (1954).

612. Lawton, E. J. et al., Some Effects of High Velocity Electrons on Wood, Science *113*, 380 (1951).

613. Lawton, E. J. et al., Irradiation of Polymers by High Energy Electrons, Nature *172*, 76 (1953).

614. Leivo, W. J., Density Change in Proton Irradiated Potassium Chloride, Phys. Rev. (2) *91*, 245 (1953).

615. Leivo, W. and R. Smoluchowski, X-Ray Coloring of 400 mev Proton-Irradiated KCl, Phys. Rev. (2) *93*, 1415–16 (1954).

616. Levy, P. W., Reactor and Gamma Ray Induced Coloring in Crystalline Quartz and Corning Fused Silica, J. Chem. Phys. *23*, 764 (1955).

617. Levy, P. W. and G. J. Dienes, Color Centers Induced in Al_2O_3 by Reactor and Gamma-Ray Irradiation, Atomic Energy Comm. Report BNL-1975 (1954); also in "Defects in Crystalline Solids", Phys. Soc. London, 1955, p. 256–60.

618. Levy, P. W. and O. F. Kammerer, Radiation Induced Amorphism in Diamond, Phys. Rev. *100*, 1787–8 (1955).

619. Levy, M. and J. H. O. Varley, Radiation Induced Color Centers in Fused Quartz, Proc. Phys. Soc. *B68*, 223–33 (1955).

620. Lewis, J. G. et al., Polymerization of Ethylene by Gamma Radiation, Intntl. Congress on Nuclear Eng. 62, June, 1954, Chem. Eng. Progress *50*, 249–54 (1954).

621. Lind, S. C., The Chemical Effects of Alpha Particle and Electrons (Book), Chem. Catalog Co., Inc., New York, 1928 (2nd ed.).

622. Lindsey, M. H. et al., Effect of Co^{60} Gamma Radiation on Formation and Degradation of Polymers, Bull. Am. Phys. Soc. *29* (3) 14 (1954).

623. Link, W. T. and D. Walker, Light Output of Potassium Iodide Crystals under Bombardment by Heavy Charged Particles, Proc. Phys. Soc. (London) *A66*, 767–70 (1953).

624. Little, K., Some Effects of Irradiation on Nylon and Polyethylene Terephthalate, Nature *173*, 680 (1954).
625. Little, K., Irradiation of Linear High Polymers, Nature *170*, 1075 (1952).
626. Loewe, S., Polymerization by Means of High Energy Electrons, Science *114*, 555 (1951).
627. Loughborough, D. L. et al., A Study of the Effects of Nuclear Radiations on Elastomeric Compounds and Compounding Materials, Air Force Report WADC-TR-55-58 (1954).
628. Lukesh, J. S., Neutron Damage to the Structure of Vitreous Silica, Phys. Rev. *97*, 345-6 (1955).
629. Lukesh, J. S., An X-Ray Study of the Effects of Intense Neutron Irradiation on the Structure of Some Glasses, Atomic Energy Comm. Report KAPL-1307 (1955).
630. McCarthy, P. B., Flexure Tests on Irradiated Teflon Bellows, Atomic Energy Comm. Report HW-35284 (1955).
631. McClelland, J. D., Change in Magnetic Susceptibility of Irradiated Graphite During Pulse Annealing, Atomic Energy Comm. Report NAA-SR-211 (1952).
632. McClelland, J. D. and J. J. Donoghue, The Effect of Neutron Bombardment upon the Magnetic Susceptibility of Several Pure Oxides, J. Appl. Phys. *24*, 963 (1953); see also AEC Report NAA-SR-263 (1953).
633. McLennan, D. E., Study of Ionic Crystal Under Electron Bombardment, Canad. J. Phys. *29*, 122-8 (1951.)
634. McClinton, A. T. et al., Radiation Effects on Dielectrics, NRL Memo. Report 146, Apr. 1953 and Oct. 1953.
635. Mador, I. L. et al., Production and Bleaching of Color Centers in X-Rayed Alkali Halide Crystals, Phys. Rev. *96*, 617-28 (1954).
636. Magee, J. L., Radiation Chemistry, Ann. Rev. of Nucl. Sci. *3*, 171 (1953).
637. Malmstrom, C. R., Studies on Nuclear Reactors. 10. Experimental Method for the Determination of Resistivity Change in Graphite Bombarded with Deuterons and Alpha Particles, Atomic Energy Comm. Report NAA-SR-10 (1955).
638. Mandeville, C. E. and H. O. Albrecht, The Alpha Particle Induced Phosphorescence of Silver-Activated Sodium Chloride, Phys. Rev. *90*, 25-8 (1953).
639. Manion, J. P. and M. Burton, Radiolysis of Hydrocarbon Mixtures, J. Phys. Chem. *56*, 560 (1952).
640. Mannal, C., Testing Electrical Insulation for Use in Gamma Ray Fields, Nucleonics *12* (6), 49 (1954).
641. Manowitz, B., Industrial Future of Radiation Chemistry, Nucleonics *11* (10), 18 (1953).
642. Manowitz, B., Nuclear Reactors, Fission Products and Their Possibilities and Limitations for the Industrial Future of Radiation Chemistry, Atomic Energy Comm. Report BNL-1519 (1953).
643. Manowitz, B. et al., Preliminary Studies on Industrial Applications of Intense γ-Radiation, Atomic Energy Comm. Report BNL-141 and T-27, (1950 and 1951, resp.).
644. Mapother, D., Effect of X-Ray Irradiation on the Self-Diffusion Coefficient of Na in NaCl, Phys. Rev. (2) *89*, 1231-2 (1953).
645. Markham, J. J., Speculation on the Formation of F Centers During Irradiation, Phys. Rev. *88*, 500-9 (1952).
646. Martin, J. J. et al., Polymerization of Ethylene by Means of Gamma Radiation, Atomic Energy Comm. Report COO-198 (1954), p. 12.

647. Martin, J. J. et al., Effect of Radiation on Chemical Reactions (including Polymerization), Atomic Energy Comm. Report COO-196 (1953) p. 21.

648. Mayburg, S., Conductivity Change in Polyethylene During Gamma Irradiation, Conference on Elec. Insulation (1952), p. 34.

649. Mayburg, S. and W. L. Lawrence, Conductivity Change in Polyethylene During Gamma Radiation, J. Appl. Phys. 23, 1006 (1952).

650. Mayburg, S., Conductivity Change in Good Insulators During γ-Radiation The Conductivity of Teflon, Atomic Energy Comm. Report WAPD-RM-122 (1952).

651. Mayer, G. and J. Gueron, Cinetique de la Decoloration de Verres Colores Par Irradiation Dans la Pile de Chatillon, J. Chim. Phys. 49, 204 (1952).

652. Mayer, G. et al., Modification Produced in Nonmetallic Materials by Radiation and the Thermal Healing of these Effects, Intntl. Conf. on Peaceful Uses of Atomic Energy, P/362; see also Comm. energie atomique (France), Rapp ≠433 (1955).

653. Mesrobian, R. B. and P. Ander, Gamma Ray Polymerization of Acrylamide in the Solid State, J. Chem. Phys. 22, 565 (1954).

654. Meyer, R. A. et al., Radiation Induced Conductivity in Polyethylene and Teflon, J. Appl. Phys. 27, 1012–18 (1956).

655. Miller, A. A., Effect of Chemical Structure of Vinyl Polymers on Cross Linking and Degradation by Ionizing Radiation, J. Polymer Sci. 14, 503–4 (1954).

656. Miller, C. W., Applications of High Energy Electrons to the Sterilization of Pharmaceuticals and the Irradiation of Plastics, J. Brit. Inst. Radio Engrs. 14, 637–52 (1954).

657. Mincher, E. L., Summary of Available Data on Radiation Damage to Various Nonmetallic Material, Atomic Energy Comm. Report KAPL-731 (1952).

658. Monk, G. S., Coloration of Optical Materials by High Energy Radiations, Nucleonics 10 (11) 52–5 (1952); see also AEC Report ANL-4536 (1950).

659. Montet, G. et al., Tracer Studies on Radiation Damaged Graphite, Nuclear Sci. and Eng. 1 (1) 33 (1956).

660. Mueller, H. and E. Schmid, An Example of an Increase in the Rate of a Phase Transition by Radiation, Monatsh. 85, 719–21 (1954).

661. Muller, F. A., Effects of Ionizing Radiation on the Electrical Conductivity of High Quality Insulating Materials, Annual Report on Elec. Insulation, N.R.C. (1952), p. 32–3.

662. Mund, W., Radiochemical Polymerization of Vinyl Chloride at Constant Pressure, Bull. Soc. Chim. Belges 62, 190 (1953).

663. Mund, W. et al., Polymerization of Vinyl Chloride under the Action of Rays, Bull. Classe Sci. Acad. Roy. Belg. 35, 656 (1949).

664. Myron, G. B. and H. Linschitz, Nonelectronic Dose Rate Indicating Systems, Atomic Energy Comm. Report NP-4400.

665. Nelson, C. M. et al., Conductivity Changes in KCl Produced by γ- and n-Irradiation, Phys. Rev. (2) 90, 364 (1953).

666. Neubert, T. J. et al., Neutron Induced Decomposition of Graphite, Atomic Energy Comm. Report ANL-5472 (1956).

667. Newman, J. B., Dissociation of Sodium Chloride by Electron Bombardment, Virginia J. Sci. (new series) 1, 341 (1950).

668. Nozaki, K., Irradiation Catalyzed Polymerization of Vinyl Compounds, U. S. Pat. 2,666,025 (1954).

669. Otley, K. O. and W. A. Weyl, Blue Glass Which Fades Upon Nuclear Radiation, J. Appl. Phys. *23*, 499 (1952).

670. Otley, K. O., Effects of High Energy Radiation on Glasses, Glass Ind. *33*, 24–7 (1952).

671. Parkins, W. E., Studies on Nuclear Reactions: 3. Effects of Cyclotron Bombardment on the Physical Properties of Graphite, Atomic Energy Comm. Report NAA-SR-3 (1947).

672. Parkins, W. E. et al., Results of Pulse Annealing Measurements on the Electric Resistivity of Irradiated Graphite, Atomic Energy Comm. Report NAA-SR-23 (1955).

673. Patrick, W. N. and M. Burton, Polymer Production in Radiolysis of Benzene, J. Am. Chem. Soc. *76*, 2626 (1954).

674. Pearlstein, E. A., Change of Electrical Conductivity of Alkali Halides upon Irradiation with 350 mev Protons, Bull. Am. Phys. Soc. *29* (3), 11 (1954).

675. Pearlstein, E. A., Change of Electrical Conductivity of Sodium Chloride upon Bombardment with High Energy Protons, Phys. Rev. (2) *92*, 881–2 (1953); see also AEC Report NYO-3127 (1953).

676. Pearlstein, E. A., Changes in Conductivity of NaCl Produced by Bombardment with 360 mev Protons, Phys. Rev. (2) *91*, 244–5 (1953).

677. Pfaff, E. R and R. D. Shelton, The Effects of Nuclear Radiation on Electronic Components, Air Force Report AD-77763 (1955).

678. Pickard, D. F., The Effect of Gamma Radiation Upon Lead Sulfide Coated Glass Fire Detection Cells ("Fireye"), Atomic Energy Comm. Report CF-52-5-211 (1952).

679. Pigg, J. C. et al., The Effect of Reactor Irradiation on Electrical Insulation, Communications and Electronics *22*, 717–23 (1956).

680. Prestwich, G. D. et al., Average Energy of Secondary Electrons in Anthracene Due to γ-Irradiation, Phys. Rev. *87*, 1030 (1952).

681. Prevot, A., Determination of X-Ray Dosage by Polymerization Reactions, Compt. rend. *230*, 288 (1950).

682. Primak, W., The Metamict State, Phys. Rev. *95*, 837 (1954).

683. Primak, W. and L. H. Fuchs, Radiation Damage to the Electrical Conductivities of Natural Graphite Crystals, Phys. Rev. *103*, 541–4 (1956).

684. Primak, W. and H. Szymanski, Radiation Damage in Vitreous Silica: Annealing of the Density Changes, Phys. Rev. *101*, 1268–71 (1956).

685. Primak, W. et al., Effects of Nuclear Reactor Exposure on Some Properties of Vitreous Silica and Quartz, J. Am. Ceram. Soc. *38* (4), 134 (1955).

686. Primak, W. et al., Photoelastic Observations of the Expansion of Alkali Halides on Irradiation, Phys. Rev. *98*, 1708–14 (1955).

687. Primak, W. et al., Radiation Damage in Insulators, Phys. Rev. *92*, 1064 (1953).

688. Primak, W. et al. Radiation Damage in Diamond and Silicon Carbide, Phys. Rev. *103*, 1184–92 (1956).

689. Przibram, K., Coloration and Luminescence Caused by Becquerel Rays and Related Phenomena. V., Z. Physik *130*, (3) 269–82 (1951) (in German).

690. Ranadive, J. S. et al., Chemical Effect of Beta, Gamma-Radiations on Solutions of Nucleic Acid, Purines and Pyrimidines, Intntl. Conf. on Peaceful Uses of Atomic Energy, P/905.

691. Rappaport, P. and E. G. Linder, Radioactive Charging Effects with a Dielectric Medium, J. Appl. Phys. *24*, 1110–14 (1953).

692. Rasor, N. S., Technique for the Measurement of Changes in Thermal and Elec-

trical Properties of Pulse-Annealed Irradiated Graphite, Atomic Energy Comm. Report NAA-SR-43.

693. Rasor, J. S. and A. W. Smith, Low Temperature Thermal and Electrical Conductivities of Normal and Neutron Irradiated Graphite, Atomic Energy Comm. Report NAA-SR-862 (1954).

694. Rexer, E., Accelerated Polymerization with Gamma and Roentgen Quanta, Reichsber. Physik. (Beihefte Physik Z.) *1*, 111 (1944).

695. Roberts, L. E. J., Adsorption on Irradiated Graphite, AERE C/M 144 (1952).

696. Robinson, C. C., The Effects of Nuclear Radiation on Electronic Components, Proc. 1956 Electronic Components Symposium, Washington, D. C. May 1956, p. 102–5.

697. Robinson, W. H. et al., Small Angle Scattering of X-Rays by Irradiated Diamond, Bull. Am. Phys. Soc. *29* (3), 37 (1954).

698. Rogers, F. T., Jr., Effect of Pile Irradiation on the Dielectric Constant of Ceramic $BaTiO_3$, J. Appl. Phys. *27*, 1066 (1956).

699. Rosenblum, C., Benzene Formation in the Radiochemical Polymerization of Acetylene, J. Phys. Colloid Chem. *52*, 474 (1948).

700. Ross, M., Changes in Some Physical Properties of Polyethylene by Pile Irradiation at 80°C, AERE-M/R 1401 (1954).

701. Ross, M. and A. Charlesby, Effect of Pile Radiation on Methyl Methacrylate, AERE-M/R 1067 (1953).

702. Ross, M. and A. Charlesby, Effect of Pile Radiation on Polymethyl Methacrylate ("Perspex"), Atomics *4*, 189 (1953).

703. Rothwell, W. S., Radiation Shielding Window Glasses, Report, Corning Glass Works, Corning, N. Y.

704. Ruechardt, H., Ionic Disorder in X-Irradiated KBr Crystals, Phys. Rev. *103*, 873–6 (1956).

705. Ryan, J. W., Effects of Radiation on Organic Materials, Atomic Energy Comm. Report GEL-57, DF 52 GL 242, Dec. 1952.

706. Ryan, J. W., Effect of Gamma Radiation on Certain Rubbers and Plastics, Nucleonics *11* (8), 13 (1953).

707. Ryan, J. W., Effect of Pile Radiation on Electrical Insulation, Modern Plastics *31*, 148 (1954).

708. Ryan, J. W., Radiation of Polytetrafluoroethylene, Modern Plastics *31*, 152 (1953).

709. Sachs, F., Effect of α-β-γ and X-Rays on Organic Compounds. A Literature Search, Atomic Energy Comm. Report Y-904 (1952).

710. Saeman, J. F. et al., Effect of High Energy Cathode Rays on Cellulose, Ind. Eng. Chem. *44*, 2848 (1952).

711. Sampson, J. B. and C. W. Tucker, Jr., Study of Interstitial Atoms and Vacancies in Irradiated Crystals Using X-Ray Measured Lattice Parameter Together with Density Measurements, Atomic Energy Comm. Report KAPL-M-JBS-8 (1954).

712. Sandford, E. R. and P. A. Nicoll, Pile Irradiation of U-Plastic Fuel Tape, Delivered at Am. Nuclear Soc., June 1956, Chicago.

713. Sarah Mellon Scaife Radiation Laboratory, Radiation Damage Study. Effects of Ionizing Radiation on Certain Materials, Atomic Energy Comm. Report NP-5218 (1954).

714. Schneider, E. E., Paramagnetic Resonance of X-Rayed Teflon, J. Chem. Phys. *23*, 978 (1955).

715. Schmitz, J. V. and E. J. Lawton, Initiation of Vinyl Polymerization by Means of High Energy Electrons, Science *113*, 718 (1951).
716. Schneider, E. E. et al., Effects of X-Rays upon Plastics: Paramagnetic Resonance, Nature *168*, 645 (1951).
717. Schuler, R. H. and W. H. Hamill, The Fast Electron and X-Ray Decomposition of the Alkyl Halides, J. Am. Chem. Soc. *74*, 6171-4 (1952).
718. Schulman, J. H. et al., The Effect of High Energy Radiation on the Absorption and Luminescence of Glasses and Crystals, Presented at Am. Ceram. Soc., Chicago, Apr. 1951. Abs. in Am. Ceram. Soc. Bull. *30*, 97 (1951).
719. Seifert, R. L., Energy of Activation of Dislocated Carbon Atoms as Determined from the Irreversible Resistance Changes in Irradiated Graphite, Atomic Energy Comm. Report ANL-4196 (1948).
720. Seitzer, W. H. et al., β-Ray Initiation of Polymerization of Styrene and Methyl Methacrylate, J. Am. Chem. Soc. *75*, 755 (1953).
721. Sheard, H. and N. J. Pattenden, The Effect of Pile Irradiation on the Linear Dimensions of AGXP Graphite, Atomic Energy Comm. Report CRNE-496 (1952).
722. Shelton, R. D., The Effects of Nuclear Radiation on Electronic Components, Air Force Report AD-82829 (1956).
723. Shelton, R. D. and J. G. Kenney, How Radiation Affects Materials: Damaging Effects on Electronic Components, Nucleonics *14* (9), 66 (1956).
724. Shirley, E. L. and A. D. Aird, The Effect of High Intensity Gamma Rays on the Optical Transmission of Cerium Stabilized Glass, Atomic Energy Comm. Report KAPL-759 (1952).
725. Simon, I., Structure of Neutron Disordered Silica, Phys. Rev. *103*, 1587-9 (1956)
726. Sisman, O., Effect of Irradiation on Some Plastic Materials, Delivered at ASTM,. Los Angeles, Calif., 9/20/56.
727. Sisman, O. and C. D. Bopp, Effect of Radiation on the Physical Properties of Plastics, Atomic Energy Comm. Report AECD 2078 (1943).
728. Sisman, O. and C. D. Bopp, Physical Properties of Irradiated Plastics, Atomic Energy Comm. Report ORNL-928 (1951).
729. Smith, A. W., Effect of Neutron Bombardment on a Zinc Sulfide Phosphor, Phys. Rev. *101*, 1263 (1956).
730. Smith, A. W., The Effect of Radiation Damage on the Thermal Conductivity of Graphite, Atomic Energy Comm. Report AECD 3652 (1954).
731. Smith, A. W. and J. D. McClelland, Electronic Properties of a Graphitized Lampblack and Their Dependence on Neutron Irradiation, Atomic Energy Comm. Report NAA-SR-248 (1953).
732. Smith, A. W. and J. Turkevich, Effect of Neutron Bombardment on a Zinc Sulfide Phosphor, Phys. Rev. *94*, 857-65 (1954); J. Chem. Phys. *21*, 367-8 (1953); see also AEC Report NYO-3280 (1952).
733. Smith, J. C., The Effect of High Energy Radiations on the Physical Properties of Textile Fibers Irradiated in Air, Presented at 30th Nat. Colloid Symposium, Am. Chem. Soc., Madison, Wis. June 1956.
734. Smith, W. J. et al., Surface Studies of X-Ray Irradiated Potassium Chloride Crystals, Phys. Rev. *101*, 37-40 (1956).
735. Smith, W. J. et al., Interferometric Study of the Surface of X-Ray and Proton Irradiated KCl Crystals, Bull. Am. Phys. Soc. *29* (3), 37 (1954).
736. Smoluchowski, R., On the Influence of Nuclear Radiation on Electrical Conductivity of Alkali Halides, Bull. Am. Phys. Soc. *29* (3), 11 (1954).

737. Smoluchowski, R., Behavior of Defects in Alkali Halides Produced by High Energy Protons and γ-Rays, in "Defects in Crystalline Solids", Phys. Soc. London, 1955, p. 252.

738. Snelgrove, J. A., Effects of High Energy Electrons on Polyvinyl Acetate, Presented at 30th Nat. Colloid Symposium, Am. Chem. Soc., Madison, Wis. June 1956.

739. Sowman, H. G. and J. S. Lukesh, An Exploratory Investigation of Glasses Exposed to Neutron Radiations, Atomic Energy Comm. Report KAPL-1242 (1954).

740. Stark, H. H. and C. G. Garton, Electric Strength of Irradiated Polythene, Nature 176, 1225-6 (1955).

740a. Stech, B., Structural Changes in Crystals by Bombardment with Alpha Particles, Z. Naturforsch. 7a, 175 (1952) (in German).

741. Steidlitz, M. E. and M. H. Feldman, Formation of Nitrogen Oxides by Alpha Particle Irradiation of the System N_2-CO_2, Atomic Energy Comm. Report AECD 3883 (1953).

742. Steigman, J. et al., Some Chromophore-tagged Polymers and Their Radiation Chemistry, Presented at meeting Am. Chem. Soc., Polymer Div., Chicago, 1953.

743. Stilson, C. E., The Effect of Radiation on a Differential Transformer, Atomic Energy Comm. Report ORNL-277 (1948).

744. Sun, K. H., Effects of Atomic Radiation on High Polymers, Modern Plastics 32, 141-50, 229-39 (1954).

745. Suran. J. J., Effect of Weak Betas on the Breakdown of Dielectric Gaps, Nucleonics 8 (6), 34-5 (1951).

746. Todd, A., Pile Irradiation of Polyethylene Terephthalate, Nature 174, 613 (1954).

747. Tokuyasu, K., On Damage to Specimens by Shadowing Bombardment. I. Experiment, J. Appl. Phys. 24, 953 (1953).

748. Trillat, J. J., Investigation by Diffraction and Electron Microscopy of the Behavior of Silver Bromide under the Action of Fast Electrons, Compt. rend. 236, 60-2 (1953) (in French).

749. Tuck, D. G., Bombardment of Glass by α-Particles, Nature 177, 434-5 (1956).

750. Tucker, C. W., Jr., X-Ray Scattering by Lattice Defects in Neutron Irradiated Single Crystals of Boron Carbide, Atomic Energy Comm. Report KAPL W-31-103 ENG -52 (1954).

751. Tucker, C. W., Jr., and P. Senio, Radiation Damage in Boron Carbide, Atomic Energy Comm. Report AECD 3939 (1956).

752. Tucker, C. W., Jr., and P. Senio, Annealing of Radiation Damage in Boron Carbide, Atomic Energy Comm. Report AECD 3871 (1955).

753. Tucker, C. W., Jr., and P. Senio, X-Ray Scattering by Neutron Irradiated Single Crystals of Boron Carbide, Atomic Energy Comm. Reports KAPL-1180 (1954) and AECD-3613 (1954).

754. Tucker, C. W., Jr., and P. Senio, Some Factors in the Resistance of Crystals to Radiation Damage, Atomic Energy Comm. Report KAPL-1301 (1955).

755. Urbanek, J., Photoelectric Investigations on Naturally Colored Rocksalt, on Radiation-Colored Fluorite, and on Vitreous Borax, Acta Phys. Aust. 5, 69-76 (1951) (in German).

756. Valovage, W. D., Effect of Irradiation on Hot Pressed Boron Carbide, Atomic Energy Comm. Report KAPL-1403 (1955).

757. Varley, J. H. O., A New Interpretation of Irradiation-Induced Phenomena in Alkali Halides, J. Nuclear Energy *1*, 130–43 (1954).

758. Vaughan, W. H. et al., Mechanical Properties of Proton Irradiated Alkali Halides, Phys. Rev. (2) *91*, 245 (1953).

759. Wall, L. A., Gamma Irradiation of Polymethyl Methacrylate and Polystyrene, Presented at 30th Nat. Colloid Symposium, Am. Chem. Soc., Madison, Wis. June 1956.

760. Wall, L. A., and M. Magat, Degradation of Polymers by γ-Rays and Neutrons, J. Chim. Phys. *50*, 308 (1953).

761. Wall, L. A., and M. Magat, Effects of Atomic Radiation on Polymers, Modern Plastics *30*, 111–12, 114, 116, 176, 178 (1953).

762. Warner, A. J. et al., Electrical Conductivity Induced by Ionizing Radiation in Some Polymeric Materials, J. Appl. Phys. *25*, 130 (1954).

763. Watson, J. H. L. et al., Solids Condensed from Carbon Monoxide by Alpha Particles, J. Phys. Chem. *54*, 391 (1950).

764. Warner, A. J., Effect of Ionizing Radiation on High Quality Insulating Materials, Conference on Elec. Insulation, 1951, p. 26.

765. Warrick, E. L., Effects of Radiations on Organopolysiloxanes, Ind. Eng. Chem. *47*, 2388–93 (1955).

766. Weeks, R. A., Paramagnetic Resonance of Lattice Defects in Irradiated Quartz, J. Appl. Phys. *27*, 1376–81 (1956).

767. Weeks, R. A. and D. Binder, Effect of Radiation on the Dielectric Constant and Attenuation of Two Coaxial Cables, Atomic Energy Comm. Report ORNL-1700 (1954).

768. Weisz, P. B. and E. W. Swegler, Catalytic Activity Induced by Neutron Irradiation of Inert Silica, J. Chem. Phys. *23*, 1567–8 (1955).

769. Westervelt, D. R., Mechanical Effects of Ionizing Radiation in the Alkali Halides, Atomic Energy Comm. Report NAA-SR-888 (1954).

770. Westervelt, D. R., Thermal Annealing of Radiation Induced Harness in Alkali Halides, Acta Met. *1*, 755–8 (1953).

771. Wieninger, L., Irradiation of Natural Colored Rocksalt Crystals with Alpha Particles from Radium F, Oesterr. Akad. Wiss., Math.-naturw. Kl. Sitzber. Abt. *11a*, 159, 113–28 (1950).

772. Wieninger, L. and N. Adler, Formation of Microscopic Crystals on Crystal Surfaces Irradiated by Po α-Rays, Acta Phys. Aust. *4*, 81–4 (1950) (in German).

773. Wittels, M. C., Lattice Expansion of Quartz Due to Fast Neutron Bombardment, Phys. Rev. *89*, 656 (1953).

774. Wittels, M. C. and F. A. Sherrill, Structural Effects Resulting from Irradiation in Nonmetals, Presented at Am. Ceram. Soc. meeting, Apr. 1956.

775. Wittels, M. and F. A. Sherrill, Radiation Damage in SiO_2 Structures, Phys. Rev. (2) *93*, 1117–8 (1954).

776. Woods, W. K. et al., Irradiation Damage to Artificial Graphite, Intntl. Conf. on Peaceful Uses of Atomic Energy, P/746.

777. Yasaitis, E. L. and B. Smaller, Paramagnetic Resonances in Irradiated Glasses, Phys. Rev. *92*, 1068–9 (1953).

778. Yokota, R., Thermoluminescence of Quartz and Fused Quartz Colored by X-Ray Irradiation, Phys. Rev. *91*, 1013–4 (1953).

779. Young, J. R., Deterioration of Luminescent Phosphors under Positive Ion Bombardment, J. Appl. Phys. *26*, 1302–6 (1955).

INDEX